# INSTRUCTOR'S SOLUTIONS MANUAL

# MANUFACTURING ENGINEERING AND TECHNOLOGY

FIFTH EDITION

Serope Kalpakjian • Steven R. Schmid

UPPER SADDLE RIVER, NJ 07458

Vice President and Editorial Director: *Marcia Horton*
Associate Editor: *Dee Bernhard*
Executive Managing Editor: *Vince O'Brien*
Managing Editor: *David A. George*
Production Editor: *Rose Kernan*
Cover Designer: *Wendy Kopf*
Manufacturing Manager: *Alexis Heydt-Long*
Manufacturing Buyer: *Lisa McDowell*
Senior Marketing Manager: *Holly Stark*

Pearson Prentice Hall
Pearson Education, Inc.
Upper Saddle River, NJ 07458



Printed in the United States of America

10 9 8 7 6 5 4 3 2 1

ISBN 0-13-187157-9

Pearson Education Ltd., *London*
Pearson Education Australia Pty. Ltd., *Sydney*
Pearson Education Singapore, Pte. Ltd.
Pearson Education North Asia Ltd., *Hong Kong*
Pearson Education Canada, Inc., *Toronto*
Pearson Educación de Mexico, S.A. de C.V.
Pearson Education—Japan, *Tokyo*
Pearson Education Malaysia, Pte. Ltd.
Pearson Education, Inc., *Upper Saddle River, New Jersey*

# Contents

# Preface

This solutions manual is intended to assist instructors in the organization of assignments and discussions associated with courses in manufacturing engineering and in the use of the *Manufacturing Engineering and Technology*, Fifth Edition textbook. In addition to these solutions, instructors can find other educational resources at the Prentice Hall website, (www.prenhall.com/onekey) and at Steven Schmid's website (www.nd.edu/~manufact).

Manufacturing presents a number of challenges and opportunities to instructors. As a topic of study it is exciting because of its breadth and unending ability to provide fascinating opportunities for research, analysis, and creativity. Literally every discipline and sub-discipline in engineering has strong ties to manufacturing, and a number of universities have used design and manufacturing as the basis of a capstone course which culminates in a bachelor's degree in mechanical engineering. To manufacturing students, it is at first a field so enormous that any single semester or academic year in manufacturing can do nothing but scratch the surface of the subject. This perception is absolutely true; manufacturing, like so many other areas of specialization within engineering, truly is an area where lifelong learning is necessary.

As educators, we have a responsibility to prepare our students as best we can for a life of continued education. Lifelong learning need not be restricted to formal classroom training, but it should be impressed upon students that they need to continually and systematically examine the physical world in order to achieve continued levels of improvement.

A challenging question, and perhaps one without any one good answer, is how one should effectively teach a manufacturing course? We have seen many examples of successful strategies, some based solely on analytical methods, others involving surveys of manufacturing, and still others emphasizing the impact of manufacturing on engineering design. Most instructors develop hybrid approaches which are not restricted to any one area. We have attempted to include problems at the end of every chapter in order to accommodate each of these approaches, and it is our hope that instructors will find good homework assignments in the book.

Manufacturing is also a challenge to instructors. There are a number of courses—such as statics, dynamics, solid and fluid mechanics—where topics for study are broken down into small enough portions and where closed-form, quantitative problems are routinely solved during lectures by both students and faculty. Such problems are important for learning concepts, and they provide students a sense of security in knowing that absolute answers can be determined. In manufacturing practice, such closed-form solutions do exist, but they are relatively rare. Usually, multiple disciplines are blended and the information available is insufficient to truly optimize a desired outcome. In practice, manufacturing engineers need to apply good judgment after they have researched a problem as best they can given budgetary and time restrictions. These difficult open-ended problems are much more demanding than closed-form solutions and require a different mindset. Instead of considering a number as valid or invalid (usually by checking against the answer provided in the book or by the instructor), an open-ended problem can be evaluated only with respect to whether or not the result is reasonable and if good scientific methods were used to obtain it. This textbook has been intentionally designed with a large number of open-ended problems. Such problems are, in our experience, extremely valuable when teaching manufacturing engineering. However, a solutions manual is well-suited for closed-form solutions, not open-ended problems. We have attempted to describe the pitfalls and methods that will be valuable in solving the open-ended problems, but it is difficult to give a correct answer to these problems due to their nature. We encourage faculty to communicate with us and to give us feedback on any areas of the book.

**Serope Kalpakjian**
**Steven Schmid**

# Chapter 1

# The Structure of Metals

## QUALITATIVE PROBLEMS

**1.15 What is the significance of the fact that some metals undergo allotropism?**

Allotropism (also called polymorphism) means that a metal can change from one crystal structure to another. Since properties vary with crystal structures, allotropism is useful and essential in heat treating of metals to achieve desired properties (Chapter 4). A major application is hardening of steel, which involves the change in iron from the fcc structure to the bcc structure (see Fig. 1.4 on p. 49). By heating the steel to the fcc structure and quenching, it develops into martensite, which is a very hard, hence strong, structure.

**1.16 Is it possible for two pieces of the same metal to have different recrystallization temperatures? Is it possible for recrystallization to take place in some regions of a part before it does other regions of the same part? Explain.**

Two pieces of the same metal can have different recrystallization temperatures if the pieces have been cold worked to different amounts. The piece that was cold worked to a greater extent (higher strains), will have more internal energy (stored energy) to drive the recrystallization process, hence its recrystallization temperature will be lower. Recrystallization may also occur in some regions of the part before others if it has been unevenly strained (since varying amounts of cold work have different recrystallization temperatures), or if the part has different thicknesses in various sections. The thinner sections will heat up to the recrystallization temperature faster.

**1.17 A cold-worked piece of metal has been recrystallized. When tested, it is found to be anisotropic. Explain the probable reason.**

The anisotropy of the workpiece is likely due to preferred orientation remaining from the recrystallization process (see pp. 59-60). Copper is an example of a metal that has a very strong preferred orientation after annealing. Also, it has been shown that below a critical amount of plastic deformation, typically 5%, no recrystallization occurs.

**1.18 Explain the advantages and limitations of cold, warm, and hot working, respectively.**

As described in Section 1.7 on p. 60, cold working a metal results in higher strength, usually a smoother surface finish, and closer dimensional accuracy than hot working, but the ductility of the piece is lower. Hot working is accompanied by recrystallization of the deformed metal, which preserves the ductility of the workpiece; also, the stress required to deform the metal is lower. The workpiece, however, will have a rougher surface finish due to oxidation at higher temperatures, and the thermal expansion and contraction prevents achieving close dimensional control. Also, because of inherent limitations in bulk deformation processes, the desired shape may not be attainable in hot working. For example, hot-rolled foils are not routinely available. Warm working has advantages intermediate to both hot and cold working; the forces required are lower than cold working, and the dimensional accuracy and surface finish are better than for hot working.

**1.19 Do you think that it might be important to know whether a raw material for a manufacturing process has anisotropic properties? What about anisotropy in the finished product? Explain.**

Anisotropy is important in cold-working processes, especially sheet-metal forming where the material's properties should preferably be uniform in the plane of the sheet and stronger in the thickness direction. As shown in Section 16.7, these characteristics allow for deep drawing of parts (like beverage cans) without earing, tearing, or cracking in the forming operations involved. In a finished part, anisotropy is important so that the strongest direction of the part can be designed to support the largest load in service. Also, the efficiency of transformers can be improved by using a sheet steel with anisotropy that can reduce *magnetic hysteresis* losses. Hysteresis is well known in ferromagnetic materials. When an external magnetic field is applied to a ferromagnet, the ferromagnet absorbs some of the external field. When sheet steel is highly anisotropic, it contains small grains and a crystallographic orientation that is far more uniform than for isotropic materials, and this orientation will reduce magnetic hysteresis losses.

**1.20 Explain why the strength of a polycrystalline metal at room temperature decreases as its grain size increases.**

Strength increases as more entanglements of dislocations occur with grain boundaries (Section 1.3.2 on p. 54). Metals with larger grains have less grain-boundary area per unit volume, and hence will not be as able to generate as many entanglements at grain boundaries, thus the strength will be lower.

**1.21 What is the significance of the fact that such metals as lead and tin have recrystallization temperatures at about room temperature?**

Recrystallization around room temperature prevents these metals from work hardening when cold worked. This characteristic prevents their strengthening and hardening, thus requiring a recrystallization cycle to restore their ductility. This behavior is also useful in experimental verification of analytical results concerning force and energy requirements in metalworking processes (see Part III of the text).

**1.22 It has been noted that the more a metal has been cold worked, the less it strain hardens. Explain why.**

This phenomenon can be observed in stress-strain curves, such as those shown in Figs. 2.2, 2.3, 2.5, and 2.7. Recall that the main effects of cold working are that grains become elongated and that the average grain size becomes smaller (as grains break down) with strain. Strain hardening occurs when dislocations interfere with each other and with grain boundaries. When a metal is annealed, the grains are large, and a small strain results in grains moving relatively easily at first, but they increasingly interfere with each other as strain increases. This explains that there is strain hardening for annealed materials at low strain. To understand why there is less strain hardening at higher levels of cold work, consider the extreme case of a very highly cold-worked material, with very small grains and very many dislocations that already interfere with each other. For this highly cold-worked material, the stress cannot be increased much more with strain, because the dislocations have nowhere else to go - they already interfere with each other and are pinned at grain boundaries.

## QUANTITATIVE PROBLEMS

**1.23 Plot the data given in Table 1.1 in terms of grains/mm$^2$ vs. grains/mm$^3$, and state your observations.**

The plot is shown below. It can be seen that the grains per cubic millimeter increases faster than the grains per square millimeter. This relationship is to be expected since the volume of an equiaxed grain depends on the diameter cubed, whereas its area depends on the diameter squared.

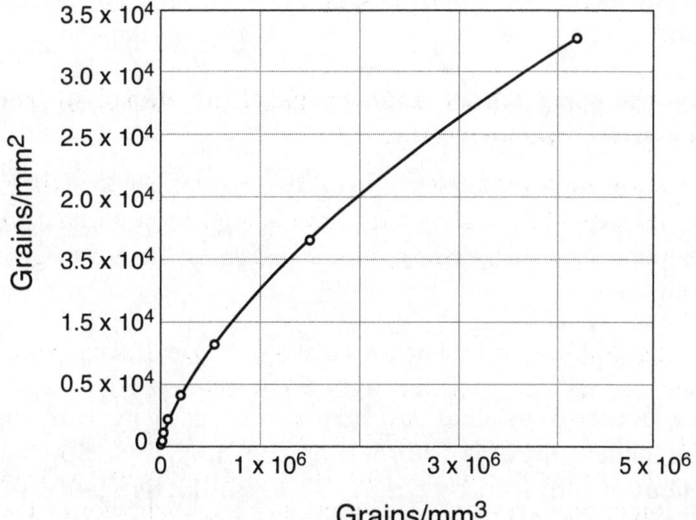

**1.24 By cold working, a strip of metal is reduced from 40 mm in thickness to 20 mm. A similar strip is reduced in a similar way from 40 mm to 30 mm. Which one of these cold-worked strips will recrystallize at a lower temperature? Why?**

The first strip undergoes a reduction of (40-20)/40=0.5, or 50% in thickness, while the second strip undergoes a reduction of (40-30)/40=0.25, or 25% reduction. Since the first strip has undergone a higher amount of cold work, it will recrystallize at a lower temperature. The extra cold work adds stored energy in the form of dislocations to the strip, hence the energy needed for recrystallization (in the form of thermal energy) is reduced.

**1.25 A paper clip is made of wire that is 5 in. long and 1/32-in. in diameter. If the ASTM grain size is 9, how many grains are there in the paper clip?**

From Table 1.1 on p. 55, we find that a metal with an ASTM grain size of 9 has about 185,000 grains/mm$^3$. The volume of the paper clip is

$$V = \frac{\pi}{4}\left(\frac{1}{32}\text{ in.}\right)^2 (5\text{ in.}) = 0.00383\text{ in}^3$$

Converting this to cubic millimeters gives a volume of 62.8 mm$^3$. Multiplying the volume by the grains per millimeter cube gives the number of grains in the paper clip as about 11.6 million.

**1.26 How many atoms are on the surface of the head of a pin? Assume the head of a pin is spherical with a 1 mm diameter and has an ASTM grain size of 2.**

If a pin has a spherical head with a diameter of 1 mm, then its surface area is

$$A = \pi d^2 = \pi\text{ mm}^2 = \pi \times 10^{-6}\text{ m}^2$$

Note from Table 1.1 on p. 55 that for ASTM grain size of 2, there are 32 grains per square millimeter. Therefore, we expect that there will be $\pi$(32)=100 grains on the head of a pin. The number of atoms depends on the particular material used, but let's assume we have a steel pin. The diameter of an iron atom is 2.5 angstroms, so this is the value that will be used. The number of atoms actually on the surface will depend on how well the atoms are packed, but an estimate can be made by assuming that one-half the area of an atom is on the surface, so that the area per atom is

$$A_{\text{atom}} = \frac{1}{2}\pi d^2 = \frac{1}{2}\pi\left(2.5 \times 10^{-10}\text{ m}\right)^2 = 6.283 \times 10^{-20}\text{ m}^2$$

Therefore the number of atoms is

$$n = \frac{3.1415 \times 10^{-6}}{6.283 \times 10^{-20}} = 5 \times 10^{13}\text{ atoms}$$

**1.27 A technician determines that the grain size of a certain etched specimen is 8. Upon further checking, it is found that the magnification used was 180x instead of the 100x that is required by the ASTM standards. Determine the correct grain size.**

If the grain size is 8, then there are 2048 grains per square millimeter (see Table 1.1 on p. 55). However, the magnification was too large, meaning that too small of an area was examined. For a magnification of 100×, the area is reduced by a factor of 1/1.82=0.309. Therefore, there really are 632 grains per mm$^2$, which corresponds to a grain size between 6 and 7.

**1.28 If the diameter of the aluminum atom is 0.5 nm, how many atoms are there in a grain with ASTM grain size 5?**

If the grain size is 5, there are 2900 grains per cubic millimeter of aluminum. Each grain has a volume of $1/2900 = 3.45 \times 10^{-4}$ mm$^3$. Note that for an fcc material there are four atoms per unit cell, with a total volume of $16\pi R^3/3$, and that the diagonal, $a$, of the unit cell is given by

$$a = \left(2\sqrt{2}\right) R$$

Hence,

$$\text{APF}_{\text{fcc}} = \frac{(16\pi R^3/3)}{\left(2R\sqrt{2}\right)^3} = 0.74$$

Note that as long as all the atoms in the unit cell have the same size, the atomic packing factors do not depend on the atomic radius. Therefore, the volume of the grain which is taken up by atoms is $(3.45 \times 10^{-4})(0.74) = 2.55 \times 10^{-4}$ mm$^3$. (Recall that 1 mm=$10^6$ nm.) If the diameter of an aluminum atom is 0.5 nm, then its radius is 0.25 nm or $0.25 \times 10^{-6}$ mm. The volume of an aluminum atom is then $V = 4\pi R^3/3 = 4\pi(0.25 \times 10^{-6})^3/3 = 6.54x10-20$ mm$^3$. Dividing the volume of aluminum in the grain by the volume of an aluminum atom yields the total number of atoms in the grain as $(2.55 \times 10^{-4})/(6.54 \times 10^{-20}) = 3.90 \times 10^{15}$.

## SYNTHESIS, DESIGN, AND PROJECTS

**1.29 By stretching a thin strip of polished metal (as in a tension-testing machine) demonstrate and comment on what happens to its reflectivity as it is stretched.**

The polished surface is initially smooth, which allows light to be reflected uniformly across the surface. As the metal is stretched, the reflective surface of the polished sheet metal will begin to become dull. The slip and twin bands developed at the surface cause roughening (see Fig. 1.7), which tends to scatter the reflected light.

**1.30 Draw some analogies to mechanical fibering (for example, layers of thin dough sprinkled with flour or butter between each layer).**

By the student. A wide variety of acceptable answers are possible based on the student's experience and creativity. Some examples of mechanical fibering include: (a) food products such as lasagna, where layers of noodles bound sauce, or pastries with many thin layers, such as baklava; (b) log cabins, where tree trunks are oriented to construct walls and then sealed with a matrix; and (c) straw-reinforced mud.

**1.31 Draw some analogies to the phenomenon of hot shortness.**

Some analogies to hot shortness include: (a) a brick wall with deteriorating mortar between the bricks, (b) time-released medicine, where a slowly soluble matrix surrounds doses of quickly soluble medicine, and (c) an Oreo cookie at room temperature compared to a frozen cookie.

**1.32 Obtain a number of small balls made of plastic, wood, marble, and so forth, and arrange them with your hands or glue them together to represent the crystal structures shown in Figs. 1.2 through 1.4. Comment on your observations.**

By the student. There are many possible comments, including the relative densities of the three crystal structures (hcp is clearly densest). Also, the ingenious and simple solid-ball models are striking when performing such demonstrations.

**1.33 Take a deck of playing cards, put a rubber band around them, and slip them against each other to represent Figs. 1.6a and 1.7. If you repeat the same experiment with more and more rubber bands around the same deck, what are you accomplishing as far as the behavior of the material is concerned?**

By the student. With an increased number of rubber bands, you are physically increasing the friction force between each card. This is analogous to increasing the magnitude of the shear stress required to cause slip. Furthermore, the greater the number of rubber bands, the higher the shear or elastic modulus of the material (see Section 2.4 on p. 78). This problem can be taken to a very effective extreme by using small C-clamps to highly compress the cards; the result is an object that acts like one solid, with much higher stiffness than the loose cards.

**1.34 Give examples where anisotropy is scale dependent. For example, a wire rope may contain wires that are isotropic on a microscopic scale, but the rope as a whole is anisotropic.**

All materials may behave in an anisotropic manner when considered at atomic scales, but when taken as a continuum, many materials are isotropic. Other examples include:

- Clothing, which overall appears to be isotropic, but clearly has anisotropy defined by the direction of the threads in the cloth. This anisotropic behavior can be verified by pulling small patches of the cloth in different directions.
- Wood has directionality (orthotropic) but it can be ignored for many applications.
- Human skin: it appears isotropic at large length scales, but microscopically it consists of cells with varying strengths within the cell.

**1.35 In Section 1.3, the movement of an edge dislocation was described by means of an analogy involving a hump in a carpet, and how the whole carpet can be moved by moving the hump forward. The entanglement of dislocations was described in terms of two humps at different angles. Demonstrate these phenomena using a piece of cloth placed on a flat surface.**

By the student. This can be clearly demonstrated, especially with a cloth that is compliant (flexible) but has high friction with a flat surface. Two methods of ensuring this is the case are (a) to use a cotton material (as found in T-shirts) and wetting it before conducting the experiments, or (b) spraying the bottom side of the fabric with temporary adhesives, as found in most arts and office supply stores. The experiments (single and two lumps) can then be conducted and observations made.

# Chapter 2

# Mechanical Behavior, Testing, and Manufacturing Properties of Materials

## QUALITATIVE PROBLEMS

**2.16 Using the same scale for stress, the tensile true stress-true strain curve is higher than the engineering stress-engineering strain curve. Explain whether this condition also holds for a compression test.**

During a compression test, the cross-sectional area of the specimen increases as the load is increased. Since true stress is defined as load divided by the instantaneous cross-sectional area of the specimen, the true stress in compression will be lower than the engineering stress for a given load, providing that frictional forces (between the platens and the specimen) are negligible.

**2.17 With the aid of a simple sketch, explain whether it is necessary to use the offset method to determine the yield stress, $Y$, of a material that has been highly cold worked.**

As can be seen by reviewing Fig. 2.3 on p. 68, a highly cold-worked metal will have a distinct change in slope on its stress-strain curve occurring at the yield point, so that the offset method is not necessary. See also Fig. 2.6 on p. 72.

**2.18 Explain why the difference between engineering strain and true strain becomes larger as strain increases. Does this difference occur for both tensile and compressive strains? Explain.**

The answer lies in the fact that the definitions of engineering strain and true strain are different, the latter being based on the actual or instantaneous dimensions, as can be seen in

Eqs. (2.2) and (2.7) on p. 67 and p. 70, respectively. In both cases of tension and compression, the difference increases as strain increases. This is shown quantitatively in Problem 2.51.

**2.19 If a material does not have an endurance limit (for example, aluminum), how would you estimate its fatigue life?**

Materials without endurance limits have their fatigue life defined as a certain number of cycles to failure at a given stress level. For engineering purposes, this definition allows for an estimate of the expected lifetime of a part. The part is then usually taken out of service before its lifetime is reached. An alternative approach is to use nondestructive test techniques (Section 36.10 on p. 1132) to periodically measure the accumulated damage in a part, and then use fracture mechanics approaches to estimate the remaining life.

**2.20 Which hardness tests and scales would you use for very thin strips of metal, such as aluminum foil? Why?**

A hardness test that produces small indentations would have to be used; also, since aluminum foil is relatively soft, a very light load would be required. Two scales that satisfy these requirements are the Knoop microhardness (HK) and the Vickers hardness (HV) at very light loads (see Fig. 2.12 on p. 80). An area of current research is the use of atomic force microscopy and nanoindenters to obtain the hardness of very thin materials and coatings. The shape of the indenter used is not exactly the same as in Fig. 2.12, and the loads are in the micro- to milli-Newton range.

**2.21 Which of the two tests, tension or compression, requires higher capacity of testing machine, and why?**

The compression test requires a higher capacity machine since the cross-sectional area of the specimen increases as the test progresses. The increase in area requires a load higher than that for the tension test to achieve the same stress level. Also, there is friction between the flat dies (platens) and the workpiece surfaces in a compression test (see Sections 2.3 and 14.2 on p. 373) which results in higher pressures than in tension; this higher pressure then requires larger forces for the same cross-sectional area. In addition, there is more redundant work in compression testing than in tension testing, so the material will work harden more (unless the test is conducted at elevated temperatures).

**2.22 List and explain briefly the conditions that induce brittle fracture in an otherwise ductile metal.**

Brittle fracture can be induced by high deformation rates, lower temperatures (particularly those with bcc structure), the presence of stress concentration (notches and cracks), state of stress, radiation damage, corrosion (including hydrogen embrittlement). In each case, the stress needed to cause yielding is raised above the stress needed to cause failure, or the stress needed for a crack to propagate is below the yield stress of the material (as with stress concentration).

**2.23 List the factors that you would consider in selecting a hardness test and in then interpreting the results from this test.**

Hardness tests mainly have three differences: (a) type of indenter, (b) applied load, and (c) method of indentation measurement, i.e., depth or surface area of indentation, or rebound of indenter. The hardness test selected would depend on the estimated hardness of the workpiece, its size and thickness, and if average hardness or the hardness of individual microstructural components is desired. For instance, the scleroscope, which is portable, is capable of measuring the hardness of large pieces that cannot be used for measurement by other techniques.

The Brinell hardness test leaves a fairly large indentation, thus providing a good measure of average hardness, while the Knoop test leaves a small indentation that allows for determination of the hardness of the individual phases in a two-phase alloy. The small indentation of the Knoop test also allows it to be useful in measuring the hardness of very thin layers or plated layers on parts. Note that the depth of indentation should be small relative to part thickness, and that any change in the appearance of the bottom surface the part will make the test results invalid.

Figure 2.14 on p. 84 is a useful guide for determining which hardness test is valid for a class of material. Note that often numerous hardness tests are suitable for a material. In these cases, the best hardness test is the one that has one or more of the following characteristics:

- The best hardness test is often one that can be performed quickly; thus, it may be desirable to also select a hardness test based on available equipment.
- Hardness tests are often specified by customers as part of a quality control requirement. Whatever form of hardness test is specified by the customer is the appropriate one to use.
- A hardness test that is most commonly used in a plant may be the best choice since technicians will be most familiar with the test protocol and the equipment is most likely to be in good calibration.
- Experimental error can be minimized by selecting a hardness test that gives the largest penetration or indentation size.

**2.24 Using Fig. 2.6 only, explain why you cannot calculate the percent elongation of the materials listed.**

Recall that elongation (total) is defined by Eq. (2.4) on p. 69 and depends on the original gage length ($l_o$) of the specimen. Note that if the gage length encompasses a necked region only, it will register a larger percent elongation than if the gage length is four or five times as long as the necked region, for example. From Fig. 2.6 on p. 72, the true necking and fracture strains can be determined. Since this is a true strain, it is not dependent on the gage length. That is, regardless of the gage length, the same true stress will be measured. Since there is no way of incorporating gage length, one cannot obtain the percent elongation from Fig. 2.6. (See also the answer to Problem 2.36.)

**2.25 If you pull and break a tension-test specimen rapidly, where would the temperature be highest, and why?**

Since temperature rise is due to work input, it is obvious that the temperature will be highest in the necked region because that is where the strain is highest and, hence, the energy dissipated per unit volume in plastic deformation is highest.

**2.26 Will the disk test be applicable to a ductile material? Why or why not?**

With a ductile material, a point load on a disk results in the circular disk being flattened at the platens and attaining elliptical shape of the originally round specimen. The flattening converts the point load to a distributed load, completely changing the stress state in the piece. Therefore, Eq. (2.10) on p. 77 is not valid, and the usefulness of the test is compromised.

**2.27 What hardness test is suitable for determining the hardness of a thin ceramic coating?**

For a thin ceramic coating, it is still important that the hardness of the coating and not the substrate be measured. Most ceramics have limited ductility (Section 8.3 on p. 224), so that Knoop or Vickers tests are suitable, although the Mohs test can also be used to obtain a qualitative value. Because of the increasing importance of coatings, special microhardness tests have been developed for their hardness measurement.

**2.28 In a Brinell hardness test, the resulting impression is found to be an ellipse. Give possible explanations for this result.**

Two possible explanations for an elliptical impression after a Brinell test are: (a) An obvious reason is the possible presence of asymmetric residual stresses in the surface layers of the material before the test. (b) The material itself may be highly anisotropic, such as a fiber-reinforced composite material, or due to severe cold working.

**2.29 Some coatings are extremely thin - some, as thin as a few nanometers. Explain why even the Knoop test is not able to obtain reasonable results for such coatings. Recent research has attempted to use highly polished diamonds (tip radius around 5 nanometers) to indent such coatings in atomic force microscopes. What concerns would you have regarding the appropriateness of the results?**

With a coating of thickness of 5 nm, the stressed volume has to be approximately one-tenth this depth, which begins to approach the size of individual atoms. Thus, a knoop indentor would need to have a tip radius that was atomically sharp in order to get results. Even with highly polished diamond tips in atomic force microscopes, this scale problem is unavoidable. However, there are additional concerns in that the diamond indenter may not be symmetric, there are large adhesive forces at the small scales, there are complicated elastic and viscoelastic recovery at small length scales, there may be residual stresses at the surface, and the stressed volume may or may not contain a dislocation (whereas with Knoop tests, there is always a number of dislocations).

**2.30 Select an appropriate hardness test for each of the following materials. Justify your answer.**

a) **Cubic boron nitride**

b) **Lead**

c) **Cold-drawn 0.5% C steel**

d) **Diamond**

e) **Caramel (candy)**

**f) Granite**

Figure 2.14 on p. 84 is a useful guide for selecting hardness tests.

(a) Cubic boron nitride is very hard, and useful data can be obtained only from the Knoop and Mohs tests. The Mohs scale is qualitative and does not give numerical values for hardness, so the Knoop test is preferable.

(b) Lead. As shown in Fig. 2.14, lead is so soft that only the Brinell and Vickers tests yield useful data. Recognizing that lead is very soft, the lightest loads in these tests should be used. Consider the expected results in this test if a typical value of hardness is 4 HB or 4 HV. For the Brinell test, Fig. 2.12 suggests that the expected indentation for a 500 kg load is:

$$\mathrm{HB} = \frac{2P}{(\pi D)\left(D - \sqrt{D^2 - d^2}\right)}$$

Therefore, solving for $d$,

$$d = \sqrt{D^2 - \left(D - \frac{2P}{(\pi D)(\mathrm{HB})}\right)^2} = \sqrt{10^2 - \left(10 - \frac{2(500)}{[\pi(10)]\,(4)}\right)^2} = 9.79 \text{ mm}$$

Note that this dimension is almost the same as the diameter of the indentor, and makes the usefulness of the test highly questionable. For the Vickers test, the expected indentation test, using the lowest allowable load of 1 kg, is:

$$\mathrm{HV} = \frac{1.854P}{L^2} \quad \rightarrow \quad L = \sqrt{\frac{1.854P}{\mathrm{HX}}} = \sqrt{\frac{1.854(1)}{4}} = 0.68 \text{ mm}$$

This is much more reasonable, suggesting that the Vickers test is the best alternative for lead.

(c) Cold-drawn 0.5% steel. From Fig. 2.14, all of the hardness tests are suitable for this material. As discussed in Problem 2.23, the best choice for this material will depend on a number of factors.

(d) Diamond. The hardness of diamond is difficult to obtain. The hardness of diamond is really determined by extrapolating the hardness on the Mohs curve to another scale in Fig. 2.14. The hardness of diamond is usually quoted as 8000 to 10,000 HK.

(e) Caramel (candy). This would be an interesting experiment to perform, but the result will be that none of the hardness tests can be used for this material because it is far too soft. Also, the hardness of caramel is strongly temperature-dependent and that it creeps, so that hardness measurement may be meaningless.

(f) Granite. The hardness of granite varies according to the source, but it is approximately around apatite on the Mohs scale. Thus, various hardness tests can give valuable information on granite. Note, however, that in inspecting granite surfaces, one can see various regions within which there would be hardness variations. The particular hardness test selected will depend on various factors, as discussed in part (c) above.

## QUANTITATIVE PROBLEMS

**2.31 A paper clip is made of wire 1 mm in diameter. If the original material from which the wire is made is a rod 18 mm in diameter, calculate the longitudinal engineering and true strains that the wire has undergone during processing.**

Engineering strain is defined by Eq. (2.2) on p. 67. Thus, because of volume constancy in plastic deformation, we may write

$$e = \frac{l_f}{l_o} = \left(\frac{d_o}{d_f}\right)^2 = \left(\frac{18}{1.0}\right)^2 = 324$$

Also, letting lo be unity, the engineering strain is (324 – 1)/1 = 323. True strain is defined by Eq. (2.7) on p. 70. Hence

$$\epsilon = \ln\left(\frac{323}{1}\right) = 5.78$$

Note the large difference in strains, even though they both describe the same phenomenon. (See also the last paragraph in Sec. 2.2.3 on p. 70.)

**2.32 A strip of metal is 250 mm long. It is stretched in two steps, first to 300 mm and then to 400 mm. Show that the total true strain is the sum of the true strains in each step - that is, that true strains are additive. Show that, in the case of engineering strains, the strains cannot be added to obtain the total strain.**

We first calculate the true strains for each step:

Step 1: $\epsilon_1 = \ln(300/250) = 0.182$

Step 2: $\epsilon_2 = \ln(400/300) = 0.288$

Thus the total true strain is

$$\epsilon_{\text{total}} = 0.182 + 0.288 = 0.470$$

The total strain may also be calculated from the final and initial dimensions as

$$\epsilon_{\text{total}} = \ln(400/250) = 0.470$$

thus giving the same answer.

Engineering strains are calculated likewise. Thus,

Step 1: $e_1 = (300 - 250)/250 = 0.200$

Step 2: $e_2 = (400 - 300)/300 = 0.333$

Thus the total engineering strain is 0.200+0.333=0.533. However, when calculated from the initial and final dimensions, the total engineering strain is

$$e_{\text{total}} = (400 - 250)/250 = 0.600$$

which is higher than the sum of the engineering strains. Consequently, engineering strains are not additive, whereas true strains are.

**2.33 Identify the two materials in Fig. 2.6 that have the lowest and the highest uniform elongations. Calculate these quantities as percentages of the original gage lengths.**

The magnitude of uniform elongation is directly related to the true strain at the onset of necking. As we see in Fig. 2.5c on p. 71, the necking strain on a true stress-true strain curve corresponds to the beginning of the straight portion of the curve. Thus, from Fig. 2.6 on p. 72 we note that the lowest uniform elongation is for 1112 cold-rolled steel, with a necking strain of about 0.05. The highest is for 304 stainless steel, although 70-30 annealed brass is close to it, with a necking strain of about 0.45.

To relate these values to a percentage of the gage length ($l_o$), we convert true strain to percent elongation as follows:

$$\epsilon = ln(l/l_o)$$

Or, $l/l_o = e^{\epsilon}$. Hence,

$$\text{Elongation} = (e^{\epsilon} - 1) \times 100$$

Thus, for 1112 cold-rolled steel

$$\text{Elongation} = (e^{0.05} - 1) \times 100 = 5\%$$

And for 70-30 brass, the specific value is

$$\text{Elongation} = (e^{0.45} - 1) \times 100 = 57\%$$

**2.34 Plot the ultimate strength versus stiffness for the materials in Table 2.2, and prepare a three-dimensional plot for the metals in Table 2.2 where the third axis is maximum elongation in 50 mm.**

The graphs are constructed using the minimum values in Table 2.2 on p. 67 when ranges of values exist. They are as follows:

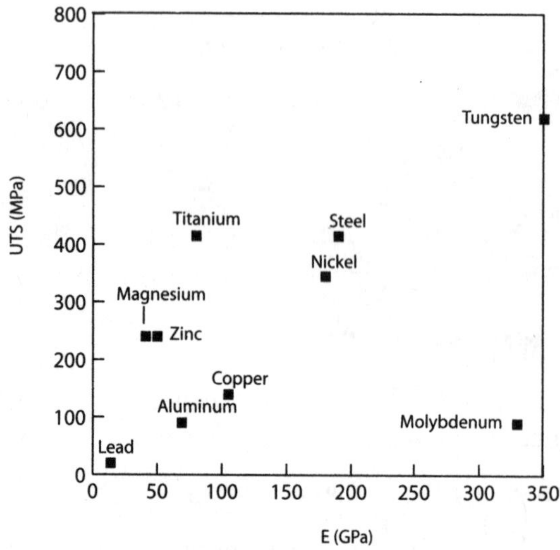


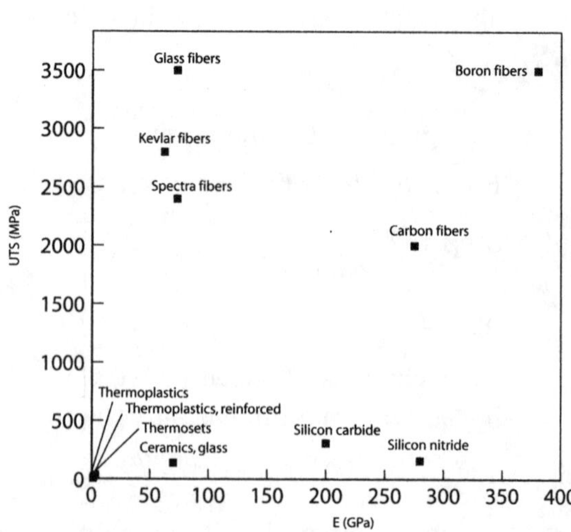

**2.35 If you remove the layer of material *ad* from the part shown in Fig. 2.29d - for instance, by machining or grinding - which way will the specimen curve? (Hint: Assume that the part shown in sketch d in the figure is composed of four horizontal springs held at the ends. Thus, from the top down you have compression, tension, compression, and tension springs.)**

The part will bow downward, with the center of curvature below the part (that is, it will hold water). The internal forces will have to achieve a state of static equilibrium. The top layer of material *ad*, which is under compression, has the tendency to bend the bar upward. When this stress is relieved, such as by removing the top layer by machining or grinding, the bar will compensate by bending downward. Such residual stress systems can be modeled with a set of horizontal tension and compression springs. Thus, starting at the top, we have a compression, tension, compression, and tension spring.

**2.36 Percent elongation is always described in terms of the original gage length, such as 50 mm or 2 in. Explain how percent elongation varies as the gage length of the tensile specimen increases. (Hint: Recall that necking is a local phenomenon, and think of what happens to the elongation as the gage length becomes very small.)**

As gage length increases, the percent elongation (total) will decrease to a value representing uniform elongation. For instance, consider taking a gage length that just encompasses the necking region (thus approaching zero gage length); the percent elongation in this region will be very high because the effect of localized deformation will tend to greatly increase the elongation. As gage length increases, however, the localized deformation zone has less and less effect on the total elongation.

**2.37 Make a sketch showing the nature and distribution of residual stresses in Fig. 2.30a and b, before they were cut. (Hint: Assume that the split parts are free from any stresses, then force these parts back to the shape they had before they were cut.)**

As the problem states, we assume that the split parts shown in Fig. 2.30a and b on p. 96 are free of stresses. After unbending the two halves (that is, closing the gap by pushing the two halves together), you will note that the inner (mating) surfaces will now be subjected to longitudinal compressive stresses, while the outer surfaces are in tension. Consequently, this represents the state of stress prior to slitting.

**2.38 You are given the K and n values of two different metals. Is this information sufficient to determine which metal is tougher? If not, what additional information do you need?**

Although the K and n values may give a good estimate of toughness, true fracture stress and true strain at fracture are also required for accurate calculation of the toughness of the metals. The modulus of elasticity and yield strength would provide information about the area under the elastic region (known as modulus of resilience; see Problem 2.45), but this region is very small and is negligible compared to the rest of the curve.

**2.39 A cable is made of two strands of different materials, A and B, and cross-sections**

**as follows:**

$$\text{For material } A: \quad K = 70,000 \text{ psi}, \quad n = 0.5, \quad A_o = 0.6 \text{ in}^2$$

$$\text{For material } B: \quad K = 25,000 \text{ psi}, \quad n = 0.5, \quad A_o = 0.3 \text{ in}^2$$

**Calculate the maximum tensile force that this cable can withstand prior to necking.**

Note that necking will occur when $\epsilon = n = 0.5$. At this point, the true stresses in each cable are (using $\sigma = K\epsilon^n$), respectively,

$$\sigma_A = 70,000\epsilon^{0.5} = 49,500 \text{ psi}$$

and

$$\sigma_B = 25,000\epsilon^{0.5} = 17,700 \text{ psi}$$

The true areas at necking can be calculated as follows:

$$A_A = 0.6e^{-0.5} = 0.364 \text{ in}^2$$

and

$$A_B = 0.3e^{-0.5} = 0.182 \text{ in}^2$$

Thus the total load that the cable can support is

$$P_{\text{total}} = (49,500)(0.364) + (17,700)(0.182) = 21,200 \text{ lb}$$

**2.40 On the basis of the information given in Fig. 2.6, calculate the ultimate tensile strength (engineering) of annealed copper.**

Recall that the definition of engineering stress is $\sigma_{\text{eng}} = P/A_o$, and that for true stress it is $\sigma = P/A$. From Fig. 2.6, the true stress at necking for copper is found to be about 50,000 psi, while the true strain is about 0.4. We also know that the ratio of the original to the necked areas of the specimen is given by

$$\ln\left(\frac{A_o}{A_{\text{neck}}}\right) = 0.4$$

or

$$\frac{A_{\text{neck}}}{A_o} = e^{-0.4} = 0.67$$

Thus, the engineering stress is calculated as

$$\sigma_{\text{eng}} = (50,000)(0.67) = 33,500 \text{ psi}$$

**2.41 In a disk test performed on a specimen 1.25 in. in diameter and 1/2 in. thick, the specimen fractures at a stress of 30,000 psi. What was the load on it?**

For this problem, we use Eq. (2.10) on p. 77. Thus,

$$\sigma = \frac{2P}{\pi dt}; \quad P = \frac{\sigma\pi dt}{2} = \frac{(30,000 \text{ psi})\pi(1.25 \text{ in.})(0.375 \text{ in.})}{2} = 22,100 \text{ lb}$$

**2.42 A piece of steel has a hardness of 300 HB. Calculate the tensile strength in MPa and in psi.**

Using Eq. (2.13) and (2.14) on pp. 82 and 83, respectively, we find that

$$\text{UTS} = 3.5(\text{HB}) = 3.5(300) = 1050 \text{ MPa}$$

and

$$\text{UTS} = 500(300) = 150,000 \text{ psi}$$

**2.43 A material has the following properties: UTS = 50,000 psi and $n$ = 0.25. Calculate its strength coefficient, $K$.**

Let's first note that the true UTS of this material is given by $\sigma = Kn^n$. We can then determine the value of this stress from the UTS by following a procedure similar to the Example 2.1 on p. 73. Since $n = 0.25$, we can write

$$\text{True UTS} = \text{UTS}\,(A_o/A_{\text{neck}})$$

where $A_o/A_{\text{neck}} = e^n = 0.25^{0.25} = 1.28$. Hence, true UTS=50,000 (1.28)=64,200 psi. Therefore,

$$K = 64,200/(0.25)^{0.25} = 90,800 \text{ psi}$$

**2.44 A material has a strength coefficient $K$ = 100,000 psi and $n$ = 0.2. Assuming that a tensile-test specimen made from this material begins to neck at a true strain of 0.2, show that the ultimate tensile strength of this material is 59,340 psi.**

The approach is very similar to that for Problem 2.43. The true UTS is given by

$$\text{True UTS} = Kn^n = 100,000(0.2)^{0.2} = 72,500 \text{ psi}$$

The true UTS is also related to the UTS by:

$$\text{True UTS} = \text{UTS}(A_o/A_{\text{neck}}) = \text{UTS}e^n = 1.22 \text{ UTS}$$

Hence, UTS=72,500/1.22=59,340 psi.

**2.45 Modulus of resilience is defined as the area under the elastic region of the stress-strain curve of the material; it has the units of energy-per-unit volume. Derive an expression for the modulus of resilience in terms of the yield stress and modulus of elasticity of the material.**

The area under the elastic portion of the curve is simply

$$\text{Area} = (\text{Yield stress})(\text{Yield strain})/2$$

The modulus of resilience is therefore

$$\text{MR} = (Y)(Y/E)/2 = Y^2/2E$$

**2.46 What is the modulus of resilience for a highly cold-worked piece of steel having a hardness of 275 HB? For a piece of highly cold-worked copper with a hardness of 100 HRB?**

From the first paragraph in Section 2.6.2 on p. 82, we note that the yield strength of a cold-worked metal is about three times the yield stress, $Y$. For the cold-worked steel with a hardness of 275 HB, the yield strength is then 825 MPa. From Table 2.2 on p. 67, $E_{\text{steel}} = 190$ GPa. Therefore, using the expression derived in Problem 2.45,

$$\text{MR}_{\text{steel}} = \frac{Y^2}{2E} = \frac{(825 \text{ MPa})^2}{2(190 \text{ GPa})} = 1.79 \text{ MPa}$$

Similarly, for the cold-worked copper, $Y = 300$ MPa, $E = 105$ GPa, and thus

$$\text{MR}_{\text{copper}} = \frac{Y^2}{2E} = \frac{(300 \text{ MPa})^2}{2(105 \text{ GPa})} = 0.43 \text{ MPa}$$

**2.47 Using only Fig. 2.6, calculate the maximum load in tension testing of a 304 stainless steel specimen with an original diameter of 5 mm.**

We note from the figure that the necking strain for 304 stainless steel is 0.45 and that the true stress at necking is about 900 MPa. The true area at necking is therefore

$$A_{\text{neck}} = A_o e^{-n} = \left[\frac{\pi}{4}5^2\right] e^{-0.45} = 12.5 \text{ mm}^2$$

Hence the maximum load is

$$P_{\text{max}} = (900 \text{ MN/m}^2)(12.5 \text{ mm}^2) = 11,270 \text{ N}$$

**2.48 Calculate the major and minor pyramid angles for a Knoop indenter and compare to Vickers and Rockwell A indenters.**

Refer to Fig. 2.12 on p. 80 for the geometry of the indenters. For a Knoop indenter with $b/t = 4$, the pyramid's minor angle is given by

$$\beta = \tan^{-1}(2) = 63^\circ$$

Also, since $L/b = 7.11$ and $b/t = 4$, then

$$\frac{L}{t} = \frac{L}{b}\frac{b}{t} = (7.11)(4) = 28.44$$

Therefore, the major pyramid angle is

$$\alpha = \tan^{-1}(14.22) = 86^\circ$$

**2.49 If a material has a target hardness of 350 HB, what is the expected indentation diameter?**

From Fig. 2.12 the indentation diameter depends on the load and the Brinell hardness according to the equation

$$\text{HB} = \frac{2P}{(\pi D)\left(D - \sqrt{D^2 - d^2}\right)}$$

where $P$ is the load (either 500, 1500 or 3000 kg) and $D$ is the diameter of the indenting ball (10 mm). This equation can be solved for $d$ as:

$$d = \sqrt{D^2 - \left(D - \frac{2P}{\pi D(\text{HB})}\right)^2}$$

Thus, (a) for a load of 500 kg, $d$ is 1.34 mm, (b) a load of 1500 kg, $d$ is 2.32 mm, and (c) for a load of 3000 kg, $d$ is 3.25 mm.

**2.50 A Rockwell A test was conducted on a material and a penetration depth of 0.1 mm was recorded. What is the hardness of the material? What material will typically give such hardness values? If a Brinell hardness test were to be conducted on this material, give an estimate of the indentation diameter if the load used is 1500 kg.**

From Fig. 2.12, the Rockwell hardness is calculated from

$$\text{HRA} = 100 - 500t = 100 - 500(0.1) = 50 \text{ HRA}$$

From Fig. 2.14 on p. 84, a material with a 50 HRA should have a Brinell hardness of 140 HB. Therefore, from Fig. 2.12,

$$\text{HB} = \frac{2P}{(\pi D)\left(D - \sqrt{D^2 - d^2}\right)}$$

or, solving for $d$,

$$d = \sqrt{D^2 - \left(D - \frac{2P}{(\pi D)(\text{HB})}\right)} = \sqrt{10^2 - \left(10 - \frac{2(1500)}{(\pi(10))(140)}\right)} = 3.6 \text{ mm}$$

**2.51 A material is tested in tension. Over a 1-in. gage length, the engineering strain measurements are 0.01, 0.02, 0.03, 0.04, 0.05, 0.1, 0.15, 0.2, 0.5, and 1.0. Plot the true strain versus engineering strain for these readings.**

The engineering strain is easy to calculate from Eq. (2.2) on p. 67, and the true strain is given by Eq. (2.7) on p. 70 as

$$\epsilon = \ln\left(\frac{l}{l_o}\right)$$

The following chart can then be made of the data points:

| $e$ | 0.01 | 0.02 | 0.03 | 0.04 | 0.05 | 0.1 | 0.15 | 0.2 | 0.5 | 1.0 |
|---|---|---|---|---|---|---|---|---|---|---|
| $\epsilon$ | 0.01 | 0.0198 | 0.0296 | 0.0392 | 0.0488 | 0.0953 | 0.1397 | 0.182 | 0.405 | 0.69 |

The plot is as follows:

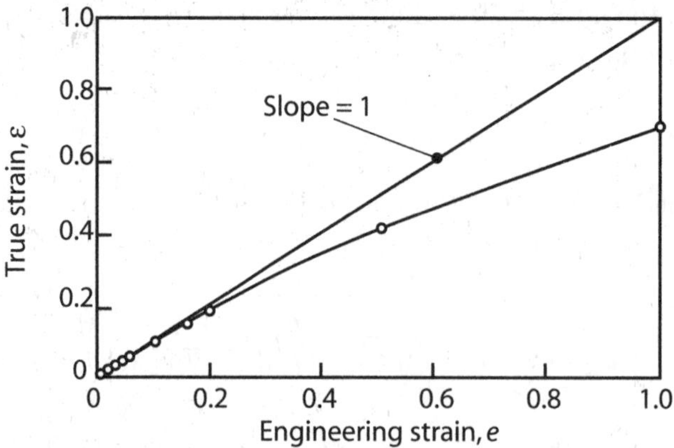


## SYNTHESIS, DESIGN, AND PROJECTS

**2.52 List and explain the desirable mechanical properties for (a) an elevator cable, (b) a paper clip, (c) a leaf spring for a truck, (d) a bracket for a bookshelf, (e) piano wire, (f) a wire coat hanger, (g) a gas-turbine blade, and (h) a staple.**

(a) Elevator cable: The cable should not elongate elastically to a great extent or undergo yielding under the load applied. These requirements call for a material with a high elastic modulus and yield stress. The cable should also be sufficiently flexible and ductile to be wrapped around the drums during its use.

(b) Paper clip: The clip material must possess high ductility to allow it to be formed without fracture. In its normal use, the clip should recover elastically when removed as well as apply sufficient force to hold papers together (thus should possess high elastic modulus).

(c) Leaf spring: The function of the leaf spring is to absorb energy elastically upon static or dynamic loading. The energy should be absorbed in an elastic manner because after absorbing the energy, the spring should return to its original shape. This requires a high yield stress and high elastic modulus that maximizes the area under the elastic portion of the stress-strain curve (modulus of resilience).

(d) Bracket: Much like an elevator cable, but not as critical, a material with a high yield stress and elastic modulus would be required. These properties would keep the shelf from sagging excessively under load.

(e) Piano wire: A piano wire is under high tension (hence high stress) to achieve the desired tone. The wire should be able to maintain this stress level for a period of time, or the piano would become out of tune. Thus, its yield stress should be high in order to sustain the tension required to produce the tone, and should not be susceptible to stress relaxation. Furthermore, it should be sufficiently ductile to be able to be wound around the tightening mechanisms.

(f) Wire coat hanger: Much like the paper clip, the hanger requires a large amount of deformation in its manufacturing, so the material must possess high ductility. The hanger should also be able to maintain its shape when clothes are hung on it, hence it should possess sufficient yield strength and elastic modulus.

(g) Gas turbine blade: A gas turbine blade is required to operate at high temperatures (depending on its location or stage in the engine), so it should have high-temperature strength and be resistant to creep, as well as oxidation and corrosion due to combustion products during use.

(h) Staple: The properties should closely parallel a paper clip. The staple should have high ductility to allow it to be deformed without fracture, and also a low yield stress so the staple can be bent (as well as removed) easily without requiring the user to exert a great amount of force.

**2.53 When making a hamburger, have you observed the type of cracks shown in Fig. 2.19d? What can you do to avoid such cracks? Note: Test hamburger patties by compressing them at different temperatures and observe the crack path (i.e., through the fat particles, the meat particles, or their interface).**

These cracks do occur, and they can be eliminated by making sure that the chunk of ground meat is not too cold. In experiments, which can be performed by the student, it can be observed that when cold, cracks propagate through the meat particles rather than through the fat. As temperature increases, cracks would propagate through the fat, which eventually softens and melts as higher temperatures are reached (which is easily observed when frying ground meat in a pan to make, for example, meat sauce).

**2.54 An inexpensive claylike material, called Silly Putty®, is often available in stores that sell toys and games. Obtain some and do the following experiments. (a) Shape it into a ball and drop it onto a flat surface. (b) Put the re-rounded ball on a table, and place a heavy book on it for five minutes. (c) Shape it into a long cylindrical piece, and pull it apart - first slowly, then quickly. Describe your observations and refer to the specific sections in this chapter where each particular observation is relevant.**

Silly putty is an extremely strain-rate sensitive material. When shaped into a ball and bounced, it undergoes a high strain rate and acts as very rigid, elastic material; i.e., it bounces. When placed on a table and subjected to a static force such as placing a book in it, it deforms as a very soft, plastic material and there is very little elastic recovery. When stretched slowly, it is very ductile; when stretched quickly, it can be seen that the ductility is drastically reduced, and the stiffness and strength are also much higher.

**2.55 Make individual sketches of the mechanisms of testing machines that, in your opinion, would be appropriate for tension, for torsion, and for compression testing of specimens at different rates of deformation. What modifications would you make to include the effects of temperature on material properties?**

By the student. The important features are that the jaws of the machine must move at constant speed; this can be simply done using a power screw drive, with a load cell to measure force. More elaborate machines can use hydraulic power sources and control systems to achieve any desired mode of loading. For testing at elevated temperatures, the machine must be protected, and the specimen must be insulated from the environment to maintain constant temperature during the test. This clearly requires a test chamber that is thermally insulated.

**2.56 In Section 2.6.1, we described the Mohs hardness test. Obtain small pieces of several different metallic and nonmetallic materials, including stones. Rub them against each other, observe the scratches made, and order them in a manner similar to the Mohs numbering system.**

By the student. Some subtle points are that scratches may be difficult to detect and measure when the hardness of the specimen and that of the harder body are close to each other. Also, the materials to be tested may have hardness variations along their surfaces.

**2.57 Demonstrate stress relaxation by tightly stretching thin plastic strings between two nails on a long piece of wood. Pluck the strings frequently, to test the tension as a function of time and of temperature. (Note: Alter the temperature by placing the fixture in an oven set on "low.")**

By the student. This experiment can be easily performed with a fishing line, but one must be careful with a wooden support in an oven. The string tone decreases in frequency over time, demonstrating stress relaxation.

**2.58 Demonstrate the impact toughness of a round piece of chalk by first using a triangular file to produce a V-notch, as shown in Fig. 2.18a, and then bending the chalk to break it.**

By the student. Chalk is relatively easy to break by hand. With a carefully filed, sharp notch, a dramatic reduction in the required force can be easily observed. With a simple fixture (such as using a vise), the chalk can be cantilevered and small weights dropped from ever higher distances to demonstrate the level of energy required to fracture the chalk.

**2.59 Using a large rubber band and a set of weights, obtain the force-displacement curve for the rubber band. How is this different from the stress-strain curves shown in Fig. 2.5?**

By the student. See also Fig. 7.14 on p. 214 and note that the behavior of rubber is highly nonlinear elastic. Two qualitative examples of load-elongation or stress-strain curves are given below. Some rubber bands have a prestress, so that a non-zero force is needed to obtain a small deflection, but these are rare. Most have section where the slope of the stress-strain curve is low, but the curve is very steep near fracture. This can be easily felt with a rubber band. Occasionally, there will be an initial stiff section as shown.

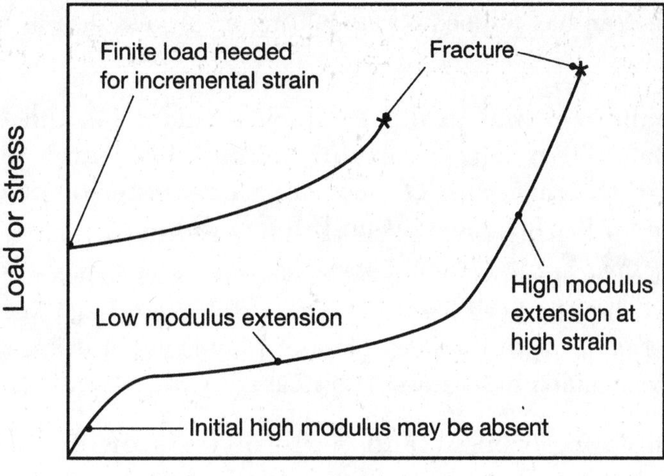


**2.60 Find or prepare some solid circular pieces of brittle materials (such as chalk, ceramics, etc.) and subject them to the type of test shown in Fig. 2.9 by using the jaws of a simple vise. Describe your observations as to how the materials fracture. Repeat the tests using ductile materials (such as clay, soft metals, etc.) and describe your observations.**

By the student. When carefully performed, one can demonstrate the failure mode as described in the disc test on p. 77, namely, that the brittle material fractures in tension along the midplane of the specimen. Note that most vises have a knurled, rough surface finish which can influence the results; a hard and flat spacer may need to be inserted into the jaws of the vise on opposite ends of the disk. Also, for a ductile material, the disk will flatten, and it may be very difficult to actually cause fracture if a soft specimen is being used in the experiment.

**2.61 Devise a simple fixture for the bend tests shown in Fig. 2.11 and test sticks of brittle materials by loading them with dead weights until they break. Verify the statement that the specimens on the right in the figure will break sooner than the ones on the left.**

By the student. This test can be performed using specially fabricated fixtures on a tension test machine. However, it can also be done very simply by using a small-diameter rod, suspended between two desks and the load applied by a basket with two strings. Three-point bending can be simulated by placing both strings at the same location, and four-point bending by spacing the strings along the rod. The load in the basket can be increased until the rod fails. Other alternatives are also possible.

**2.62 By pushing a ball bearing against the top surfaces of various materials (such as clay, dough, etc.) observe with a magnifier the shape of the indentation, similar to those shown in Fig. 2.13a and b.**

By the student. Note that with simple materials, the indentation shape (when viewed from above) will always be circular. An interesting specimen can be carefully prepared by reinforcing threads placed in the material so that a non-circular patch can be created. A side view of a deformed zone can be obtained by laminating materials, such as using clays with different colors.

**2.63 Embed a small steel ball in a soft block of material and compress it as shown in Fig. 2.23a. Then cut it carefully along the center plane and observe the deformation of the material. Repeat the same experiment by embedding a small round jelly bean in the material and deforming it.**

By the student. The steel ball will not deform, just as is shown in the middle sketch of Fig. 2.23b on p. 90. The jelly bean has to be soft in order to simulate the behavior shown in Fig. 2.23a. An alternative is to use two colors of Play-Doh® in a carefully prepared specimen, with one material chilled to increase its stiffness.

**2.64 Devise a simple experiment and perform tests on materials commonly found in a kitchen by bending them for a qualitative assessment of their transition temperature, as shown in Fig. 2.24.**

By the student. This experiment can be performed fairly easily on materials such as butter, chocolate, or cheese. The temperature can be varied and controlled by putting the materials in a freezer or increasing it by immersion into water heated to different temperatures. A qualitative assessment of transition temperature can thus be done; also, a number of experiments can be performed to assess ductility (such as shearing the material and observing the strains that can be achieved - shearing can include smearing with a knife).

**2.65 Locate some solid and some tubular metal pieces, and cut them as shown in Fig. 2.30 to determine if there are any residual stresses in the parts prior to cutting them.**

By the student. The answers can vary widely depending on the materials and their processing history. Most tubes have been extruded and drawn and will have some residual stresses notable. Some tubes may be annealed and therefore be residual stress free.

# Chapter 3

# Physical Properties of Materials

## QUALITATIVE PROBLEMS

**3.10 Describe the significance of structures and machine components made of two materials with different coefficients of thermal expansion.**

The structural fit of the machine components will depend on the thermal expansion coefficient. For instance, if two materials with different thermal expansion coefficients are assembled together by some means and then heated, the structure will develop internal stresses due to uneven expansion. If these stresses are high enough, the structure will warp, bend, or buckle in order to balance or relieve the stresses; it will possibly retain some internal (residual) stresses as well. If prevented from warping, the structure will develop high internal stresses which can lead to cracks. This is not always detrimental; shrink fits are designed recognizing that materials may have different coefficients of thermal expansion, and some machine elements such as thermocouples and temperature probes are based on a mismatch of thermal expansion coefficients.

**3.11 Which of the properties described in this chapter are important for (a) mechanical pencils, (b) cookie sheets for baking, (c) rulers, (d) paper clips, (e) door hinges, (f) beverage cans? Explain your answers.**

(a) Mechanical pencil: Requires good environmental corrosion resistance to keep parts functioning. Also, its weight (density) should make it comfortable to write with.

(b) Cookie sheet: Requires corrosion resistance at high temperatures, the specific heat should allow for rapid heating of the sheet, and a high thermal conductivity should allow for even distribution of heat across the sheet. The melting temperature should be high enough that the sheet can safely withstand baking temperatures.

(c) Ruler: Should have low thermal expansion to maintain the measurements accurately and a low density to make it easy to carry.

(d) Paper clip: Should be corrosion resistant, with a stiffness that holds papers together without requiring excessive force.

(e) Door hinge: Should be corrosion resistant for functional as well as aesthetic purposes.

(f) Beverage can: Should have a high thermal conductivity, low density, and good corrosion resistance.

**3.12 You will note in Table 3.1 that the properties of the alloys of metals have a wide range as compared to the properties of the pure metals. What factors are responsible for this?**

Alloying elements tend to disturb the crystal lattice of the base metal, and they do so by distorting the lattice by occupying lattice sites (substitutional atoms), spaces between lattice sites (interstitials), or forming a second phase (an intermetallic compound of the two elements). Lattice distortion will reduce properties that depend on a repeating lattice, such as thermal conductivity and melting points. Properties such as density and specific heat generally depend on the properties of the alloying elements, and range around the value for the alloy base metal. Also, 'alloys' is a generic term, and can include a very wide range of concentration and types of alloying element, whereas pure metals have, by definition, only one chemistry.

**3.13 Does thermal conductivity play a role in the development of residual stresses in metals? Explain.**

Thermal conductivity is one of the most important material properties affecting thermal stress (along with thermal expansion). In terms of residual stresses, it is much less important than the processing history. However, uneven cooling of castings (Part II) or welds (Part VI), for example, can cause warpage and residual stresses.

**3.14 What material properties are desirable for heat shields, such as those placed on the space shuttle?**

Material properties required for heat shields are sufficient strength so that they do not fail upon takeoff, reentry, and landing; they must have a high melting point so that they do not change phase or degrade at the high temperatures developed during reentry, and they must be exceptionally high thermal insulators so that the shuttle cabin does not heat significantly during reentry.

## QUANTITATIVE PROBLEMS

**3.15 If we assume that all the work done in plastic deformation is converted into heat, the temperature rise in a workpiece is (a) directly proportional to the work done per unit volume and (b) inversely proportional to the product of the specific heat and the density of the workpiece. Using Fig. 2.6, and letting the areas under the**

**curves be the unit work done, calculate the temperature rise for (i) 8650 steel, (ii) 304 stainless steel, and (iii) 1100-H14 aluminum.**

We use the following information given in Chapters 2 and 3: The area under the true stress-true strain curve and the physical properties for each of the three metals. We then follow the procedure discussed on pp. 96-97 and use Eq. (2.15). Thus, for (a) 8650 steel, the area under the curve in Fig. 2.6 on p. 72 is about $u = 72,000$ in-lb/in$^3$. Let's assume a density of $\rho = 0.3$ lb/in$^3$ and a specific heat $c = 0.12$ BTU/lb °F. Therefore, we have

$$\Delta T = \frac{72,000}{(0.3)(0.12)(778)(12)} = 214°\text{F}$$

For (b) 304 stainless steel, we have $u = 175,000$, $\rho = 0.3$ and $c = 0.12$, hence $\Delta T = 520°$F. For (c) 1100-H14 aluminum, we have $u = 25,000$ in.-lb/in$^3$, $\rho = 0.0975$ and $c = 0.215$; hence $\Delta T = 128°$F.

**3.16 The natural frequency, $f$, of a cantilever beam is given by**

$$f = 0.56\sqrt{\frac{EIg}{wL^4}}$$

**where $E$ is the modulus of elasticity, $I$ is the moment of inertia, $g$ is the gravitational constant, $w$ is the weight of the beam per unit length, and $L$ is the length of the beam. How does the natural frequency of the beam change, if at all, as its temperature is increased? Assume that the material is steel.**

Let's assume that the beam has a square cross-section with a side of length $h$, although as we shall see, the cross-section of the beam does not affect the final result. The beam's moment of inertia is then

$$I = \frac{h^4}{12}$$

The moment of inertia will increase as temperature increases, because the cross-section will become larger due to thermal expansion. The weight per length is given by

$$w = \frac{W}{L}$$

where $W$ is the weight of the beam and $L$ is the beam length. Since $L$ increases with increasing temperature but $W$ is constant, the weight per length will decrease with increasing temperature. Also, note that the modulus of elasticity will decrease with increasing temperature (see, for example, Fig. 2.7 on p. 74). Consider the ratio of initial frequency (subscript 1) to frequency at elevated temperature (subscript 2):

$$\frac{f_1}{f_2} = \frac{0.56\sqrt{\frac{E_1 I_1 g}{w_1 L_1^4}}}{0.56\sqrt{\frac{E_2 I_2 g}{w_2 L_2^4}}} = \frac{\sqrt{\frac{E_1 I_1}{(W/L_1)L_1^4}}}{\sqrt{\frac{E_2 I_2}{(W/L_2)L_2^4}}} = \frac{\sqrt{\frac{E_1 I_1}{L_1^3}}}{\sqrt{\frac{E_2 I_2}{L_2^3}}} = \sqrt{\left(\frac{E_1}{E_2}\right)\left(\frac{I_1}{I_2}\right)\left(\frac{L_2^3}{L_1^3}\right)}$$

$$= \sqrt{\left(\frac{E_1}{E_2}\right)\left(\frac{h_1^4}{h_2^4}\right)\left(\frac{L_2^3}{L_1^3}\right)}$$

Letting $\alpha$ be the coefficient of thermal expansion, we can write

$$h_2 = h_1(1 + \alpha\Delta T)$$

$$L_2 = L_1(1 + \alpha\Delta T)$$

Therefore, the frequency ratio is

$$\frac{f_1}{f_2} = \sqrt{\left(\frac{E_1}{E_2}\right)\left(\frac{h_1^4}{h_2^4}\right)\left(\frac{L_2^3}{L_1^3}\right)} = \sqrt{\left(\frac{E_1}{E_2}\right)\left(\frac{h_1^4}{h_1^4(1+\alpha\Delta T)^4}\right)\left(\frac{L_1^3(1+\alpha\Delta T)^3}{L_1^3}\right)}$$
$$= \sqrt{\left(\frac{E_1}{E_2}\right)\left(\frac{1}{1+\alpha\Delta T}\right)}$$

To compare the effects of the modulus and the thermal expansion, consider the following plot (taken from S. Kalpakjian, *Manufacturing Engineering and Technology*, 2nd ed., Addison-Wesley, 1992):

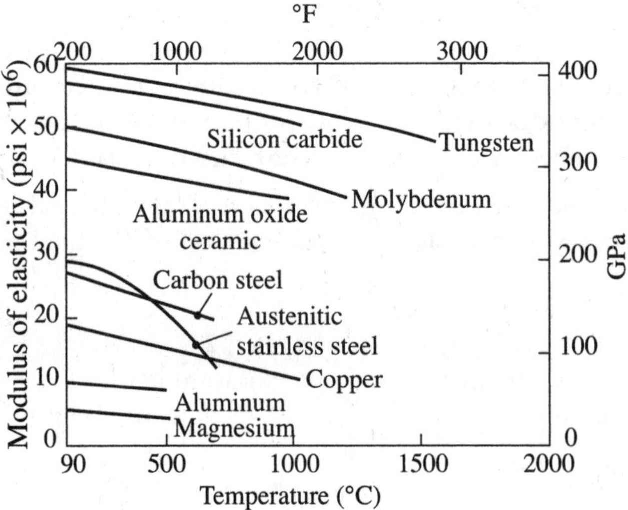


Consider, for example, carbon steel, where the elastic modulus changes from $28 \times 10^6$ psi to around $20 \times 10^6$ psi for a temperature increase of 800°C. Since the coefficient of thermal expansion for steel is 14.5 $\mu$m/m°C (see Table 3.1 on p. 103), then the change in frequency for this case is:

$$\frac{f_1}{f_2} = \sqrt{\left(\frac{E_1}{E_2}\right)\left(\frac{1}{1+\alpha\Delta T}\right)} = \sqrt{\left(\frac{28}{20}\right)\left(\frac{1}{1+(14.5\times10^{-6})(800)}\right)} = 1.18$$

Thus the frequency of the beam decreases when it is heated. This is the general trend (and not just a peculiarity for carbon steel), namely that the elastic modulus plays a larger role than the thermal expansion.

**3.17 It can be shown that thermal distortion in precision devices is low for high values of thermal conductivity divided by thermal expansion coefficient. Rank the materials in Table 3.1 according to their suitability to resist thermal distortion.**

The calculations using the data in Table 3.1 on p. 103 are as follows. When a range of values is given for an alloy, the average value has been used. These materials have been ranked according to the ratio of thermal conductivity to thermal expansion coefficient.

| Material | Thermal conductivity, $k$ | Thermal expansion coefficient, $\alpha$ | $k/\alpha$ |
|---|---|---|---|
| Tungsten | 166 | 4.5 | 36.9 |
| Molybdenum alloys | 142 | 5.1 | 27.8 |
| Copper | 393 | 16.5 | 23.8 |
| Silver | 429 | 19.3 | 22.2 |
| Silicon | 148 | 7.63 | 19.4 |
| Beryllium | 146 | 8.5 | 17.2 |
| Gold | 317 | 19.3 | 16.4 |
| Copper alloys | 234 | 18 | 13.0 |
| Aluminum | 222 | 23.6 | 9.41 |
| Tantalum alloys | 54 | 6.5 | 8.31 |
| Aluminum alloys | 180 | 23 | 7.72 |
| Columbium (niobium) | 52 | 7.1 | 7.32 |
| Nickel | 92 | 13.3 | 6.92 |
| Iron | 74 | 11.5 | 6.43 |
| Magnesium | 154 | 26 | 5.92 |
| Magnesium alloys | 106.5 | 26 | 4.10 |
| Nickel alloys | 37.5 | 15.5 | 2.42 |
| Steels | 33 | 14.5 | 2.28 |
| Titanium | 17 | 8.35 | 2.04 |
| Lead alloys | 35 | 29.1 | 1.20 |
| Lead | 35 | 29.4 | 1.19 |
| Titanium alloys | 10 | 8.8 | 1.14 |

## SYNTHESIS, DESIGN AND PROJECTS

**3.18 From your own experience, make a list of parts, components, and products that have corroded and have had to be replaced or discarded.**

By the student. This is an open-ended problem that have many possible answers, and these will vary depending on the background of the student. There are many parts, usually associated with rusted steel, e.g., automobile frames and bodies, bolts, bicycle pedals, etc. Other parts that are commonly corroded include automotive battery cable terminals, naval parts of all kinds (especially if ocean going), nameplates on old machinery, etc. If one extends the discussion to corrosion-assisted failure, one can include just about all parts which fail by fatigue, including shafts, and airplane fuselages as shown below. This photograph is a dramatic example of corrosion-assisted fatigue of an aircraft fuselage that occurred mid-flight. (*Source:* From Hamrock, B.J., et al., *Fundamentals of Machine Elements*, 2nd ed., New York, McGraw-Hill, 2005, p. 265.).

**3.19 List applications where the following properties would be desirable: (a) high density, (b) low density, (c) high melting point, (d) low melting point, (e) high thermal conductivity, and (f) low thermal conductivity.**

By the student. This is an open-ended problem, and many possible answers exist. Some examples are:

(a) High density: Adding weight to a part (like an anchor, bar bells or a boat), as an inertial element in a self-winding watch, and weights for vertically sliding windows. Also, projectiles such as bullets and shotgun particles are applications where high density is advantageous.

(b) Low density: Airplane components, aluminum tubing for tents, ladders, and high-speed machinery elements. Most sporting goods give better performance if density and hence weight is low, such as tennis rackets, skis, etc.

(c) High melting point: Creep-resistant materials such as for gas-turbine blades or oven insulation. Mold materials for die casting need to have high melting points, as do filaments for light bulbs.

(d) Low melting point: Soldering wire, fuse elements, wax for investment casting, and lubricants that depend on a phase change are examples of such applications.

(e) High thermal conductivity: Rapid extraction of heat in radiators and heat exchangers, and cooling fins for electrical circuits and transformers. Cutting tools with high thermal conductivity can help keep temperatures low in machining. Dies in injection molding with high thermal conductivity can extract heat more quickly allowing higher production rates.

(f) Low thermal conductivity: Coffee cups, winter clothing, and oven insulation require low thermal conductivity. In addition, handles on cookware, lubricants for hot forging, and thermos materials (unless evacuated) need low thermal conductivities.

**3.20 Give several applications in which specific strength and specific stiffness are important.**

By the student. This problem is open-ended and the students should be encouraged to develop answers based on their experience and training. Two examples are: (a) Tent tubing: requires lightweight material for ease of carrying, while possessing sufficiently high strength and stiffness to support the weight of the tent tarp without excessive bending or bowing. (b) Racquetball or tennis racquet: requires lightweight material for control over the racquet's direction; also, high strength and stiffness are required to efficiently transfer the energy of the racquet to the ball.

**3.21 Design several mechanisms or instruments based on utilizing the differences in thermal expansion of materials, such as bimetallic strips that develop a curvature when heated.**

By the student. Instruments will have a common principle of measuring or regulating temperatures such as thermometers or butterfly valves which regulate fluid flow when temperatures vary.

**3.22 For the materials listed in Table 3.1, determine the specific strength and specific stiffness. Describe your observations.**

Selected results are as follows (the values which give highest possible quantities have been used, e.g., high stiffness and low density). Data is taken from Table 2.2 on p. 67.

| Material | $Y$ (MPa) | $E$ (GPa) | Density (kg/m$^3$) | Spec. strength (m $\times 10^3$) | Spec. stiffness (m $\times 10^6$) |
|---|---|---|---|---|---|
| Aluminum | 35 | 69 | 2700 | 1.3 | 2.6 |
| Al alloys | 550 | 79 | 2630 | 21.3 | 3.1 |
| Copper | 76 | 105 | 8970 | 0.86 | 1.2 |
| Cu alloys | 1100 | 150 | 7470 | 15.0 | 2.05 |
| Iron | 205 | 190 | 7860 | 2.66 | 2.5 |
| Steels | 1725 | 200 | 6920 | 25.4 | 2.9 |
| Lead | 14 | 14 | 11,350 | 0.13 | 0.126 |
| Pb alloys | 14 | 14 | 8850 | 0.161 | 0.16 |
| Magnesium | 130 | 41 | 1745 | 7.6 | 2.4 |
| Mg alloys | 305 | 45 | 1770 | 17.6 | 2.6 |
| Mo alloys | 2070 | 360 | 10,210 | 20.7 | 3.6 |
| Nickel | 105 | 180 | 8910 | 1.2 | 2.06 |
| Ni alloys | 1200 | 214 | 7750 | 15.8 | 2.8 |
| Titanium | 344 | 80 | 4510 | 7.8 | 1.8 |
| Ti alloys | 1380 | 130 | 4430 | 31.7 | 3.0 |
| Tungsten | 550 | 350 | 19,290 | 2.9 | 1.8 |

**3.23 The maximum compressive force that a lightweight column can withstand before buckling depends on the ratio of the square root of the stiffness to the density for the material. For the materials listed in Table 2.1, determine (a) the ratio of tensile strength to density and (b) the ratio of elastic modulus to density. Comment on the suitability of each for being made into lightweight columns.**

This problem uses the results from Problem 3.22. To make a lightweight column, one has to maximize the specific strength and the specific stiffness. Reviewing the values obtained, one can observe that: (a) Pure metals are not useful whereas alloys are much more preferable; (b) Titanium alloys have the highest specific strength (31,700 m); (c) Aluminum alloys have the highest specific stiffness (3.1); and (d) Among the lest desirable materials are lead and copper. Note that these results are consistent with the materials of choice for modern aircraft.

**3.24 Describe possible applications and designs using alloys exhibiting the Invar effect of low thermal expansion.**

By the student. If there is essentially no thermal expansion, the material is exceptional for situations where thermal fatigue is a consideration, or for precision instruments where no thermal expansion would be highly desirable. Examples of the former include furnace sensors and electrical components, and examples of the latter include micromanipulators and micro-electromechanical systems (MEMS); see p. 908.

# Chapter 4

# Metal Alloys: Structure and Strengthening by Heat Treatment

## QUALITATIVE PROBLEMS

**4.15 You may have seen some technical literature on products stating that certain parts in those products are "heat treated." Describe briefly your understanding of this term and why the manufacturer mentions it.**

Heat treating, in general, subjects the alloys to controlled heating and cooling cycles to produce a microstructure that improves the mechanical properties of the alloy. Manufacturers mention heat treating because it generally implies an improvement in the properties of the parts, particularly strength, hardness, and wear resistance, although the process is usually accompanied by an increase in cost.

**4.16 Describe the engineering significance of the existence of a eutectic point in phase diagrams.**

A eutecic point corresponds to a composition that has the lowest melting temperature for that alloy system. The low melting temperature associated with a eutectic point is an important aspect of soldering, and also helps in controlling thermal damage to parts being joined.

**4.17 Explain the difference between hardness and hardenability.**

Hardness represents the material's resistance to permanent indentation (Section 2.6 on p. 79), whereas hardenability is the material's capability to be hardened by heat treatment processes.

**4.18 Refer to Table 4.1, and explain why the items listed under "typical applications" are suitable for surface hardening.**

Surface hardening is useful in increasing wear resistance, fatigue resistance, or indentation resistance, without producing a part that is hard and brittle throughout (which would result in low toughness). The parts listed under typical applications would either be exposed to high wear conditions (tools, dies, and gears), cyclic loading (rotating shafts and cams), or where surface damage would render the parts useless (bolts, gears, cams).

**4.19 Why is it generally not desirable to use steels in their as-quenched condition?**

Steels are rarely used in their as-quenched condition because they are very brittle and thus lack toughness. These detrimental conditions are overcome by tempering the steel, which restores toughness.

**4.20 Describe the differences between case hardening and through hardening, insofar as engineering applications are concerned.**

Case hardening is a treatment process that hardens only the outer surface of a part; the bulk retains its toughness, which allows for blunting of surface cracks as they propagate to the core. Case hardening generally induces a residual compressive stress on the workpiece surface which, in turn, helps retard fatigue crack initiation. Through-hardened parts have a high hardness level across the whole part; consequently, a crack could propagate easily through the cross-section of the part, causing failure.

**4.21 Describe the characteristics of (a) an alloy, (b) pearlite, (c) austenite, (d) martensite, and (e) cementite.**

(a) Alloy: Composed of two or more elements, at least one of which is a metal. The alloy may be a solid solution or it may form intermetallic compounds.

(b) Pearlite: A two-phase aggregate consisting of alternate lamellae of ferrite and cementite. The closer the pearlite spacing of the lamellae, the harder the steel will be.

(c) Austenite: Called gamma iron, it has a face-centered cubic structure. The fcc structure allows for higher solubility of carbon in the crystal lattice. This structure also possesses a high level of ductility, which increases the steel's formability.

(d) Martensite: Forms by quenching austenite. It has a body-centered tetragonal (bct) structure, and carbon atoms in interstitial positions impart high strength to the structure. It is very brittle and hard.

(e) Cementite, also known as iron carbide ($Fe_3C$). Cementite is a hard and brittle phase.

**4.22 Explain why carbon, of all the elements, is so effective in imparting strength to iron in the form of steel.**

The size of the carbon atom allows it to have high solubility in the high-temperature fcc phase of iron (austenite). At low temperatures, the structure is bcc and has very low solubility of carbon atoms. Upon quenching, the austenitic structure transforms to bct martensite, which produces a large amount of distortion in the crystal lattice, enough to allow the solubility of carbon, but not other larger atoms.

**4.23 How does the shape of graphite in cast iron affect its properties?**

The shape of graphite in cast iron has the following basic forms:

(a) Flakes: Have sharp edges which act as stress raisers. The shape makes cast iron low in tensile strength and ductility, but it still has good compressive strength. The flakes also act as vibration dampers.

(b) Nodules: Spheroids formed by graphite when magnesium or cerium is added to the melt. This form has increased ductility, strength, and shock resistance over flakes, but the damping capacity is reduced.

(c) Clusters: Much like nodules, except they form from the breakdown of white cast iron upon annealing. Clusters have properties similar to flakes.

(d) Compacted flakes: Short thick flakes with rounded edges. This form has properties that are between nodular and flake graphite.

**4.24 In Section 4.8, we listed several fluids in terms of their cooling capacity in quenching. Which physical properties of these fluids influence their cooling capacity?**

The main physical properties of the fluids that influence their cooling capacity are thermal conductivity and specific heat. Agitation (rapid movement of the quenching medium) is an effective way of increasing the cooling capacity of the quenching medium.

**4.25 Why is it important to know the characteristics of heat-treating furnaces?**

The size, shape, and heating media of heat-treating furnaces make them useful in various applications. For example

- Batch: Usually large furnaces that allow a large number of parts to be treated simultaneously. Batch furnaces are important for parts such as bolts or cams that are produced in large but finite quantities.
- Continuous: Offers close control over heating cycles. Some parts have complex heating cycles, requiring controlled heating and cooling rates to develop desired microstructures, and this can be best achieved in a continuous furnace.
- Gas-fired: Can be used for gas carburization of parts. Carburization is a valuable hardening process that can be used for gears, cams, etc.
- Electric: Offers closest control over furnace atmospheres. Sometimes it is important to exclude oxygen or nitrogen to avoid oxidation or the formation of nitrides during heat treating.

**4.26 Explain why, in the abscissa of Fig. 4.15, the percentage of pearlite begins to go down after 100% carbon content is reached.**

Pearlite is a eutectoid transformation of steel that occurs at 0.77 weight percent carbon. Its microstructure consists of about 88% ferrite and 12% cementite. As the carbon content is increased, more than 12% of cementite is formed. The microstructure consists of pearlite and excess cementite, and the excess cementite reduces the percentage of pearlite.

**4.27 What is the significance of decarburization? Give some examples.**

Decarburization results in a loss of carbon from the surface layers of a part. The lower carbon at the surface consequently results in lower strength and hardness. Fatigue life and wear resistance are also reduced. If a bolt or screw is decarburized during heat treatment, the tendency to strip the threads will be increased. Decarburization is especially harmful in the heat treatment of tool and die steels, since the softer surface would have less wear resistance.

**4.28 Explain your understanding of size distortion and of shape distortion in heat-treated parts, and describe their causes.**

Because of microstructural changes during heat treatment and variations in the rate of heating and cooling in different regions of a part, heat treatment can cause distortions. Size distortion involves changes in the dimensions of the part without a change in shape, whereas shape distortion involves bending, twisting, and similar nonsymmetrical dimensional changes. These are illustrated below; the red image shows a size distortion, although greatly exaggerated compared to shrinkage from heat treating or casting, for example. The green image shows a shape that has distorted, but the nominal size of the part has remained constant.

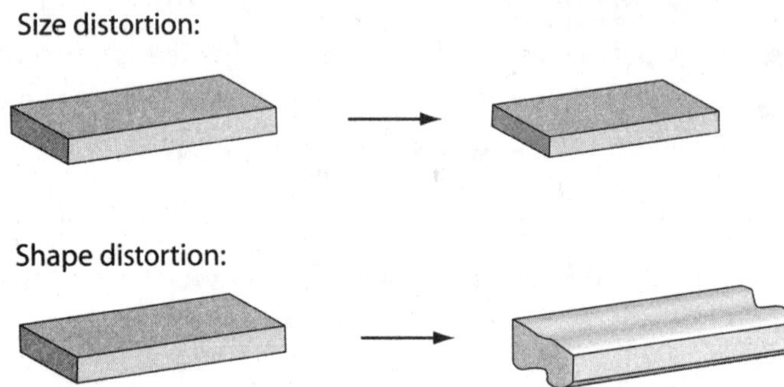


**4.29 Comment on your observations regarding Fig. 4.20.**

Several observations can be made: (a) Hardness decreases with increasing distance from the quenched end, due to the slower cooling rate. (b) For plain-carbon steels, hardness increases with increasing carbon content, as shown in Fig. 4.18 (a) on p. 131. (c) The hardness is higher for nickel- and chrome-alloy steels (see Table 5.3 and the discussion of austenite and ferrite formers on p. 125), with nickel having a greater effect on hardenability.

**4.30 Design a heat-treat cycle for carbon steel, including temperature and exposure times, to produce (a) pearlite-martensite steels and (b) bainite-martensite steels.**

The heat-treat cycle for these conditions can be obtained from Fig. 4.17c. For part (a), it is desired to produce a pearlite-martensite steel, so it is important that the cooling rate be maintained between 140° and 35°C/s when cooling the material from the eutectoid temperature. Such a cooling rate can be achieved with a salt or oil quench, where the bath temperature will determine the cooling rate and the ultimate percentage of pearlite and martensite. For part (b), it is desired to have bainite, which forms under very rapid cooling (see the discussion on pp. 127-128). Thus the two heat-treat cycles desired can be sketched as shown below.

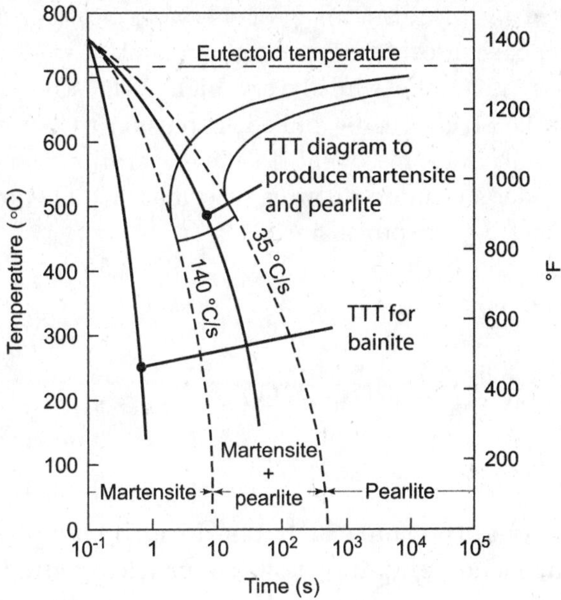


## QUANTITATIVE PROBLEMS

**4.31 Using Fig. 4.5, estimate the following quantities for a 20% Cu - 80% Ni alloy: (a) The liquidus temperature. (b) The solidus temperature. (c) The percentage of nickel in the liquid at 1400 °C (2550 °F). (d) The major phase at 1400 °C. (e) The ratio of solid to liquid at 1400 °C.**

(a) Liquidus temperature: 1400 °C (2550 °F).

(b) Solidus temperature: 1372 °C (2500 °F).

(c) At 1400 °C (2550 °F) the alloy is still all liquid, thus the nickel composition is 80% .

(d) The major phase at 1400 °C is liquid, with no solids present since the alloy is not below the liquidus temperature.

(e) The ratio is zero, since no solid is present.

**4.32 Extrapolating the curves in Fig. 4.16, estimate the time that it would take for 1080 steel to soften to 53 HRC at (a) 200 °C and (b) 300 °C.**

From the graph of hardness of tempered martensite, for 200 °C the time is $10^7$ s and for 300 °C it is $10^4$ s.

**4.33 A typical steel for tubing is AISI 1040, one for music wire 1085. Considering their applications, explain the reason for the difference in their carbon contents.**

Music wire is formed by wire drawing processes (see Sections 15.7 through 15.10), and the combination of high carbon content and large amount of work hardening (that accompanies the drawing process) gives the wire a very high yield stress. The high yield strength is necessary to allow the strings to be pulled in tension to obtain the proper pitch. Tubing requires higher ductility for subsequent forming operations (such as bending, flanging, and bulging) where it undergoes more rigorous deformation. The lower carbon content gives the steel the required ductility for processing.

## SYNTHESIS, DESIGN AND PROJECTS

**4.34 We stated in this chapter that, in parts design, sharp corners should be avoided in order to reduce the tendency toward cracking during heat treatment. If it is necessary for the part to have sharp corners in order to function properly and it still requires heat treatment, what method would you recommend for manufacturing this part?**

Cracking could be eliminated by having a sufficiently low cooling rate to avoid thermal shock. A lower cooling rate could be achieved by using a less severe quenching medium, such as air or oil instead of water; die quenching also may be beneficial. Sharp corners can be produced by subsequent machining or grinding of the heat-treated part without any danger of cracking.

**4.35 The heat-treatment processes for surface hardening are given in Table 4.1. Each of these processes involves different equipment, procedures, and cycle times; as a result, each incurs different costs. Examine available literature, and contact various facilities; then, make a similar table outlining the costs involved in each process.**

By the student. Specific costs will vary with location. Costs will also vary with the number and size of parts, specific processing parameters, and the required hardened depth.

**4.36 We have seen that, as a result of heat treatment, parts can undergo size distortion and shape distortion to various degrees. By referring to the Bibliography at the end of this chapter, make a survey of the technical literature, and report quantitative data regarding the distortions of parts having different shapes.**

By the student. This problem appears straightforward, but it is quite challenging because of the call for quantitative data. Distortions will be given as tolerances or deflections, and these need to be translated to particular shapes by the students to gain an appreciation of shape distortions.

**4.37 Figure 4.20 shows hardness distributions in end-quench tests, as measured along the *length* of the round bar. Make a simple qualitative sketch showing the hardness distribution *across the diameter* of the bar. Would the shape of the curve depend on the bar's carbon content? Explain.**

Hardness profiles will be somewhat similar to the curves shown in Fig. 4.20b on p. 133, with the abscissa indicating the distance from the outer diameter, instead of the distance from the quenched end. The shape of the curve will depend on the carbon content since the hardness of martensite increases greatly with increasing carbon content. The magnitude of the hardness will depend on the position along the length of the bar. However, because the radius is smaller than the length, the difference in the cooling rate between the outside radius and the center will not be as high as the differences along the length. An acceptable qualitative curve is as shown below. Note that the curve is increasing, and one expects higher hardness at the outside radius than at the center.

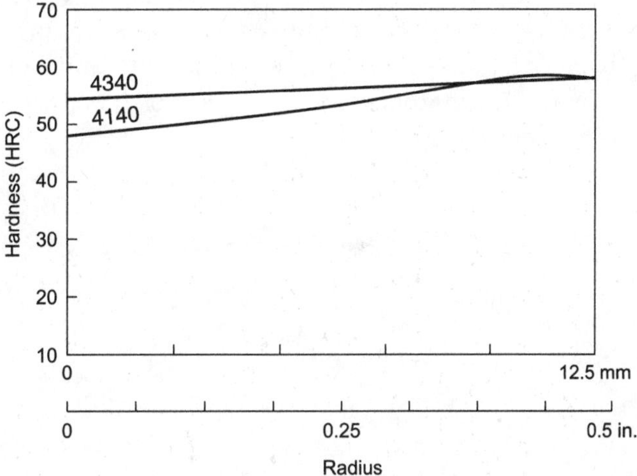


**4.38 Throughout this chapter, you have seen the importance and the benefits of heat treating parts (or certain regions of parts), and you have seen some specific examples. Make a survey of the heat-treatment literature available by referring to the Bibliography at the end of this chapter. Compile several examples and illustrations of parts that have been heat treated.**

By the student. There are numerous examples of heat-treated parts; for example, cutlery, gear teeth, nuts and bolts, hand tools, shafts, tools and dies, crankshafts, sprockets, springs, and cams. Most parts that require wear resistance have been heat treated to increase their hardness. In addition, applications where impacts occur and could lead to surface damage often use hardened parts.

**4.39 Referring to Fig. 4.26, suggest a variety of other part shapes to be heat treated, and design appropriate coils for them. Describe how your designs would change if the parts have varying shapes along their length.**

By the student. For constant cross-sections, the coils can closely match the contour of the part, and this represents a fairly straightforward design problem. If the cross-section varies, there are a number of possible solutions, such as:

- Using a series of coils that have a contour matching the profile at a given axial location. Thus, the part could be inserted into the coil over the entire length to be heat treated, and it could be treated along the entire surface at one time.

- A coil can be used that is compliant, either because of a helix integrated into the coil (like with a spring) or because of geometry as in the support for the coil ends.
- Instead of a continuous coil, a series of coil segments can be used, similar to the aperture for a camera.

**4.40 Inspect various parts in your car or home, and identify those that would have been case hardened. Explain your reasons.**

By the student. As discussed in the chapter, parts are through hardened when the mechanical properties through the thickness need to be improved, and in case hardening they are hardened to a certain depth. Case hardening is desirable when the surface should be hard but the substrate should maintain ductility. Examples are gears (as in automobile transmissions), knives, ice skate blades, hammers, screwdriver bits, nuts and bolts and woodworking tools such as drills and saws. Case hardening gives wear resistance while preserving ductility and resistance to stress concentrations.

# Chapter 5

# Ferrous Metals and Alloys: Production, General Properties, and Applications

## QUALITATIVE PROBLEMS

**5.16 Identify several different products that are made of stainless steel and explain why they are made of this material.**

Applications for stainless steel are usually centered around its corrosion resistance (see pp. 161-162). The students are encouraged to give several applications; a few examples include:

(a) Cutlery: the appearance of the cutlery will not be diminished by rust with time.

(b) Blender blades and other food processing and kitchen equipment: stainless steel will not react chemically with food products, so no unpleasant taste remains on the utensils and so that the food does not become adulterated.

(c) Chemical storage tanks: the chemicals would attack the internal surfaces and produce holes in ordinary steels, rendering them useless.

(d) Orthopedic implants: combined with their biocompatibility, the corrosion resistance of stainless steels is essential for materials placed inside the human body.

**5.17 As you may know, professional cooks prefer carbon-steel to stainless-steel knives, even though the latter are more popular with consumers. Explain the reasons for those preferences.**

Professional cooks keep their knives sharp and use them more often, so that wear resistance of the knives becomes more important. Wear resistance usually is accompanied by high strength and hardness (see Section 33.5 on p. 1046). High-carbon steels can be hardened by heat treatment to a higher degree than stainless steels, thus they have better wear resistance. On the other hand, consumer users have the perception that stainless steel is preferable to carbon steel because it will give superior performance, and this perception drives demand. Also, consumers do not use their knives as often as professional cooks, so wear is not as significant an issue.

**5.18 Why is the control of ingot structure important?**

Control of the ingot structure is important because it will affect the requirements of further processing and the amount of waste material in the ingot. For instance, porosity accompanying semi-killed or rimmed steel should be eliminated during subsequent working of the ingot, such as by forging and rolling (Section 5.3 on p. 153). If the porosity is not eliminated, the strength and ductility of the steel will generally be reduced. The segregation of alloying elements and impurities in rimmed steel generally gives the steel nonuniform properties. On the other hand, killed steels, which typically have little or no porosity, are accompanied by a large shrinkage cavity at the top of the ingot. This pipe must be scrapped (and remelted) before the ingot is processed further.

**5.19 Explain why continuous casting has been such an important technological advancement.**

Continuous casting (Section 5.4 on p. 154) eliminates processing of individual ingots and also eliminates most of the porosity, elemental segregation, and shrinkage associated with ingot casting. Continuously-cast bars can be made in a variety of shapes and sizes, significantly reducing the number of subsequent rolling operations. These major benefits make continuous casting capable of producing higher quality steels at lower cost than individual ingot processing.

**5.20 Describe applications in which you would not want to use carbon steels.**

By the student. Applications that are not suited for carbon steels are those that mainly require high corrosion resistance. A few examples include drain spouts, gutters, and ornamental applications such as cabinet hardware, coins, and faucets. Other applications where carbon steels are not well suited are those where low density is desirable, such as portable computer or camera frames, aircraft fuselages, and automotive pistons.

**5.21 Explain what would happen if the speed of the continuous-casting process (Fig. 5.4) is (a) higher or (b) lower than that indicated (typically 25 mm/s).**

(a) If the speed of the continuous casting process is higher, the metal may not have sufficient time to completely solidify before it leaves the mold area. Liquid metal will eventually start spilling out of the mold. (b) Lower speeds, on the other hand, adversely affect the economics of the process, and are obviously unnecessary.

**5.22 The cost of mill products of metals increases with decreasing thickness and section size. Explain why.**

Smaller thickness and section size generally require more metalworking processing steps, such as in rolling, extrusion, or drawing. The more reduction passes, the higher the cost of manufacturing. The relationship between cost and thickness is also not linear, since going beyond a certain size threshold may also mean that a given machine's capabilities have been exceeded. This situation would require the use of additional machinery and manufacturing steps, leading to a larger increase in cost. Also, it should be noted that as the cross-section decreases, the cost increases but so do the mechanical properties such as yield strength and hardness.

**5.23 Describe your observations regarding the information given in Table 5.7.**

By the student. In general, steels with high hardness have low toughness and high resistance to wear. Also, those having very high resistance to wear have low machinability, and those with high machinability have low resistance to wear. Additional observations can be made by the student by noting the composition of individual steels in the first column of the table.

**5.24 How do trace elements affect the ductility of steels?**

Most trace (residual) elements tend to form inclusions or segregate to grain boundaries, causing embrittlement, thus decreasing toughness and fracture resistance, as well as severe reduction in ductility.

**5.25 Comment on your observations regarding Table 5.1.**

A number of observations can be made. First, a direct comparison between steel and aluminum shows that steel is cheaper per unit weight, and, when a calculation is made, by volume as well. Other tables in the chapter show the general trend that the stronger and more heavily alloyed steels are more expensive than the more common carbon steels. Finally, there is an obvious trend that additional processing is reflected in the costs of, for example, hot-rolled versus cold-rolled steels.

**5.26 In Table 5.7, D2 steel is listed as a tool and die material for most applications. Why is this so?**

D2 tool steel is listed for many applications because, as discussed on p. 164 and shown in Table 5.6, this material has a high resistance to wear and cracking, thus making it ideal for tooling applications. In addition, this material can be formed well because, as a dual-phase steel, it has a high $n$ value (see Section 2.2.5 on p. 71). It also has a high ductility so that fracture is less likely.

**5.27 List the common impurities in steel. Which of these are the ones most likely to be minimized if the steel is melted in a vacuum furnace?**

Imperfections (such as micropores) and surface defects (such as blow holes) exist in steel, which can be reduced by hot working. Residual elements, such as antimony, hydrogen, nitrogen, oxygen and tin, can adversely affect the steel's properties. When melted in a vacuum furnace, on the other hand, the hydrogen, nitrogen and oxygen will be present in much smaller concentrations, although antimony, arsenic and tin may still be present.

**5.28 Explain the purpose of the oil in Fig. 5.4 given that the molten-steel temperatures are far above the ignition temperatures of the oil.**

The oil serves two purposes. First, a lubricant is needed between the steel and the mold to facilitate movement. As stated, the oil combusts at the casting temperatures, but it doesn't combust fully because of the argon-dominated atmosphere. Thus the oil can provide some lubrication. Secondly, the oil usually is a carrier for graphite flakes that have been suspended in the oil, and these flakes lubricate the mold.

**5.29 Recent research has identified mold-surface textures that will either (a) inhibit a solidified steel from separating from the mold or (b) force it to stay in contact in continuous casting. What is the advantage of a mold which maintains intimate contact with the steel?**

The main advantage to this kind of surface texture is that if the material keeps in contact with the mold, the thermal contact resistance between the mold and the material is much lower. Consequently, heat will be conducted faster, allowing higher traverse speeds or the use of shorter molds.

**5.30 Identify products which cannot be made of steel and explain why this is so. For example, electrical contacts are commonly made of gold or copper, because their softness results in low contact resistance, while for steel the contact resistance would be very high.**

By the student. There are many potential answers, and students should be encouraged to think creatively to respond to this question. The instructor may wish to further constrain this problem, such as by requiring five answers, where the rationale is different for each answer. Alternatively, one could request that students find examples in the automotive, aerospace, food processing, computer, and construction industries. Examples are:

- Gym-shoe soles cannot be made of steel because the shoe needs high coefficients of friction, and the sole material must have a high compliance for comfort.
- Steel cannot be used in building foundations, because it is far too expensive compared to cement.
- Steel is not used as aircraft-fuselage material, because its strength-to-weight ratio is too low (see Fig. 9.3 on p. 241).
- Steel is a bad material for a coffee cup, since it is thermally conductive and would burn the hands of someone drinking coffee, and would not keep the coffee hot as long as when using an insulator. Note that an evacuated design as with some thermos designs would be acceptable.
- Steel would not be suitable for jewelry because of aesthetic reasons.
- Steel is not suitable as a material for many children's toys because it is hard and can be dangerous in the hands of small children.
- Steel is not suitable as a crate or pallet material, since it is far more expensive than wood.
- Tennis racquets and golf clubs are not made of steel because they would be too heavy compared to titanium products.

## QUANTITATIVE PROBLEMS

**5.31 By referring to the available literature, estimate the cost of the raw materials for (a) an aluminum beverage can, (b) a stainless-steel two-quart cooking pot, and (c) the steel hood of a car.**

By the student. For examples, (a) an aluminum beverage can is approximately 4 cents, (b) a stainless-steel cooking pot is around \$40-\$100, depending on quality and the manufacturer, and (c) the hood of the car can be as low as \$75.

**5.32 In Table 5.1, more than one type of steel is listed for some applications. By referring to data in the technical literature, determine the range of properties for these steels in various conditions (such as cold worked, hot worked, and annealed).**

By the student. The information can be found in various textbooks and references, as also given in the Bibliography.

**5.33 Some soft drinks are now available in steel cans (with aluminum tops) that look similar to aluminum cans. Obtain one of each, weigh them when empty, and determine their respective wall thicknesses.**

By the student. The actual wall thicknesses vary by manufacturer. A typical thickness for an aluminum can is 0.003 in. (0.076 mm). The thickness of steel cans will typically range from this value to thinner walls, as low as 0.0015 in. (0.040 mm).

**5.34 Using strength and density data, determine the minimum weight of a two-foot long tension member which must support 1000 lb. manufactured from (a) annealed 303 stainless steel, (b) normalized 8620 steel, (c) as-rolled 1080 steel, (d) any two aluminum alloys, (e) any brass alloy, or (f) pure copper.**

The cross-sectional area required is given by $\sigma_y = F/A$; thus $A = F/\sigma_y$. The volume is then $V = AL = FL/\sigma_y$, and the weight is $W = \rho V = \rho FL/\sigma_y$. In this case, $L = 24$ in. = 0.610 m, and $F = 1000$ lb = 4440 N. Density data below is obtained from Table 3.1 on p. 103, and uses the lowest values in the range. Using this information, the following table can be compiled:

| Material | Density (kg/m$^3$) | Yield strength (MPa) | Weight required |
|---|---|---|---|
| 303 stainless steel | 6290 | 550[1] | 0.031 kg (0.30 N) |
| 8620 normalized | 6290 | 632[1] | 0.027 kg (0.26 N) |
| 1080 as rolled | 6290 | 1010[1] | 0.017 kg (0.17 N) |
| Al 1100-O | 2700 | 90[2] | 0.081 kg (0.79 N) |
| Al 1100-H14 | 2700 | 125[2] | 0.059 kg (0.58 N) |
| Copper | 8970 | 220[3] | 0.110 kg (1.08 N) |
| Red brass | 7470 | 270[3] | 0.075 kg (0.74 N) |

Notes: [1] From Table 5.2 and 5.4 on pp. 159 and 162.
[2] From Table 6.3, p. 171.
[3] From Table 6.6, p. 177.

**5.35 The endurance limit (fatigue life) of steel is approximately one-half the ultimate strength (see Fig. 2.16) but never higher than 100 ksi (700 MPa). For irons, the endurance limit is 40% of the ultimate strength but never higher than 24 ksi (170 MPa). Plot the endurance limit versus the ultimate strength for the steels described in this chapter and for the cast irons in Table 12.3. On the same plot, show the effect of surface finish by plotting the endurance limit, assuming the material is in the as-cast state (see Fig. 2.28).**

The plot is as follows:

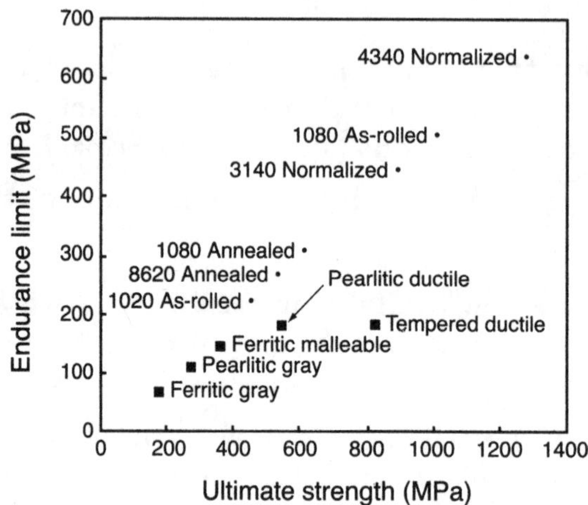


## SYNTHESIS, DESIGN AND PROJECTS

**5.36 Based on the information given in Section 5.5.1, make a table with columns for each improved property (i.e., hardenability, strength, toughness, and machinability). In each column, list the elements that improve that property and identify the element that has the most influence.**

The following table indicates the elements (in alphabetical order) that influence favorably a particular property. The element that has the most influence is given in bold letters.

| Hardenability | Strength | Toughness | Machinability |
|---|---|---|---|
| Boron | **Carbon** | Calcium | Lead |
| Carbon | Cobalt | Cerium | Manganese |
| **Chromium** | Chromium | Chromium | Phosphorus |
| Manganese | Copper | Magnesium | Selenium |
| Molybdenum | Manganese | Molybdenum | **Sulfur** |
| Phosphorus | Molybdenum | **Nickel** | Tellurium |
| Titanium | Nickel | Niobium | |
| | Niobium | Tantalum | |
| | Phosphorus | Tellurium | |
| | Silicon | Vanadium | |
| | Tantalum | Zirconium | |
| | Tungsten | | |
| | Vanadium | | |

**5.37 Assume that you are in charge of public relations for a steel-producing company. Outline all the attractive characteristics of steels that you would like your customers to know about.**

By the student. Note that the main benefits of steels are their wide range of properties and low cost in relation to nonferrous alloys. The properties of steels can be tailored to fit a specific application. By certain alloying-element additions, properties such as strength, wear resistance, toughness, formability, corrosion resistance, and magnetic properties can be optimized to best suit a particular application.

**5.38 Assume that you are in competition with the steel industry and are asked to list all the characteristics of steels that are not attractive. Make a list of these characteristics and explain their engineering relevance.**

By the student. A major drawback in using steels is their density, which is higher than aluminum, titanium, or plastics. Because of its higher density, steel is not used extensively in applications where weight is an important factor, such as the aerospace industry (which uses mainly aluminum and titanium). Also, most alloys of aluminum, titanium, copper, and nickel are naturally corrosion resistant, whereas steel requires expensive alloy additions (such as chromium) to achieve this property. The thermal and electrical conductivity of steels are not particularly high, so that copper or aluminum alloys are most suited for applications requiring these properties. Further, since early 2004, the worldwide demand for steel has resulted in increased prices and unreliable supply.

**5.39 In Section 5.5.1, we noted the effects of various individual elements (such as either lead alone or sulfur alone) on the properties and characteristics of steels. We did not, however, discuss the role of combinations of elements (such as lead and sulfur together). Review the available technical literature and prepare a table indicating the combined effects of several elements on steels.**

By the student. References on steels will discuss this subject; the usual treatment is to explain the trends of one additive and then assume that there are not interactions if one or more are used. For important additive combinations, this is a good approximation, but usually alloys are characterized individually, based on many additives.

**5.40 In the past, waterfowl hunters used lead shot in their shotguns, but this practice resulted in lead poisoning of unshot birds that ingested lead pellets (along with gravel) to help them digest food. Recently, steel and tungsten have been used as replacement materials. If all pellets have the same velocity upon exiting the shotgun barrel, what concerns would you have regarding this material substitution? Consider environmental and performance effects.**

From the hunter's standpoint, steel is less dense than lead, thus it is not as effective. Tungsten has a much higher density than lead and does not have this drawback; however, it is much more expensive. From an environmental standpoint, there is an obvious advantage to replacing lead with steel or tungsten, in that the toxic lead pellets would not be thrown into the environment where they can pollute groundwater. There has been a well-known problem, in that lead particles are often ingested by birds to help digest food, leading to lead poisoning, which does not occur if the birds ingest pebbles. However, wounded waterfowl are often able to escape to nearby sanctuaries (such as national parks) where large flocks congregate. These wounded birds eventually perish and the decaying birds then spread disease among the flock. Thus, as is often the case, there are drawbacks and benefits to the material substitution and firm conclusions are difficult to obtain.

**5.41 Aluminum has been cited as a possible substitute material for steel in automobiles. What concerns would you have before purchasing an aluminum automobile?**

By the student. There are many concerns, a few of which are discussed here. Aluminum is more expensive than steel, and this will undoubtedly be reflected in total cost. Much of this cost is due to aluminum requiring greater energy to produce than steel, so even improved gas mileage may never pay off in the life of a car. Steel is a proven material in the automotive industry and performs well from a safety standpoint.

**5.42 In the 1940s, the Yamato was the largest battleship that had ever been built. Find out the weight of this this ship, and determine how many automobiles could be built from the steel in this one ship. How long would it take to cast this much steel by continuous casting?**

By the student. The research can have some minor variations, depending on the source and details of the figures obtained; thus a general outline of an acceptable approach is given here. The *Yamato* displaced about 72,000 tons. Admittedly, some of this weight was not steel, but was wood, brass and decorative material as well. Consider if it was all steel, and a typical automobile in 1995 used around 650 kg of steel (or 1430 lb = 0.715 tons). Therefore, the *Yamato's* steel could have been used to make approximately 100,000 automobiles.

As for the time needed to produce this much continuously cast steel, it is stated on p. 155 that the steel is withdrawn at a speed of around 25 mm (1 in.) per second. The largest openings for billets are 15 in. by 23 in. (see www.steel.org/learning/howmade/concast.htm), so that the highest flow rate in continuous casting can be estimated as 345 in$^3$/s = 0.00565 m$^3$/s. Since steel has a density of 8025 kg/m$^3$ (mid-range value from Table 3.1 on p. 103), the mass flow rate of steel in continuous casting is approximately 45.4 kg/s. Thus, it can be calculated that the time needed to produce the steel in the *Yamato* is $1.40 \times 10^6$ s, or 16.2 days.

**5.43 Search the technical literature and add more parts and materials to those shown in Table 5.1.**

By the student. Some examples are:

| Product | Steel | Product | Steel |
|---|---|---|---|
| Screw machine parts, spindles, pins, rods | 1018 | Simple structural applications such as cold formed fasteners | 1020 |
| Moderate strength, cold-formed fasteners and bolts | 1022 | Couplings and cold-headed parts | 1040 |
| Aircraft engine mounts and welded tubing | 4130 | Aircraft landing-gear axles, power transmission shafts | 4330 |
| Gears and studs | 1045 | Hand tools such as screw-drivers and pliers | 1060 |

*Source:* http://www.coburnmyers.com/technical/carbon-steel.asp.

# Chapter 6

# Nonferrous Metals and Alloys: Production, General Properties, and Applications

## QUALITATIVE PROBLEMS

**6.15 Explain why cooking utensils are generally made of stainless steels, aluminum, or copper.**

Cooking utensils require noncorrosive materials (to maintain their appearance and prevent unpleasant taste in cooked products) as well as good thermal conductivity for even heating. These metals satisfy these requirements and are also able to be easily formed into the various shapes.

**6.16 Would it be advantageous to plot the data in Table 6.1 in terms of cost-per-unit weight rather than of cost-per-unit volume? Explain and give some examples.**

Such a table would better reflect more the actual prices of stock materials (steel, gold, copper, etc.), which is usually sold in price per weight unlike wood from a lumber yard, for instance. However, when we determine the amount of material required in a product or structure, we do so from its dimensions (hence volume), as derived from strength or aesthetic considerations. Note, for example, that the dimensions of beams and shafts for a particular application are determined from formulas in mechanics of solids textbooks. We then order the materials, the cost of which is based on weight.

**6.17 Inspect Table 6.2 and comment on which of the two hardening processes (heat treating and work hardening) is more effective in improving the strength of aluminum alloys.**

According to Table 6.2, those alloys designated with a T are heat treated, while those designated with an H are cold worked. Heat treating (Chapter 4) increases the strength to higher levels than cold working. The reason that cold working is not as effective of a hardening process is due to the low strain hardening capability of aluminum (see, for example, Table 2.3 on p. 72).

**6.18 Other than mechanical strength, what other factors should be considered in selecting metals and alloys for high-temperature applications?**

Because high temperatures tend to increase corrosion rates, the alloy should have good high-temperature corrosion resistance. Also, creep resistance should be high, since high temperatures promote creep (Section 2.8 on p. 86). If the particular application requires cycling through temperature ranges, the alloy should also possess thermal-fatigue resistance.

**6.19 Explain why you would want to know the ductility of metals and alloys before selecting them.**

It is important to know the ductility of a metal or alloy since ductility is a measure of how much the metal can be cold worked, if at all, without requiring an intermediate annealing cycle. In addition to the metal's formability, the toughness of the metal increases with increasing ductility. Materials with high ductility can be less susceptible to stress concentrations and can have better fatigue lives.

**6.20 Explain the techniques you would use to strengthen aluminum alloys.**

The main techniques used in strengthening aluminum alloys are strain hardening and precipitation hardening (see Section 4.9 on p. 134). The precipitation-hardening process is capable of imparting higher strength levels to aluminum. This process starts with a solution treatment of the alloy so that the alloying elements are in an unstable supersaturated solution. The alloy can then be either cold worked, naturally aged (at room temperature), or artificially aged (at higher temperatures). The aging process forms small precipitates in the microstructure which decrease dislocation movement and, thus, increase strength. Strain hardening involves cold working of the alloy, which produces dislocation networks that hinder dislocation motion, and, thus, increase strength.

**6.21 Assume that, for geopolitical reasons, the price of copper increases rapidly. Name two metals with similar mechanical and physical properties that can be substituted for copper. Comment on your selection and observations.**

Two metals having the closest properties to copper are probably aluminum and magnesium. Aluminum has the closest overall properties, both physical and mechanical, to copper. The table below shows the similarities of mechanical properties (see Table 3.1 on p. 103 for correlation of physical properties).

| Property | Copper | Aluminum | Magnesium |
|---|---|---|---|
| Yield stress (MPa) | 70-55 | 35-500 | 200-300 |
| Tensile strength (MPa) | 220-900 | 100-570 | 255-380 |
| Elongation (%) | 66-1700 | 45-800 | 15-700 |

**6.22 If planes (such as a Boeing 757) are made of 79% aluminum, why are automobiles predominantly made of steel?**

Automobiles are predominantly made of steel for a number of reasons. A major reason is that a design history exists with steel but not with aluminum, and material changes have a certain initial drawback (for example, aluminum is more difficult to form than steel, and welding process parameters differ). Also, the weight reduction consideration which dominates aerospace design is not as pressing in automobiles. In recent years, there have been some models of automobiles that have used very high amounts of aluminum (such as the Audi A6 and the Plymouth Prowler), demonstrating that aluminum can be successfully applied to automobiles.

**6.23 Portable (notebook) computers have their housing made of magnesium. Why?**

The main reason that the notebook computer housings are magnesium is because of the need to reduce weight. Because magnesium is the lightest of all metals (see Table 3.1 on p. 103), it can produce the lightest housing of a given volume. Furthermore, magnesium can easily be die cast into intricate shapes (see Section 11.3.5 on p. 306).

**6.24 Table 6.3 lists the manufacturing properties of wrought aluminum alloys. Compare their relative characteristics with those of other metals.**

By the student. There are many trends which can be identified in Table 6.3 on p. 171, but, as examples, note that wrought aluminums have much better corrosion resistance than wrought steels. Machinability is somewhat poorer than that for copper, but better than refractories. Weldability is usually excellent in wrought form, compared to that of other metals.

**6.25 Most household wiring is made of copper wire. By contrast, grounding wire leading to satellite dishes and the like is made of aluminum. Explain the reason for this.**

Grounding wire is used as an exterior conductor on a house for protection against lightning strikes. In this case, the current flow is extremely high. Thus, it is thus essential to minimize resistance inside the wire. Aluminum has a lower resistivity than copper, so it is the better choice for this application provided that good electrical contact is obtained using proper terminals. Aluminum is not used for conventional household wiring because it is too stiff and not as ductile as copper, and this is a drawback when the wire is bent and twisted in conduits around beams and joists during installation. (See also the example, "Electrical Wiring in Homes", on p. 97 in *Manufacturing Engineering and Technology*, 3rd ed.)

## QUANTITATIVE PROBLEMS

**6.26 A simply-supported rectangular beam is 25 mm wide and 1 m long, and it is subjected to a vertical load of 30 kg at its center. Assume that this beam could be made of any of the materials listed in Table 6.1. Select three different materials**

**and calculate for each the beam's height that causes each beam to have the same maximum deflection. Calculate the ratio of the cost for each of the three beams.**

This is a simple problem of mechanics of solids, and the student is to select three different materials. The governing equation for maximum deflection, $d$, for this type of loading of a beam is:

$$d = \frac{PL^3}{48EI}$$

where $P$ is the load (30 kg, or 294 N), $L$ is the beam length (1 m), $E$ is the elastic modulus, and $I$ is the moment of inertia, where $I = bh^3/12$ and $b = 25$ mm. For a constant deflection, the relationship between $E$ and $h$ is as follows:

$$d = \frac{PL^3}{48EI} = \frac{PL^3}{4Ebh^3} \quad \rightarrow \quad h = \sqrt[3]{\frac{PL^3}{4Ebd}}$$

For illustrative purposes, we will proceed with the following materials:

| Material | Young's modulus (GPa) |
|---|---|
| Carbon steel | 190 |
| Aluminum | 70 |
| Nickel | 180 |

Note: See Table 2.2 on p. 67.

(a) Using carbon steel as the reference, consider the beam height, $h$, required to restrict the deflection to 1 mm (0.001m). For steel, $h$ is

$$h = \sqrt[3]{\frac{(294)(1)^3}{4(190 \times 10^9)(0.025)(0.001)}} = 0.0249 \text{ m}$$

The required volume, $V$, of the steel beam is then

$$V = bhl = (25)(24.9)(1000) = 622,500 \text{ mm}^3$$

(b) For aluminum,

$$h = \sqrt[3]{\frac{(294)(1)^3}{4(70 \times 10^9)(0.025)(0.001)}} = 0.0348 \text{ m}$$

so that the required volume is 870,000 mm$^3$.

(c) For nickel,

$$h = \sqrt[3]{\frac{(294)(1)^3}{4(180 \times 10^9)(0.025)(0.001)}} = 0.0254 \text{ m}$$

so that the volume is 635,000 mm$^3$.

Table 6.1 on p. 170 allows us to calculate the relative costs. The steel beam is the reference. By comparison, the aluminum will cost, at a minimum, twice the cost of steel by volume. The aluminum beam requires a larger volume, so that the cost of the aluminum will be $(827{,}500/592{,}500)(2) = 2.79$ times the cost of the steel beam. Similarly, the nickel beam will cost 35.7 times the cost of the carbon steel beam.

**6.27 Obtain a few aluminum beverage cans, cut them, and measure their wall thicknesses. Using data in this chapter and simple formulas for thin-walled, closed-end pressure vessels, calculate the maximum internal pressure these cans can withstand before yielding.**

Aluminum beverage can thicknesses can vary slightly depending on the canmaker. This solution will use typical numbers of a thickness of 0.075 mm and a radius of 33 mm. Using 3003-H14 aluminum with a yield strength of 145 MPa (see Table 6.3 on p. 171), noting that the two of the principal stresses are the hoop stress and the axial stress:

$$\sigma_h = \frac{pr}{t} = 452p \qquad \sigma_a = \frac{pr}{2t} = 226p$$

The radial stress is essentially zero for a thin-walled pressure vessel. Thus, the maximum shear stress is equal to one-half the hoop stress, or $226p$. Using the maximum shear stress (Tresca yield criterion) gives

$$\frac{Y}{2} = 226p \quad \rightarrow \quad p = \frac{Y}{452} = \frac{145 \text{ MPa}}{452} = 321 \text{ kPa}$$

which is approximately three atmospheres.

**6.28 Beverage cans are usually stacked on top of each other in stores. By using information from Problem 6.27 and referring to textbooks on the mechanics of solids, make an estimate of the crushing load each of these cans can withstand.**

The buckling analysis of such cans is complicated, especially since the fluid contents can eliminate local buckling. However, considering only the effect of a compressive stress on the wall, and assuming the can contents are at ambient pressure, the effect of a load is one of an axial stress. Using the same can dimensions and material as in Problem 6.27 above,

$$\sigma_a = \frac{F}{2\pi rt} \quad \rightarrow \quad F = \sigma_a(2\pi rt) = (145 \text{ MPa})(2\pi)(0.033 \text{ m})(0.000075 \text{ m}) = 2.25 \text{ kN}$$

**6.29 Using strength and density data, determine the minimum weight of a two-foot long tension member which must support 750 pounds, if it is manufactured from (a) 3003-O aluminum, (b) 5052-H34 aluminum, (c) AZ31B-F magnesium, (d) any brass alloy, and (e) any bronze alloy.**

The cross-sectional area required is given by $\sigma_y = F/A$; $A = F/\sigma_y$. The volume is then $V = AL = FL/\sigma_y$, and the weight is $W = \rho V = \rho FL/\sigma_y$. In this case, $L = 24$ in. $= 0.610$ m, and $F = 1000$ lb $= 4440$ N. Density data comes from Table 3.1 on p. 103 and uses the lowest values in the range. Using this equation, the following can be compiled:

| Material | Density ($kg/m^3$) | Yield strength (MPa) | Weight needed (N) |
|---|---|---|---|
| 3003-O Al | 2630 | 40[1] | 1.75 |
| 5052-H34 Al | 2630 | 215[1] | 0.32 |
| AZ31B-F Mg | 1770 | 200[2] | 0.24 |
| Red brass | 7470 | 70[3] | 2.8 |
| C38500 bronze | 7470 | 140[4] | 1.4 |

Notes:

1. From Table 6.3 on p. 171.
2. From Table 6.5 on p. 176.
3. From Table 6.6 on p. 177.
4. From Table 6.7 on p. 178.

**6.30 An automobile engine operates at up to 7000 rpm. If the stroke length for a piston is 6 in. and the piston is made of a 10-lb. steel casting, estimate the inertial stress on the 1-in. diameter connecting rod. If the piston is replaced by the same volume of aluminum alloy, what would be the speed for the same inertia-induced stress?**

First, note that the operating speed is 100 rev/sec; however, the velocity distribution of the piston is a function of location in the cylinder. As a first approximation, let's assume sinusoidal motion of the piston, so that from the middle of the piston, the position is described by

$$x = (3 \text{ in.}) \sin(200\pi t)$$

The acceleration is, then

$$a = \ddot{x} = -120,000\pi^2 \text{ in./sec}^2 (\sin 200\pi t)$$

with a maximum value of $1.18 \times 10^6$ in./sec$^2$ = 98,700 ft/sec$^2$. From inertia,

$$F = Ma = \frac{10 \text{ lb}}{32.2}(98,700 \text{ ft/sec}^2) = 30.6 \text{ kip}$$

For a 1-in. diameter connecting rod, $A = 0.78$ in$^2$, hence the stress is 39 ksi. If the piston is made of aluminum, with the same volume as the steel, its weight will be (2700/6290)=0.429 times that of the steel piston (numbers taken from Table 3.1 on p. 103). Therefore, the weight would be about 4.3 lb. Performing the same calculation, the stress would be 16.7 ksi.

**6.31 Plot the following for the materials described in this chapter: (a) yield strength versus density, (b) modulus of elasticity versus strength, and (c) modulus of elasticity versus relative cost.**

The plot for selected materials are as follows for parts (a) and (c); part (b) is to be completed the student.

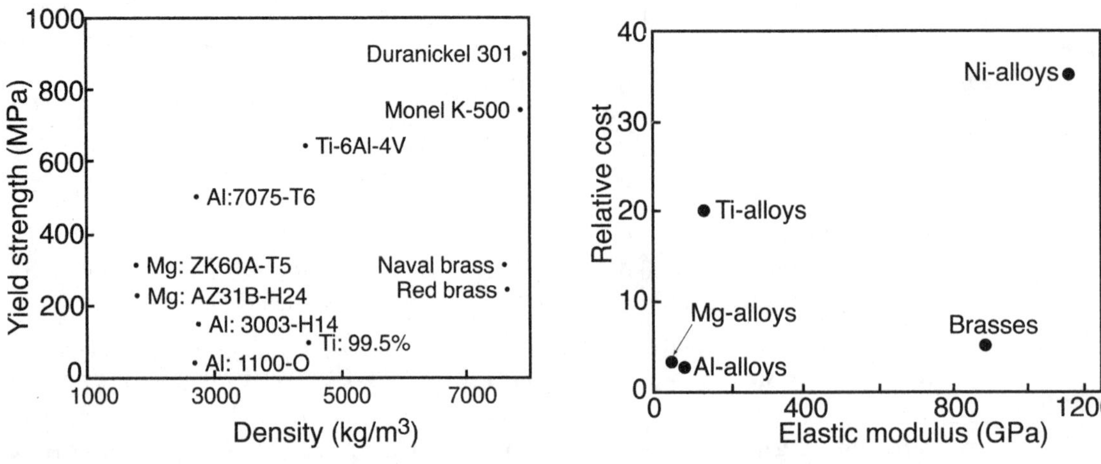


## SYNTHESIS, DESIGN AND PROJECTS

**6.32 Because of the number of processes involved in making them, the cost of raw materials for metals depends on their condition (hot or cold rolled), shape (plate, sheet, bar, tubing), and size. Make a survey of the available literature and price lists (or get in touch with suppliers) and prepare a list indicating the cost per 100 kg of the nonferrous materials described in this chapter, as available in different conditions, shapes, and sizes.**

By the student. As a helpful guide, there are some sources which deal in one particular metal, while others are sources for all materials. There will be a wide range, depending on the size of cross-sections selected. Thus, for example, the data from Small Parts, Inc. will be different than those from McMaster-Carr.

**6.33 The materials described in this chapter have numerous applications. Make a survey of the available literature and prepare a list of several specific products and applications, indicating the types of materials used.**

By the student. An example could be the stem of an artificial hip replacement (see Example I.5 on p. 26), which can be made from stainless steel, cobalt-chrome alloy, or titanium. As another example, automobile body panels can be constructed from steel, aluminum, stainless steel (the DeLorean automobile), or reinforced plastics.

**6.34 Name products that would not have been developed to their advanced stages (as we find them today) if alloys having high strength, high corrosion resistance, and high creep resistance (all at elevated temperatures) had not been developed.**

The most outstanding examples of improvements for high-temperature parts typically have occurred in the aircraft and the aerospace industry. The efficiency of many gas-turbine engines increases with higher operating temperatures. The rotors and turbine blades in these engines have constantly been improved in terms of their high-temperature strength and creep and corrosion resistance. These improvements have allowed the engines to achieve greater thrust and speeds. Also, casings and other components of rockets have made space exploration possible.

**6.35 Assume that you are the technical sales manager of a company that produces nonferrous metals. Choose any one of the metals and alloys described in this chapter and prepare a brochure, including some illustrations, for use as sales literature by your staff in their contact with potential customers.**

By the student. The brochure should mainly promote the products that the company markets. The information given in the brochure about the metal should list benefits over other competitive materials, and should also show how the company's product is better than those of the competitors. Special production processes should be described and how the metal is improved by these advances should be explained. Plant facilities, equipment, and the capabilities of the personnel at all levels are usually also shown. Important sales information such as a wide range of reliable applications, trends in sales, and any concerns that may arise regarding the material and its uses should also be given.

**6.36 Inspect several metal products and components and make an educated guess as to what materials each is made from. Give reasons for your guesses. If you list two or more possibilities, explain your reasoning.**

By the student. Students are encouraged to respond to this question by developing a comprehensive list of products and explaining their observations. As an example, a U.S. quarter or a dime, when viewed from the side clearly shows a sandwiched structure (see Example 31.1 on p. 982). The interior is clearly reddish brown, indicating a copper alloy, and the exterior is shiny and bright, as well as corrosion resistant. These properties are typical of silver, platinum, and nickel. Reviewing cost information in Table 6.1 on p. 170, a nickel-alloy appears the most likely material.

**6.37 Give applications for (a) amorphous metals, (b) precious metals, (c) low-melting alloys, and (d) nanomaterials.**

By the student. Some examples are

(a) Amorphous alloys: magnetic applications such as steel coils for electrical transformers, since they have a very low magnetic hysteresis loss. Also, their high strength and corrosion resistance can make them useful in structural applications.

(b) Precious metals: applications include jewelry, decorative fixtures, coins, dental work, tableware, and electrical contacts.

(c) Low-melting alloys: these alloys consist mainly of three elements: lead (piping, tubing, x-ray shields, solders, weight), tin (solders, coating for sheet steel for cans, bearing materials, tableware), and zinc (galvanic coating for steel, die casting, low strength and nonstructural applications).

(d) Nanomaterials: they can be used where exceptional performance is required, such as in cutting tools, medical applications, filters, and microelectromechanical systems (MEMS).

**6.38 Describe the advantages of making products with multilayer materials. (For example, aluminum bonded to the bottom of stainless-steel pots.)**

By the student. Multilayer materials are capable of incorporating and combining the beneficial properties of two distinct materials. In the case of cookware, for example, copper or aluminum provides at the bottom of the pot conducts heat evenly, whereas stainless steel has good corrosion resistance and is easy to clean because of its smooth surface. The student is encouraged to develop further applications.

**6.39 Describe applications and designs utilizing shape-memory alloys.**

By the student. Shape-memory alloys can be used for space saving applications, such as tents or antennas. The parts would be folded up at room temperature and heated to regain their initial form; this is especially useful for satellite antennas. Other applications have been described in Section 6.13 on p. 185.

**6.40 The Bronze Age is so known because the hardest metals known at the time were bronzes. Therefore, tools, weapons, and armor were made from bronze. Investigate the geographical sources of the metals needed for bronze, and identify the known sources in the Bronze Age. (Note: Does this explain the Greek interest in the British Islands?)**

By the student. Since both copper and tin are needed to produce bronze weapons and tools, sources of these materials were extremely valuable during the Bronze Age. However, at the time there were a number of Mediterranean sources of copper, but only two known sources for tin. The first and larger source was the Danube River valley in what is now Austria; the second source was in Wessex, in southern England. There is considerable evidence of Bronze Age trade, such as various Mycenean (2000 to 1100 B.C.) tools and weapons unearthed at various architectural sites in southern England. (See also Table I.2 on pp. 5-7.)

**6.41 Aluminum beverage-can tops are made from 5182 alloy, while the bottoms are made from 3004 alloy. Study the properties of these alloys and explain why they are used for these applications.**

The can tops are made of 5182 aluminum alloy mainly because of the ductility requirements in the material (see also top of p. 173). The key feature is the integral rivet which holds the pop top lever in place; this region undergoes a very large strain in forming. The 3004 alloy is a common can-making alloy because it has good formability and doesn't foul tooling. It appears that the iron-silicon constituent particles in the alloy gently remove aluminum-magnesium particles that may adhere to the tooling surfaces (galling), which is an important consideration.

**6.42 Obtain specimens of pure copper, pure aluminum, and alloys of copper and aluminum. Conduct tension tests on each, plot the stress-strain diagrams, and evaluate the results.**

By the student. Note that pure metals can undergo much higher strains to failure. Pure copper is the material of choice to demonstrate classical, well-behaved materials in stress-strain curves. Pure aluminum also gives classical-shaped curves, but with pure aluminum and aluminum alloys, there is a noise at fracture that is startling at first.

**6.43 Comment on your observations regarding the type of materials used in particular sections of the jet engine shown in Fig. 6.1.**

By the student. There will be several observations made, including:

- Nickel alloys are used in locations in the jet engine where extreme temperatures are encountered, reflecting the excellent strength and creep resistance of nickel alloys at elevated temperatures.
- When considered in combination with Table 6.1 on p. 170, it is clear that the performance requirements are pressing enough that the use of expensive materials can be justified.
- For lower-temperature locations, aluminum alloys are used, where the excellent strength-to-weight ratio of aluminum can be exploited.
- While nickel is used in some locations, it is not used for large structures such as the inlet fan due to its high cost and limited formability.

**6.44 Inspect various small or large appliances in your home and identify the metals and alloys that you think have been used in their construction.**

By the student. Examples are:

- Steel: desks, food containers, bolts and nuts, stamped parts as in toasters, screwdrivers and wrenches, sewing needles.
- Aluminum: baking trays, window frames, soda and beverage containers, aluminum foil.
- Tungsten: toaster burner and furnace elements
- Gold: printed-circuit boards in controllers.
- Lead and tin: soldered connections of all types.

**6.45 Referring to recent technical literature, comment on the trends in the use of metallic materials in (a) military vehicles, (b) sports equipment, (c) medical equipment, (d) automotive applications, and (e) aircraft.**

By the student. Each of these topic areas has extensive technical literature associated with them. Competing concerns such as reliable performance, weight, manufacturability, cost, and availability are important common themes to be explored.

# Chapter 7

# Polymers: Structure, General Properties, and Applications

## QUALITATIVE PROBLEMS

**7.17 Inspect various plastic components in your automobile and state whether you think that they are made of thermoplastic materials or of thermosetting plastics.**

By the student. Some typical parts that are thermoplastics are dashboard trim, cup holders, plastic fasteners, seat components, radio and dashboard knobs, carpeting, and seat-belt holders. Thermosets can be found as steering wheels, battery casings, structural parts in door frames, and car bodies in some models. (See also Sections 7.6 and 7.7 on pp. 208-211.)

**7.18 Give applications for which flammability of plastics would be of major importance.**

By the student. A major concern is their use in aircraft and the subsequent effects during fires and crash landing. In these circumstances it is not only the flammability of the polymers that is a concern, but also the toxicity of combustion byproducts. The same concerns hold for use of polymers inside buildings, where it is essential to contain and prevent the spreading of fires. There are numerous applications where flammable polymers cannot be used, such as pressure vessels or containers for flammable materials, and cooking implements. (See also top of p. 208.)

**7.19 What characteristics make polymers advantageous for applications such as gears? What characteristics are drawbacks for such applications?**

By the student. The advantages include the low friction of polymers, even when not lubricated, and the high adhesive and abrasive wear resistance (see pp. 1044 and 1050). In addition, polymers have good damping characteristics so that sound and impact forces are not as severe with plastic gears. Plastics used for gears also have manufacturing characteristics that allow the production of tooth profiles with superior surface finish (Chapter 19). The main drawbacks to polymers used in gears are associated with their low stiffness, especially at elevated temperature. Also, polymers have lower strength than metals, especially the steels used in gears, so the loads that can be transferred for an equivalent sized gear is much lower.

**7.20 What properties do elastomers have that thermoplastics in general do not have?**

Elastomers (Section 7.9 on p. 214) are capable of returning to their original shape after being stretched, while thermoplastics cannot do so. In addition, there is a pronounced hysteresis loop in the loading and unloading of an elastomer, making these materials very valuable in vibration damping applications.

**7.21 Do you think that the substitution of plastics for metals (in products traditionally made of metal) is viewed negatively by the public at large? If so, why?**

By the student. The public may negatively view the substitution of plastics for metals if they consider plastics as a cheap material (rather than cost effective), are lower in strength (even if the strength is suitable for the particular application), and not as hard or durable. For some applications, there is an environmental perception polymers cannot be recycled as easily.

**7.22 Name three plastics that are suitable for use at elevated temperatures.**

By the student. Three plastics suitable for use at elevated temperatures are polyvinyl chloride, polyamides, and epoxies.

**7.23 Is it possible for a material to have a hysteresis behavior that is the opposite of that shown in Fig. 7.14, so that the arrows run counterclockwise? Explain.**

If the arrows in Fig. 7.14 on p. 214 were counterclockwise, the material would have a hysteresis gain, rather than a loss. This would mean that the energy put into the material is lower than the energy recovered during unloading, which is not possible.

**7.24 Observe the behavior of the specimen shown in Fig. 7.13 and state whether the material has a high or a low strain-rate sensitivity exponent $m$. (See Section 2.2.7.) Explain why it does.**

The m value represents the strain-rate sensitivity of a material (see Section 2.2.7 on p. 74). The material in Fig. 7.13 on p. 205 elongates considerably by the orientation of molecules; thus the material would be expected to have a high strain-rate sensitivity, i.e., a high m value. This is equivalent to diffuse necking, as opposed to localized necking commonly observed with most metals in tension tests.

**7.25 Add more to the applications column in Table 7.3.**

By the student. Some examples are:

| Design requirements | Applications |
|---|---|
| Mechanical strength | Hangers, cables |
| Functional and decorative | Electrical outlets, light switches |
| Housings and hollow shapes | Pens, electrical plugs |
| Functional and transparent | Cassette holders, food containers |
| Wear resistance | Rope, car seats |

**7.26 Discuss the significance of the glass-transition temperature, $T_g$, in engineering applications.**

In engineering applications, where thermoplastics would be expected to carry a load (structural members), the material should have a glass-transition temperature higher than the maximum temperature to which it would be subjected in service. If it didn't, the plastic would soften and eventually fail.

**7.27 Why does cross-linking improve the strength of polymers?**

Cross-linked polymers (p. 197) have additional bonds linking adjacent chains together. The strength is increased because these cross-linking bonds give additional resistance to material flow; these bonds must be broken before the molecules can slide past one another.

**7.28 Describe the methods by which optical properties of polymers can be altered.**

Optical properties can be altered by additives which can alter the color or translucence of the plastic. Additives can either be dyes or pigments; they impart color to the plastic. Also, stress whitening makes the plastic appear lighter in color or more opaque. As stated in the last paragraph in Section 7.2.2 on p. 200, optical properties are also affected by the degree of crystallinity of the polymer.

**7.29 Can polymers be made to conduct electricity? How?**

Polymers can be made to conduct electricity. As stated on p. 206, there are electrically conductive polymers such as polyacetylene, polyaniline, and polythiophene. Other polymers can be made more conductive by doping them with metal particles or whiskers. If continuous wire reinforcement is present, the polymer can be directionally conductive; it can be conductive in a plane if a mesh reinforcement is used. An electroless nickel plating of a polymer part can make it conductive.

**7.30 Explain the reasons for which elastomers were developed. Are there any substitutes for elastomers? Explain.**

Elastomers were developed to obtain a material that could undergo a large amount of deformation without failure. They provide high friction and nonskid surfaces, shock and vibration isolation, and protection against corrosion.

**7.31 Give several examples of plastic products or components in which creep and stress relaxation are important considerations.**

By the student. Obviously, it is in high-temperature, low-stress situations where creep is important. Low temperature, high stress circumstances are where stress relaxation is important. As an example of the creep's importance, polymers used in cookware as for pot handles must have creep resistance. As an example of stress relaxation, seat cushions will deform to provide a uniform stress distribution and provide comfort for the occupant.

**7.32 Describe your opinions regarding the recycling of plastics versus the development of plastics that are biodegradable.**

By the student. Some arguments that may be made are that recycling actually has a cost associated with it, for example, in the fuel which must be consumed and other costs involved in collecting the material to be recycled. Also, the properties of the recycled polymer my be inferior compared to the virgin polymer. Biodegradable plastics have drawbacks as well; it is difficult to design them to degrade in the intended time frame, and they may have more failures in service, as a result. They can be much more expensive than polymers that are not biodegradable.

**7.33 Explain how you would go about determining the hardness of plastics.**

Many of the hardness tests described in Section 2.6 on p. 79 are not suitable for polymers. Inelastic recovery of the surface makes tests such as Brinell and Knoop tests difficult to assess. The depth of penetration as measured in a Rockwell test will be time dependent because of stress relaxation. Consequently, durometer testing (p. 82) is an appropriate approach.

**7.34 Compare the values of the elastic modulus from Table 7.1 to the values for metals given in Chapters 2, 5, and 6.**

Individual comparisons can be made, but the obvious trend is that metals have an elastic modulus of at least an order of magnitude higher than those for polymers, even for the softest of metals. Consider the following plot showing the elastic modulus of various materials and note that the moduli for polymers are far lower than those for metals (or ceramics).

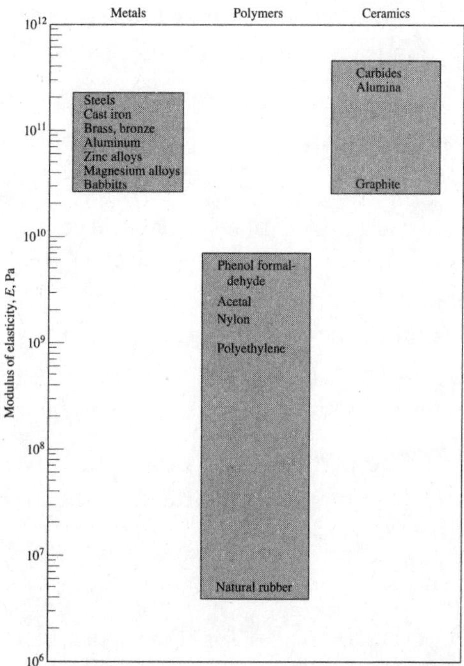


**7.35 Why is there so much variation in the stiffness of polymers?**

Table 7.1 on 192 shows a wide range of stiffness; for example, for polyethylene the change can be 1400%. This is mainly due to the varying degree of polymerization and crystallinity, and the number of crosslinks, if any, present, as well as the effects of the reinforcements. Stiffness will increase with any of these variables.

**7.36 Explain why thermoplastics are easier to recycle than thermosets.**

Thermoplastics are processed by melting or plasticizing polymer pellets or powders and then forming them into desired shape. If a polymer's chemistry can be identified, then a formed polymer can be cut into small shapes (such as pellets or particles) and fabricated as is done with so-called virgin polymers. There is some degradation of mechanical properties and a measurable loss of molecular weight, but if properly sorted, these drawbacks can be minimized. It is difficult to recycle thermosets because it is impossible to break down a thermosetting resin into its mer components. Thus, the manufacturing strategies for the original polymer and for its recycled counterparts have to be different. Furthermore, the recycled thermoset cannot be chopped up and melted as thermoplastics would.

**7.37 Give an example of a process where crazing is desirable.**

By the student. As one example, plastic strips with adhesive on one side are commonly used as labels, where a die with a letter or number is pushed into the plastic (embossing, see pp. 457-458), locally crazing it to form a visible imprint.

**7.38 Describe how shrink-wrap works.**

Shrink wrap consists of branched thermoplastics. When deformed above their glass-transition temperature, the branches attain a preferred orientation, similar to the effect of combing hair. The plastic is then quickly lowered in temperature, preventing stress relaxation. When the sheet is then wrapped around an object and then heated, the plastic relieves the stresses and shrinks around the object.

**7.39 List and explain some environmental pros and cons of using plastic shopping bags instead of paper bags.**

By the student. Some advantages of plastic bags over paper bags: trees are not consumed to make the plastic bags; plastic bags can be recycled; since they use less energy during manufacture than paper bags. Some environmental advantages of paper bags over plastic bags: paper is biodegradable; it is a renewable resource; trees filter the atmosphere and remove carbon dioxide and carbon monoxide, so by manufacturing bags and then burying them or disposing of them in landfills, the atmosphere is actually cleaned.

**7.40 List the characteristics required of a polymer for: (a) a total hip replacement insert, (b) a golf ball, (c) an automobile dashboard, (d) clothing, (e) laminated flooring, and (f) fishing nets.**

By the student. For example:

(a) Some of the characteristics needed for a polymer insert in a total hip replacement (see Example I.5 on p. 26) are that it be biocompatible; not dissolve or warp in the presence of bodily fluids; support the loads developed during normal walking, sitting, and standing; not wear excessively; provide low friction. Cost is not as imperative as other applications, given the high cost of surgery for hip replacement.

(b) For a golf ball, abrasion resistance is important, as well as impact strength and toughness. The polymer needs to have a stiffness consistent with most golf balls (NOT CLEAR). The polymer must be coatable, so that it can be made into a bright color. Cost is also important.

(c) An automobile-dashboard polymer needs to be formable into the desired (and quite demanding) shape. It also has to be available in a range of desired colors, and should have reasonable manufacturing cost.

(d) The polymer in clothing needs to be produced into very small-diameter fibers and in continuous lengths. The fibers need to be sufficiently flexible so that they can be woven into cloth and withstand normal wear and tear. The polymer needs to have low elastic modulus but sufficient strength so that the cloth feels soft but doesn't tear easily. It must also be inexpensive.

(e) Laminated flooring needs to have high hardness to resist abrasion, and should be made with proper decoration and texture, and easy to clean. Laminated flooring also should have high friction so that people can walk on the surface without slipping.

(f) Fishing nets must be strong, to efficiently capture fish without tearing. There is an interesting feature in some new fishing nets, intended to address the problem when a net is lost at sea, and floats in the ocean continuing to catch fish. Some novel fishing nets are degradable so that prolonged exposure to saline solutions causes them to lose strength and become gels; these then fall apart and do not cause uncontrolled devastation to an ecosystem.

**7.41 How can you tell whether a part is made of a thermoplastic?**

By the student. There are several nondestructive and destructive tests (see Sections 36.10 and 36.11 on pp. 1132 and 1136, respectively) that can be performed. Tension tests will demonstrate the difference: a pronounced plasticity is indicative of a thermoplastic. Exposure to high temperatures is another test: the presence of a glass-transition temperature is indicative of a thermoplastic. The shape of the part is often a clue; for example, thin films (roughly as thick as a sheet of paper) must be made of thermoplastics because they are blown from extruded tubing.

**7.42 As you know, there are plastic paper clips available in various colors. Why are there no plastic staples?**

Paperclips must function completely in the elastic range. Because of their nature, staples require plastic deformation, with little or no elastic recovery. Thermoplastics will recover dramatically, making them unsuitable as staples, and thermosets will readily fracture before beginning to achieving the desired shape of a staple.

**7.43 By incorporating small amounts of blowing agent, it is possible to manufacture hollow polymer fibers with gas cores. List applications for such fibers.**

By the student. If a polymer has a gas core, it has clear benefits in that the fiber has lower density; if used for clothing, the cloth will be lighter for the same thickness. Also, since gases have lower thermal conductivity than polymers, a fiber with a gas core will have better thermal insulation properties. This means that very thin layers of the polymer fiber will be suitable for cold-weather clothing.

**7.44 In injection molding operations, it is common practice to remove the part from its runner, to place the runner into a shredder, and to recycle the resultant pellets.**

**List the concerns you would have in using such recycled pellets as opposed to so-called "virgin" pellets.**

The main concerns about shredded polymers are that the properties of the polymer may be deteriorated as a result of shredding. This can happen if dirt or contaminants get into the polymer, or if there is so much shredding that the molecular weight of the polymer is reduced. Also, there is concern that lubricants present in the system may contaminate the polymer, and for critical applications, there is the additional concern that wear particles from the shredder may end up in the polymer. Obviously, one cannot tolerate, for example, metal particles in pacifiers for infants or in food packaging.

**7.45 Based on the subject matter in this chapter, describe how human DNA is similar to a terpolymer.**

Human DNA has a helical carbon structure, with amino acids attached as branches. Whereas a terpolymer has simple species attached to a carbon chain, DNA has very complex species. However, the basic structure is very similar; it consists of long chains with alternating amino acids attached to the chain. Note that the DNA chain is much longer and contains far more species and complexity than all artificial polymers, so there are also clear differences.

## QUANTITATIVE PROBLEMS

**7.46 Calculate the areas under the stress-strain curve (toughness) for the materials in Fig. 7.11, plot them as a function of temperature, and describe your observations.**

By the student. The area under each curve in Fig. 7.11 on p. 203 is estimated by adding the areas under the initial elastic region and the flat regions under the curve. The points and a plot are as follows:

| Temperature (°C) | Toughness (MJ/m³) |
|---|---|
| -25 | 140 |
| 0 | 635 |
| 25 | 760 |
| 50 | 730 |
| 65 | 520 |
| 80 | 270 |

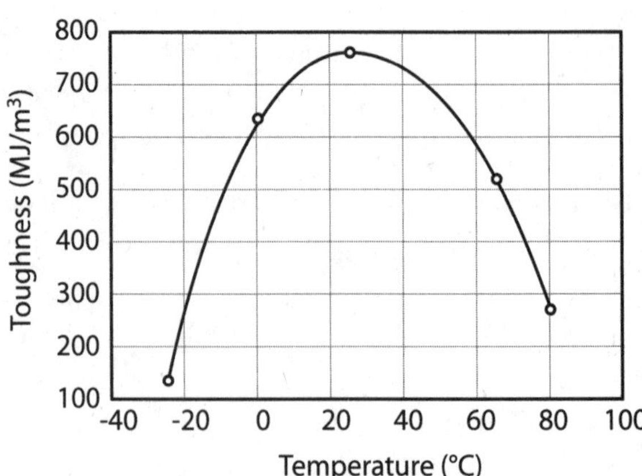


Note that the toughness is a maximum somewhere around 25°C. As temperature increases, the polymer begins to soften and melt; consequently its toughness will approach zero.

**7.47 Note in Fig. 7.11 that, as expected, the elastic modulus of the polymer decreases as temperature increases. Using the stress-strain curves in the figure, make a plot of the modulus of elasticity versus the temperature. Comment on the shape of the curve.**

By the student. The curve is as follows. Note that the shape is very nearly linear.

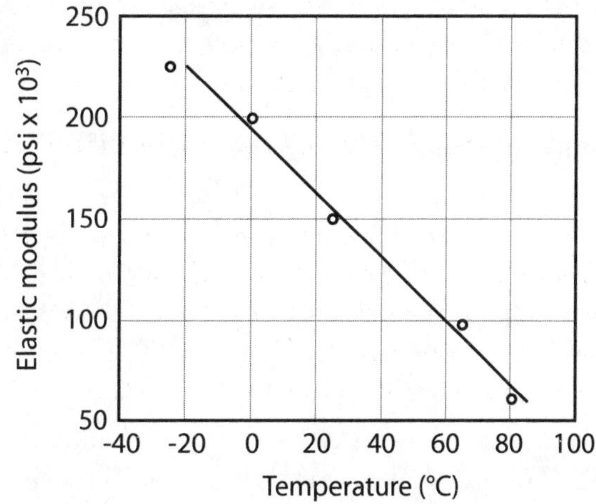


**7.48 A rectangular cantilever beam 120 mm high, 20 mm wide, and 1.5 m long is subjected to a concentrated load of 100 kg at its end. From Table 7.1, select three unreinforced and three reinforced materials and calculate the maximum deflection of the beam in each case. Then select aluminum and steel for the same beam dimensions, calculate the maximum deflection, and compare the results.**

The formula for maximum deflection, $d$, for a cantilevered beam is

$$d = \frac{PL^3}{3EI}$$

where $P$ is the load (100 kg or 981N), $L$ is the beam length (1.5 m), $E$ is the elastic modulus, and $I$ is the moment of inertia $= bh^3/12$, where $b = 0.02$ m and $h = 0.120$ m; hence, $I = 2.88 \times 10^{-6}$ m$^4$. Substituting into the equation above,

$$d = \frac{PL^3}{3EI} = \frac{(981)(1.5)^3}{3(2.88 \times 10^{-6})} \frac{1}{E} = (3.83 \text{ N/m}) \frac{1}{E}$$

As samples of calculations, the following have been taken from Table 7.1 on p. 192, using mean values when a range is given for Young's modulus:

| Material | Young's modulus (GPa) | Deflection (m) |
|---|---|---|
| ABS | 2.1 | 0.18 |
| Acetal | 2.45 | 0.156 |
| Epoxy | 10.25 | 0.037 |
| ABS, reinforced | 7.5 | 0.051 |
| Acetal, reinforced | 10 | 0.038 |
| Epoxy, reinforced | 36.5 | 0.010 |
| Aluminum[1] | 70 | 0.0055 |
| Steel[1] | 195 | 0.00196 |

Note: 1. From Table 2.2 on p. 67.

**7.49 Determine the dimensions of a tubular steel drive shaft for a typical automobile. If you now replace this shaft with an unreinforced and then with a reinforced plastic, what should be its new dimensions in each case, in order to transmit the same torque? Choose the materials from Table 7.1 and assume a Poisson's ratio of 0.4.**

Because each car or truck can have a different axle, the answer will vary depending on the dimensions obtained. For illustrative purposes, the following analysis assumes an outside shaft diameter of 45 mm and a wall thickness of 6 mm, with a strength of 346 MPa (typical of 1020 steel, which is a reasonable material for axles; 1040 is better, with a typical yield stress is 386 MPa, but this number is not available in Table 5.2 on p. 159). The shear stress on the material is given by Eq. (2.11) on p. 78, but this is only for a thin-walled tube. It is better to use the equation from solid mechanics:

$$\tau = \frac{Tr}{J} \quad \rightarrow \quad T = \frac{\tau J}{r}$$

Substituting for the polar moment of inertia, and for a material in shear, we can take $\tau = 0.5Y$, so that

$$T = \frac{\tau J}{r} = \frac{\left(\frac{Y}{2}\right)\left[\frac{\pi}{2}\left(r_o^4 - r_i^4\right)\right]}{r_o} = \frac{\left(\frac{346 \times 10^6}{2}\right)\left[\frac{\pi}{2}\left(0.0225^4 - 0.0165^4\right)\right]}{0.0225} = 220 \text{ Nm}$$

Note that this is a very high torque, which illustrates the high safety factor used on axles.

Of the materials given in Table 7.1, epoxy (reinforced) appears to be be a good choice to substitute for steel. In fact, the strength can be made higher or even identical to the steel strength used above, so that the axle could have the same dimensions. However, epoxy is rather brittle for this demanding application. For the purposes of this example, we will proceed with nylon, using 83 MPa and 210 MPa as the strengths in the original and reinforced states, respectively. It can be readily seen that the nylon cannot transmit the required torque for this outer diameter; a solid shaft of nylon would require a diameter given by:

$$T = \frac{\tau J}{r} = 2200 \text{ Nm} = \left(\frac{Y}{2}\right)\left[\frac{\pi}{2}\left(r_o^3\right)\right] = \left(\frac{83 \times 10^6}{2}\right)\left(\frac{\pi}{2}r_o^3\right) \quad \rightarrow \quad r_o = 0.0323 \text{ m}$$

Thus, using unreinforced nylon would require a solid bar of about 65 mm in diameter, so that a straight material substitution would require redesign of the components that interface with this axle. For reinforced nylon, we can calculate that the axle has to be a solid bar to support essentially the same load.

Note that this is a stress-based design. It would be valuable to also consider deflections, since it is poor design practice to have large deflections when a stiff design is preferable (which is certainly the case with automobile axles).

**7.50 Estimate the number of molecules in a typical automobile tire. Estimate the number of atoms.**

The number of molecules in a car tire is one because of the extensive cross linking occurring during the vulcanization process (see p. 214). Tire sizes vary, as do specific chemical makeups. If 80% of the molecules are hydrogen and the remainder carbon, the average atomic weight is 3.208 (1.0079 for hydrogen and 12.011 for carbon, as obtained from a periodic table of the elements). Recall from introductory physics courses that this means one mole of hydrogen weighs 1.0079 g. Therefore, assuming a weight of 10 kg for the tire, there are approximately 3000 moles in a tire, or $1.9 \times 10^{27}$ atoms.

**7.51 Using strength and density data, determine the minimum weight of a 2-ft long tension member which must support a load of 1000 lbs., if it is manufactured from (a) high-molecular-weight polyethylene, (b) polyester, (c) rigid polyvinyl chloride, (d) ABS, (e) polystyrene, and (e) reinforced nylon. Where appropriate, calculate a range of weights for the same polymer.**

Refer to the derivation given in Problem 5.34. The area needed is given by $\sigma_y = F/A$, or $A = F/\sigma_y$. The volume is $V = AL = FL/\sigma_y$, and the weight is $W = \rho V = \rho FL/\sigma_y$. In this case, $L$ = 24 in. = 0.610 m, and $F$ = 1000 lb = 4440 N. The numbers here were obtained from a polymer handbook and are representative of the particular polymer, but the student may use approximate numbers from Table 3.1 on p. 103 and Table 7.1 on p. 192. Also note that the calculations are based on ultimate strength, not yield strength as was done with metals. The results are shown below:

| Material | Density (kg/m$^3$) | UTS (MPa) | Required weight (N) |
|---|---|---|---|
| HMW polyethylene | 950 | 24 | 1.05 |
| Polyester | 1270 | 50 | 0.67 |
| Rigid PVC | 1400 | 41-52 | 0.91-0.71 |
| ABS | 1030 | 30-52 | 0.91-0.52 |
| Polystyrene | 1000 | 32-56 | 0.83-0.47 |
| Reinforced nylon | 1130 | 90 | 0.33 |

**7.52 Plot the following for any five polymers described in this chapter: (a) UTS versus density and (b) elastic modulus versus UTS. Where appropriate, plot a range of values.**

Typical plots are as follows:

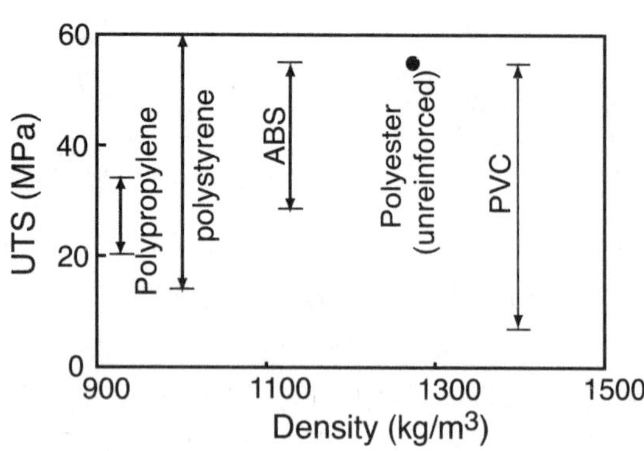


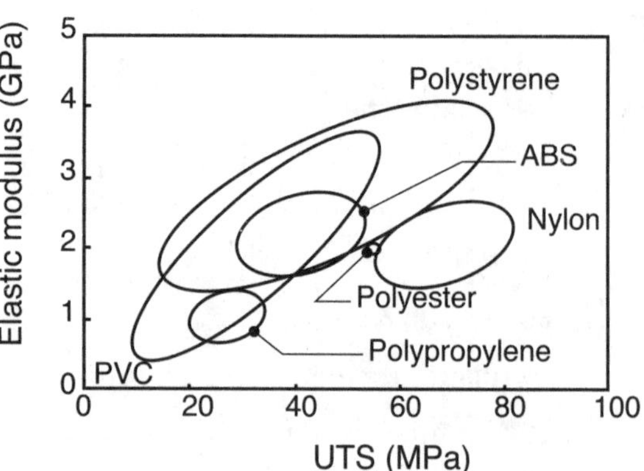


## SYNTHESIS, DESIGN AND PROJECTS

**7.53 Describe the design considerations involved in replacing a metal beverage container with one made of plastic.**

By the student. Note that the beverage can must be nontoxic and have sufficient strength (from low temperatures in the refrigerator to hot summer temperatures) to prevent from rupturing under internal pressure or buckling under a load. Because beverage cans are produced in the range of millions per day, the processing would have to be simple and highly reliable. Additional considerations include chilling characteristics, labeling, and aesthetics and feel.

**7.54 Assume that you are manufacturing a product in which all the gears are made of metal. A salesman visits you and asks you to consider replacing some of these metal gears with plastic ones. Make a list of the questions that you would raise before making a decision.**

By the student. Some of the questions to be asked are: Will the plastic retain its required strength, stiffness, and tolerances if temperature rises during its normal use? How acceptable is the wear resistance and fatigue life of the gears? Is it compatible with metal gears that it may mesh with? What are its frictional characteristics? Is the plastic gear affected adversely by any lubricants present? Will the supplier be able to meet the quality demands? How much cost savings are involved? Various other questions can be raised by the student.

**7.55 Sections 7.6 and 7.7 list several plastics and their applications. Rearrange this information by making a table of products (gears, helmets, luggage, electrical parts, etc.) which shows the types of plastic that can be used to make these products.**

By the student. Some examples are:

- Gears: Acetals, nylons, polyesters.

- Helmets: ABS, cellulosics, polycarbonates.
- Luggage: ABS, polyethylene, polypropylene, polyesters.
- Electrical parts: Fluorocarbons, nylons, polyethylenes, alkyds, urea, epoxies.
- Lenses: Acrylics, polycarbonates.
- Pipes and tubing: Acetals, ABS, cellulosics, nylon, polyethylene, polypropylene, PVC.

**7.56 Make a list of products or parts that are not currently made of plastics and offer some reasons why they are not. Support the reasons.**

By the student. Some examples are: Gas-turbine components: plastics do not possess the necessary strength at high temperatures. Keys: thermal expansion of the keys may not allow them to fit properly in keyholes, and wear resistance of plastics is generally less than that for metals.

**7.57 Review the three curves in Fig. 7.10 and give applications for each type of behavior. Explain your choices.**

By the student. Some examples are:

- Rigid and brittle: Handles, because they should not flex significantly; heat resistance, coupled with rigidity, is also useful for cookware handles.
- Tough and ductile: Helmets, because these plastics can dissipate the energy from impact without fracturing.
- Soft and flexible: Beverage bottles, because they can deform when dropped and regain their shape and not break, unlike glass bottles.

**7.58 Repeat Problem 7.57 for the curves in Fig. 7.12.**

By the student. Some examples are:

- Low-density polyethylene: The impact strength at low temperatures makes them useful for applications such as nonbreakable food containers.
- High-impact polypropylene: The high impact strength at a range of temperatures allows it to be used in automotive trim so that, in a collision, the trim will not crack and may not have to be replaced.
- Polyvinyl chloride (PVC): It can be either flexible or rigid, and either type can be used for tubing. Since it is not particularly strong or impact resistant, its use must be limited to low-pressure tubing. It is also very water resistant.
- Polymethylmethacrylate: It has moderate strength, good optical properties, and is weather resistance; Note that the main drawback to this material is low impact resistance. These properties makes it useful for lighting fixtures (that by their nature do not require high impact resistance).

**7.59 In order to use a steel or aluminum container for an acidic substance, such as tomato sauce, a polymeric barrier must be placed between the container and its contents. Describe methods of producing such a barrier.**

The most common method is to (a) dissolve a thermosetting polymer in a chemical liquid carrier, usually a ketone, (b) then spraying it onto the can interior, and (c) boiled off, leaving an adherent polymer coating. A less common approach is to laminate or coat the inside surface of the sheet stock with a metallic materials.

**7.60 Perform a study of plastics used for some products. Measure the hardness and stiffness of these plastics. (For example, dog chew toys use plastics with a range of properties.)**

By the student. The numbers will reflect the values given in Table 7.1 on p. 192.

**7.61 Add a column to Table 7.1 which describes the appearance of these plastics, including available colors and opaqueness.**

By the student. Note that most plastics can be made opaque, but only a few (such as acrylics and polycarbonates) are transparent. Most are available in more than one color, especially thermoplastics such as polyethylene and ABS.

**7.62 Perform a literature search and describe the properties and applications of polyaryletherketone (PAEK).**

By the student. PAEK and PEEK (polyetheretherketone) have a wide range of applications, from aerospace components like cable conduits and luggage compartment retainers, automotive components like starting disks in bus gears and ABS brake system components, dental instrument handles, steam faucets on espresso machines, and orthopedic implants (see Case Study 19.1 on p. 547).

**7.63 With Table 7.3 as a guide, inspect various products in your kitchen and your car and describe the types of plastics that could have been used in making their individual components.**

By the student. A wide variety of answers are acceptable for all types of applications. It can be especially beneficial if students attempt to identify the particular polymer, either by examining product literature, performing an Internet search, or simply identifying the symbol used for recycling the polymer (see p. 213).

# Chapter 8

# Ceramics, Graphite, and Diamond: Structure, General Properties, and Applications

## QUALITATIVE PROBLEMS

**8.18 Explain why ceramics are weaker in tension than in compression.**

Ceramics are very sensitive to cracks, impurities, and porosity, and thus generally have low toughness. In compression, however, the flaws in the material do not cause stress concentrations or crack propagation, as they do in tension.

**8.19 What are the advantages of cermets? Suggest applications in addition to those given in the text.**

High-temperature oxidation resistance and toughness are the advantageous properties of cermets. They also may be useful for components in furnaces (such as moving belts) and automotive-engine parts (such as pistons and cylinders).

**8.20 Explain why the electrical and thermal conductivity of ceramics decreases with increasing porosity.**

Pores in the ceramic are usually filled with air, and air has much lower thermal and electrical conductivity than ceramics. Increasing porosity will thus reduce the ceramic's thermal and electrical conductivities.

**8.21 Explain why the mechanical property data in Table 8.2 have such a broad range. What is the significance in engineering practice?**

The properties given in Table 8.2 on p. 225 vary greatly because the mechanical properties of ceramics depend greatly on the quality of the raw material, porosity in the product, and the manner in which the product is made. Engineering applications that require high mechanical properties must ensure that the material quality and processing of the part are the best available.

**8.22 What reasons can you think of that encouraged the development of synthetic diamond?**

By the student. Synthetic diamonds were first used exclusively in industrial applications; they have superior properties to natural diamonds because of the absence of impurities. The hardness of diamond makes it useful in machining and grinding hard metallic and nonmetallic materials. For widespread and economical use, diamonds are mass produced synthetically.

**8.23 Explain why the mechanical properties of ceramics are generally better than those of metals.**

Metals and ceramics have different types of bonding, metallic and ionic, respectively. Ionic bonds are stronger than metallic bonds, hence more force must be applied to the material to break the bonds. The crystal structure for ceramics is generally more complex than metals, and requires higher forces to cause slip. Also, the high-temperature properties of ceramics are very attractive in many applications.

**8.24 How are ceramics made tougher?**

Ceramics may be made tougher by using high-purity raw materials, controlled processing techniques, and adding various reinforcements. The presence of tougher second phases and microcracks (less than one $\mu$m in size) in the ceramic can also reduce the energy of propagation of an advancing crack tip. (See also partially stabilized zirconia, Section 8.2.2 on p. 221.)

**8.25 Mention and describe applications in which static fatigue can be important.**

By the student. There are numerous possible answers. Static fatigue occurs in environments where water vapor is present and the part is under a constant load. In applications such sewer piping, if a tensile stress is developed in the pipe by bending or torsion, static fatigue can be a significant problem. Any situation where a tension member is exposed to water vapor (such as mounting brackets or structural members outdoors) are also subject to static fatique. Some MEMS devices see failure of borosilicate glass layers due to static fatigue as well.

**8.26 How does porosity affect the mechanical properties of ceramics, and why does it do so?**

Porosity can be considered microscopic air pockets in the ceramic. Air has no strength or elastic modulus, thus porosity will always decrease the strength of the ceramic. The holes in the material also act (depending on their shape) as stress concentrations, thus further lowering the strength. Porosities also act as crack initiation sites, thus decreasing toughness.

**8.27 What properties are important in making heat-resistant ceramics for use on oven tops? Why?**

Heat-resistant ceramics for oven tops should possess hot corrosion resistance to maintain their appearance, hardness for wear and scratch resistance, and toughness for impact loading.

Because the heating of oven top is uneven, thermal gradients will be set up across the surface. To minimize the possibility for thermal cracking, the oven top should have low coefficient of thermal expansion and high thermal conductivity (see also pp. 107-108).

**8.28 Describe the differences between the properties of glasses and those of ceramics.**

Glasses are amorphous solids (supercooled), while ceramics are materials with a highly ordered and usually complex crystal structures. The amorphous structure of glasses allows them to be transparent, while ceramics are opaque. The hardness and elastic modulus are lower than those for ceramics, while the compressive strength of glass is in the same range as that for ceramics.

**8.29 A large variety of glasses is now available. Why is this so?**

By the student. The cost of each type of glass varies, and a high-quality glass (high cost) shouldn't be used in a low-quality application. However, high quality glasses are required for fiber optics, which need to transmit light with high efficiency. Other applications may require high strength, low cost, chemical resistance, impact resistance, abrasion resistance or resistance to thermal shock, which would be best exhibited by 96% silica or fused-silica type glass. Thus, in summary, there are a large variety of glasses available because of the large variety of applications where glass is used.

**8.30 What is the difference between the structure of graphite and that of diamond? Is it important? Explain.**

Graphite has a crystalline form of a layered structure of basal planes of close-packed carbon atoms (see Fig. 1.4 on p. 49). Diamond, on the other hand, has a covalently bonded structure. The structure of graphite permits easy slip on basal planes, while the covalent bonding of diamond greatly restricts slip, thus making it very hard.

**8.31 What materials are suitable for use as a coffee cup? Explain.**

By the student. A coffee cup must obviously be made of a material that is safe for food contact, so it should not affect or be affected by coffee. In addition, it should be inexpensive. Furthermore, it must be thermally insulating, have a melting point higher than the boiling point of water, and be easy to clean. Ceramics, polymers, porous polymers (foams), and multi-layered metals (with air or a vacuum between layers) are thus suitable.

**8.32 Aluminum oxide and partially stabilized zirconia are described as white in appearance. Can they be colored? If they can, how would you accomplish this?**

Both aluminum oxide and partially stabilized zirconia can be produced in a variety of colors. This can be done by using impurities in small concentrations in the ceramic, which develop a color. There is, of course, also the option of enameling, painting, or coloring the surfaces.

**8.33 Both ceramics and metal castings (Part II) are known to be stronger in compression than in tension. What similar reasons exist for these behaviors?**

The main common reason is that both the ceramic and the metal are porous. In tension, porosity serves as a serious stress concentration and compromises the material's strength. In compression, the stress concentration associated with porosity is far less serious, so that the strength is not compromised to nearly the same extent in compression than tension. Also, there are residual stresses which can affect both ceramics and metals, and these are both due to thermal stresses during processing.

**8.34 Why does the strength of a ceramic part depend on its size?**

Ceramic strength is mainly compromised by the presence of flaws where cracks can initiate. In a small volume, there is less likelihood that a large flaw or a number of flaws can exist, while the reverse is true for larger parts, i.e., in a large volume, it is more likely that a large flaw will exist (see also the discussion regarding Fig. 2.11 on p. 79).

**8.35 In old castles and churches in Europe, the glass windows display pronounced ripples and are thicker at the bottom than at the top. Explain why this has occurred.**

The silica in the glass is not really solid; it is merely a supercooled liquid. Over centuries, the glass has creeps or flows due to the force of gravity. This situation depends greatly on the type of glass, as some will creep faster than others.

**8.36 Ceramics are hard and strong in compression and shear. Why, then, are they not used as nails or other fasteners?**

Ceramics aren't used as nails or other fasteners because they have poor impact resistance and thus would not be able to be driven into a workpiece with impact forces as applied by a hammer. Other fasteners such as bolts depend on a tensile proof stress (the proof strength of a bolt is a common design specification) for a well-designed joint, and this would be a poor design application for a ceramic which is weak and has a wide range of strengths in tension.

**8.37 It was stated in the text that ceramics have a wider range of strengths in tension than metals. List reasons why this is so, with respect to both the ceramic properties that cause variations and the difficulties in obtaining repeatable results.**

By the student. The obvious starting point is the number and size of flaws and their distributions. Metals will often plastically deform around a flaw and will be less susceptible to them.

## QUANTITATIVE PROBLEMS

**8.38 If a fully dense ceramic has the properties that UTS$_o$ = 180 MPa and $E_o$ = 300 GPa, what are these properties at 20% porosity for values of $n$ = 4, 5, 6, and 7, respectively?**

Inserting the appropriate quantities into the Eqs. (8.1) and (8.2) on p. 225, we obtain the following:

| $n$ | UTS (MPa) | E (GPa) |
|---|---|---|
| 4 | 80.9 | 196.8 |
| 5 | 66.2 | 196.8 |
| 6 | 54.2 | 196.8 |
| 7 | 44.4 | 196.8 |

Note that the magnitude of $n$ does not affect the magnitude of $E$.

**8.39 Plot the UTS, $E$, and $k$ values for ceramics as a function of porosity $P$, describe and explain the trends that you observe in their behavior.**

Equations (8.1) through (8.3) on pp. 225-226 are needed to solve this problem. The curves can be obtained using an assumed value at zero porosity, or else they can be non-dimensionalized, as shown below. The plots are as follows:

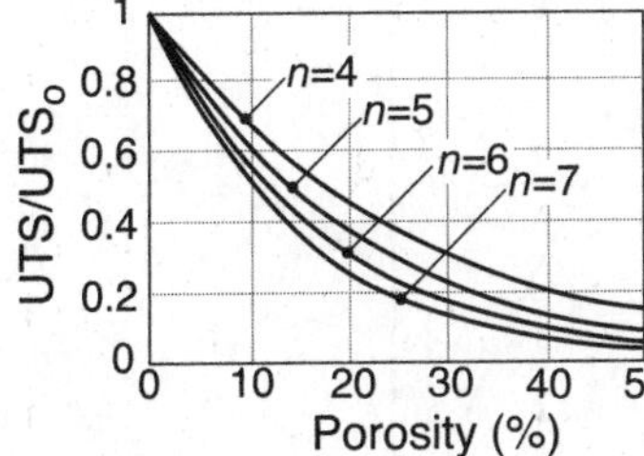


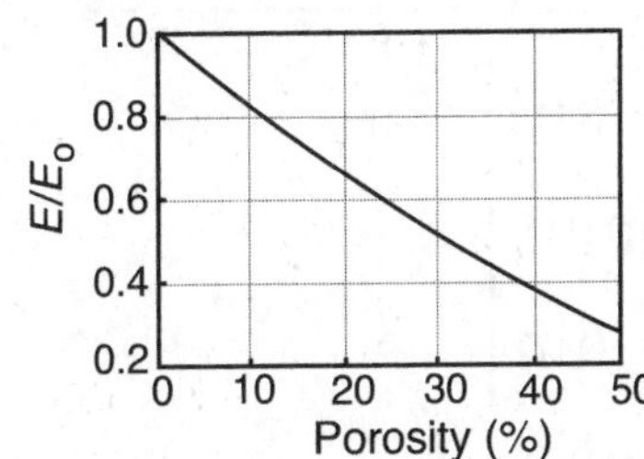


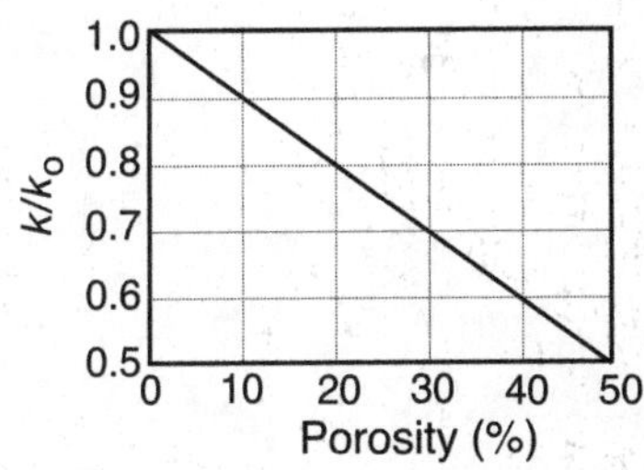


There are several observations that can be made. Most striking is the near-linear behavior of stiffness and thermal conductivity with respect to porosity, and the highly nonlinear behavior of strength. Thus, to produce high-strength ceramics, reduction of porosity is especially important.

**8.40 What would be the tensile strength and the modulus of elasticity of the ceramic in Problem 8.38, for porosities of 10% and 30%, for the four $n$ values given?**

Equations (8.1) and (8.2) on p. 225 are needed to solve this problem. Inserting the appropriate quantities into these equations, we obtain the following:

| $n$ | UTS (MPa) | |
|---|---|---|
| | $P = 0.10$ | $P = 0.30$ |
| 4 | 120 | 54.2 |
| 5 | 109 | 40.2 |
| 6 | 98.8 | 29.7 |
| 7 | 89.4 | 22.0 |

The modulus of elasticity values are as follows: for $P = 0.10$, $E = 246$ GPa, and for $P = 0.30$, $E = 177$ GPa.

**8.41 Calculate the thermal conductivities for ceramics at porosities of 10%, 20%, and 30% for $k_o = 0.7$ W/m·K.**

Equation (8.3) on p. 226 is needed to solve this problem. Inserting the values into the equation, we obtain thermal conductivities of:

| | |
|---|---|
| $P = 10\%$ | $k = 0.45$ W/mK |
| $P = 20\%$ | $k = 0.40$ W/mK |
| $P = 30\%$ | $k = 0.35$ W/mK |

**8.42 A ceramic has $k_o = 0.65$ W/m·K. If this ceramic is shaped into a cylinder with a porosity distribution given by**

$$P = 0.1(x/L)(1 - x/L)$$

**where $x$ is the distance from one end of the cylinder and $L$ is the total cylinder length, plot the porosity as a function of distance, evaluate the average porosity, and calculate the average thermal conductivity.**

The plot of porosity is as follows:

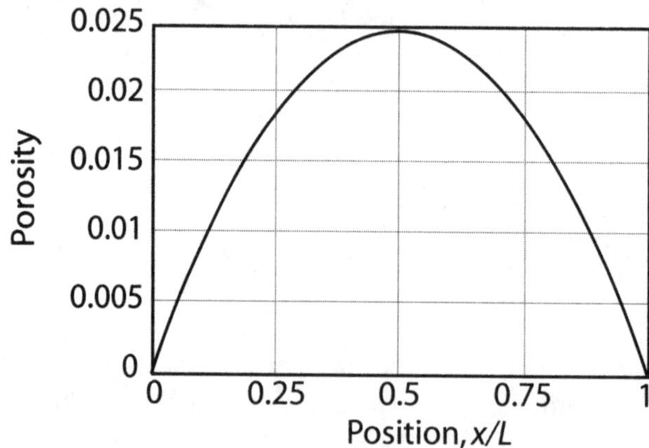


For the remainder of the problem, use $X = x/L$. The average porosity is given by

$$\bar{P} = \int_0^1 0.1X(1 - X)dX = \int_0^1 \left(-0.1X^2 + 0.1X\right) dX = 0.0167$$

Since the thermal conductivity is linearly related to the porosity, the average porosity can be used, so that the average thermal conductivity is:

$$\bar{k} = k_o\left(1 - \bar{P}\right) = (0.65)(1 - 0.0167) = 0.639 \text{ W/mK}$$

8.43 **It can be shown that the minimum weight of a column which will support a given load depends on the ratio of the material's stiffness to the square root of its density. Plot this property for a ceramic as a function of porosity.**

The stiffness of a ceramic is given by Eq. (8.2) as $E = E_o(1 - 1.9P + 0.9P^2)$. The density is given by $\rho = \rho_o(1 - P)$. Therefore, the desired quantity is:

$$\frac{E}{\sqrt{\rho}} = \frac{E_o\left(1 - 1.9P + 0.9P^2\right)}{\sqrt{\rho_o(1 - P)}}$$

The plot is as shown below.

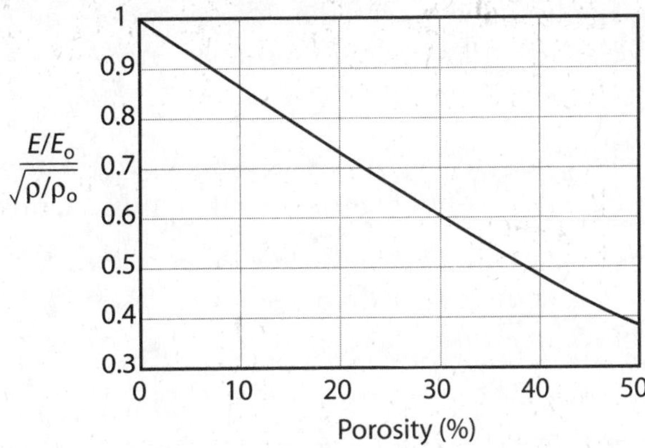


## SYNTHESIS, DESIGN AND PROJECTS

**8.44 Make a list of the ceramic parts that you can find around your house and in your car. Explain why those parts are made of ceramics.**

By the student. Some examples are: Bathroom fixtures: they will not discolor or corrode in normal use, are hard enough to resist the abrasive action of cleaning powders, and are relatively inexpensive. Coffee mugs: their smooth finish makes them easy to clean, are corrosion resistant, and are inexpensive. Light-fixture components: electric insulators and resistant to heat. Spark plugs: thermal and electrical insulation and corrosion resistance.

**8.45 Assume that you are working in technical sales and are fully familiar with all the advantages and limitations of ceramics. Which of the markets traditionally using nonceramic materials do you think ceramics can penetrate? What would you say to your potential customers during your sales visits? What kind of questions do you think they will ask?**

By the student. There are a number of acceptable answers to this question, and students should not be restricted to the answer given here. Applications that require high hot strength and wear and corrosion resistance in components such as car engines. Beneficial features of properties should be pointed out, along with recent trends in the improvement of properties. All the advantages that ceramics have over the current material should also be pointed out. Questions concerning the brittleness and low toughness would also be raised, as well as questions concerning the consistency of the quality of ceramic parts, particularly as their size and shape complexity increases.

**8.46 Describe applications in which a ceramic material with a near-zero coefficient of thermal expansion would be desirable.**

By the student. A ceramic material with a near-zero coefficient of thermal expansion will have a lower tendency of thermal cracking when exposed to temperature gradients. This property would be useful in applications where the ceramic would be cycled through temperature ranges, as with space shuttle tiles and cutting tools in machining, particularly in interrupted cutting operations such as milling.

**8.47 The modulus of elasticity of ceramics is largely maintained at elevated temperatures. What engineering applications could benefit from this characteristic?**

By the student. Note that by retaining their high stiffness at elevated temperatures, dimensional accuracy can be maintained. Some examples are bearings, cutting tools, turbine blades, machine-tool components, and electronics. The student is encouraged to expand on this answer.

**8.48 List and discuss the factors that you would take into account when replacing a metal component with a ceramic component.**

By the student. Note, for example, that the main limitations of ceramics are low tensile strength and low toughness. The application of the metal component that would be replaced should, therefore, not require high tensile strength or high impact resistance.

**8.49 Obtain some data from the available technical literature and quantitatively show the effect of temperature on the strength and the modulus of elasticity of several ceramics. Comment on how the shape of these curves differs from those for metals.**

By the student. The general trend that will be seen is that such properties as strength and stiffness do not change as drastically as in metals (see, for example, Fig. 22.1 on p. 648).

**8.50 Assume that the cantilever beam in Quantitative Problem 3.16 in Chapter 3 is made of ceramic. How different would your answer be when compared to that of a beam made of metal? Explain clearly, giving numerical examples.**

As can be seen from the answer to Problem 3.16, the relevant parameters are the modulus of elasticity, $E$, at different temperatures and the coefficient of thermal expansion, ?. We know that compared to metals, ceramics maintain their modulus of elasticity much better as temperature increases. Also, ? for ceramics is generally lower than that for metals (see Tables 3.1 and 3.2 on pp. 103 and 104, respectively). Consequently, the difference in the frequencies, $f$, will be smaller than indicated.

**8.51 It was noted in Section 8.4.1 that there are several basic types of glasses available. Make a survey of the available technical literature in the Bibliography and prepare a table for these glasses indicating various mechanical, physical, and optical properties.**

By the student. A large variety of answers are possible. For example, the following table is given in Schey, J., *Introduction to Manufacturing Processes*, 3d ed., p. 500, based on data from D.C. Boyd and D.A. Thompson:

| **Property** | **Corning glass works code number and type** | | | | | | |
|---|---|---|---|---|---|---|---|
| | 7940 fused silica | E glass | 7740 boro-silicate | 1720 alumino-silicate | 0800 soda-lime-silica | 8871 potash-lead | 8830 boro-silicate |
| Composition, wt% | | | | | | | |
| $SiO_2$ | 99.9 | 54 | 81 | 62 | 73 | 42 | 65 |
| $B_2O_3$ | | 10 | 13 | 5 | | | 23 |
| $Al_2O_3$ | | 14 | 2 | 17 | 1 | | 5 |
| $Na_2O$ | | | 4 | 1 | 17 | 2 | 7 |
| $K_2O$ | | | | | | 6 | |
| $Li_2O$ | | | | | | 1 | |
| CaO | | 17.5 | | 8 | 5 | | |
| MgO | | 4.5 | | 7 | 4 | | |
| PbO | | | | | | 49 | |
| Viscosity, at °C | | | | | | | |
| $10^{14.5}$ (hard) | 956 | 507 | 510 | 667 | 473 | 350 | 460 |
| $10^{13}$ (anneal pt.) | 1084 | 657 | 560 | 712 | 514 | 385 | 501 |
| $10^{7.6}$ (soft) | 1580 | 846 | 821 | 915 | 695 | 525 | 708 |
| $10^4$ (working) | | | 1252 | 1202 | 1005 | 785 | 1042 |
| Coefficient of thermal expansion, $\times 10^{-7}/°C$ | 55 | 60 | 33 | 42 | 92 | 102 | 49.5 |

**8.52 Ceramic pistons are being considered for a high-speed combustion engine. List the benefits and concerns that you would have regarding this application.**

By the student. Ceramic pistons would be advantageous in that they would have a high strength and potentially low wear. In addition, the inertial forces associated with a ceramic piston would be much lower than for a metal one, and the need for cooling the piston becomes less imperative. The main drawbacks are that the ceramic could excessively wear the cylinder liner; with three-body wear, any ceramic wear particles could cause severely damage in the engine. Also, the low fracture toughness of the ceramic may cause catastrophic failure of the engine.

**8.53 Pyrex cookware displays a unique phenomenon: It functions well for a large number of cycles and then shatters into many pieces. Investigate this phenomenon, list the probable causes, and discuss the manufacturing considerations that may alleviate or contribute to such failures.**

By the student. The basic phenomenon is that with each thermal stress cycle, new flaws in the material are developed and existing flaws grow. When the flaws have finally reached a critical size, the Pyrex part fails at their usual loading, such as associated with placing the part on a stove or shelf. This loading results in a stress wave; since there is a significant temper in the glass and a critical fracture site releases the stress, the resulting stress wave is sufficient to cause fracture at many of the flaws that have developed over time. Any manufacturing considerations that result in a larger initial flaw or less effective tempering will contribute to the problem.

**8.54 It has been noted that the strength of brittle materials (such as ceramics and glasses) is very sensitive to surface defects such as scratches (notch sensitivity). Obtain some pieces of these materials, make scratches on them, and test them by carefully clamping in a vise and bending them. Comment on your observations.**

By the student. Note that special care must be taken in performing these experiments, and eye protection and the like are necessary. This experiment can be performed using a glass cutter to make a deep and sharp scratch on the glass. It can be demonstrated that glass, with such a scratch, can be easily broken with bare hands (using work gloves). Note also the direction of the bending moment with respect o the direction of the scratch. As a comparison, even a highly heat-treated aluminum plate will not be nearly as weakened when a similar scratch is made on its surface.

# Chapter 9

# Composite Materials: Structure, General Properties, and Applications

## QUALITATIVE PROBLEMS

**9.18 How do you think the use of straw in clay originally came about in making brick for dwellings?**

By the student. Someone probably accidentally mixed straw with clay. When the baked clay was broken up, it was noticed that the straw held the fractured pieces together and prevented the clay block from crumbling.

**9.19 What products have you personally seen that are made of reinforced plastics? How can you tell?**

By the student. Some examples are chairs, tennis rackets, and boat hulls. The reinforced structure can be identified by observing the surface texture (small irregular bumps) and when fractured, the fracture pattern (fibers showing through). The stiffness-to-weight ratio of reinforced plastic products, as compared to ordinary plastics, is also a definitive method of identification. Perhaps the simplest technique is direct examination, since a laminate structure or even the reinforcing fibers can be seen directly, especially using a magnifying glass.

**9.20 What applications are not well suited for composite materials?**

By the student. This is an open-ended problem that can be answered in a number of ways. One of the main drawbacks to composite materials is that they are expensive, so that low-cost items such as children's toys or simple plastic parts cannot be produced economically using composites. Also, it is relatively easy to produce thin, laminated structures from reinforced polymers, but bulky shapes are difficult to produce unless they are metal-matrix or ceramic-matrix composites.

**9.21 What is the difference between a composite material and a coated material?**

This is an open-ended problem that can be answered in a number of ways. Coatings are typically very thin and do not affect the stiffness of a material. Furthermore, a coating generally does not serve a structural purpose, whereas a composite material can support high applied loads, in addition to possessing various other characteristics. Composite materials usually incorporate many reinforcements, whereas a coating covers only one item.

**9.22 Identify metals and alloys that have strengths comparable to those of reinforced plastics.**

By the student. A typical comparison is given below:

| Metal (MPa) | Reinforced plastic (MPa) |
|---|---|
| Magnesium (165-195) | Nylon (70-210) |
| | Polyester (110-160) |
| Aluminum alloys (90-600) | ABS (100) |
| | Acetal (135) |
| | Nylon (70-210) |
| | Polycarbonate (110) |
| | Polyester (110-160) |
| | Polypropylene (40-100) |
| Copper alloys (140-1310) | Nylon (70-210) |
| | Polyester (40-100) |
| Iron (185-285) | Nylon (70-210) |

Note that reinforced epoxy has such a wide range of strength levels that it can be comparable to almost all metals. It is the only reinforced plastic that is capable of achieving the strength levels of steels, and nickel and titanium alloys.

**9.23 The many advantages of composite materials were described in this chapter. What limitations or disadvantages do these materials have? What suggestions would you make to overcome these limitations?**

By the student. There are many disadvantages that could be suggested based on the student's experience. Two examples of disadvantages are anisotropy of properties and possible environmental attack of the fibers (especially water adsorption). Anisotropy of properties (which is not always undesirable) can be reduced by having a random dispersion of reinforcing materials. Environmental attack of the fibers would cause loss of fiber strength and possibly debonding from the matrix (see also Section 9.3 on p. 244). Applying a thin protective coating to the composite and selecting appropriate matrix and fiber materials can help reduce environmental attack.

**9.24 What factors contribute to the cost of reinforcing fibers? (See also Table 9.2).**

The two main factors that affect the cost of reinforcing fibers are the cost of raw materials and the cost of processing (see also Section 19.2.2 on p. 542). For example, boron fibers require a starting material made of expensive tungsten wire. Graphite fibers require relatively expensive processing techniques, making them more expensive than glass fibers. Polymer fibers need to be of high purity, and involve special processing steps to align the polymer molecules to obtain desirable mechanical properties, and these processing steps add to the cost of the material.

**9.25 Give examples of composite materials other than those stated in this chapter.**

By the student. Some additional examples of composite materials are:

(a) wood, which has a natural honeycomb structure of cellulose fibers,
(b) metal-matrix composites of aluminum and silicon carbide
(c) copper-infiltrated, powder-metal ferrous gears,
(d) particle board, which consists of wood chips and a binder, and
(e) steel-belted radial tires.

**9.26 A hybrid composite is defined as one containing two or more different types of reinforcing fibers. What advantages would such a composite have over others?**

By the student. The hybrid composites have their properties and cost dependent on the type of fibers used. Thus, for example, a certain strength level could be obtained at a lower cost by using a combination of graphite and Kevlar fibers, rather than Kevlar alone. The anisotropic properties of the composite can also be controlled in different ways, such as having Kevlar fibers oriented along the major stress direction and graphite fibers dispersed randomly in the composite.

**9.27 Explain why the behavior of the materials given in Fig. 9.5 is as shown.**

The matrix material (nylon 6,6) generally has poor thermal conductivity and creep resistance, and high electrical resistance and thermal expansion. Both carbon and glass fibers raise the endurance limit and wear resistance of the nylon because they raise the strength of the material. Both reinforcements increase the thermal conductivity since they have higher thermal conductivity than the nylon matrix. This argument also explains the increase in creep resistance and the decrease in thermal expansion coefficient of a composite by fiber addition.

**9.28 Why are fibers capable of supporting a major portion of the load in composite materials?**

Fibers can support the major portion of the load when it can be transferred from the matrix to the fiber. This transfer requires a good interfacial bond between the fiber and the matrix. The reason that the fibers can carry such a large portion of the load is that they are stiffer than the matrix, although both the matrix and the fibers undergo the same amount of deformation (see the Section 9.3.1 on pp. 247-248.

**9.29 Do metal-matrix composites have advantages over reinforced plastics? Explain.**

Metal-matrix composites have two main advantages over reinforced plastics: they can be used at higher temperatures and they are generally tougher and more ductile. Also, the manufacturing processes for metal-matrix composites (see Section 19.14 on p. 570) are better suited for making bulk forms than some of the processes used for making reinforced plastics, such as tape lay-up.

**9.30** Give reasons for the development of ceramic-matrix composites. Name some possible applications.

Ceramic-matrix composites maintain their strength, stiffness, and temperature resistance of the ceramic matrix, and have fiber added to the material to improve toughness. Typical applications include engine components, deep-sea mining equipment, and pressure vessels. These applications exploit the hard, strong (in compression), and chemically inert nature of ceramics while utilizing the additional ductility of the reinforcement to avoid fracture, especially those associated with high stress concentrations or impact.

**9.31 Explain how you would go about determining the hardness of reinforced plastics and of composite materials. Are hardness measurements on these types of materials meaningful? Does the size of the indentation make a difference? Explain.**

By the student. The important consideration here is the fact that the smaller the indentation, the more localized the hardness measurement will be (see Fig. 2.13 on p. 70). Consequently, one can then distinguish the hardness of the matrix and the reinforcements separately by using small indentations. A large indentation, such as resulting from a Brinell test, will give an overall hardness value.

**9.32 How would you go about trying to determine the strength of a fiber?**

By the student. One can either try to perform a tension test on a single fiber (with much care, as ensuring that the fiber fails within a test section is important), or else the breaking strength of a number of fibers could be determined and an average value of fiber strength can be found. Finally, one could use microhardness testing techniques on a fiber inside a sectioned and lapped composite to estimate the strength (see Section 2.6.2 on p. 82), although the anisotropic nature of the fiber will affect the results.

**9.33 What are the advantages of whiskers as a reinforcing material?**

Whiskers are small-diameter, limited-length fibers (see top of p. 244 and Section 22.10 on p. 664). The initial impression may be that whiskers have a limited beneficial role because of their limited length. However, whiskers in general have sufficient length to develop their full strength in fracture (the matrix transmits sufficient force to each fiber so that delamination is not the significant concern) The main advantage of whiskers over other fibers is that their small size means that they are generally stronger than other fibers (size effect).

**9.34 It has been stated that glass fibers are much stronger than bulk glass. Why is this so?**

The glass fibers are stronger than bulk glass for a number of reasons. The glass used for fibers is of higher purity and greater care is taken in its manufacture. A fiber with a small cross-section is far less likely to have a large flaw than one with a larger cross-section. Surface flaws, which reduce strength, are also smaller for the same reason. The drawing process which produces fibers, in effect, proof stresses the fiber, so that weak fibers do not survive the manufacturing process.

**9.35 Under what circumstances could a glass be used as a matrix?**

By the student. The matrix is generally used to provide toughness and chemical protection to the fibers. However, with glass it is not likely that this will be the case, and in fact reinforcement for glass usually consists of steel wires. The glass provides the structural strength, and the metal contributes to the tensile strength, and also keeps the fragments together if the glass fractures. A common product is glass sheet or plate reinforced by a chicken-wire type of mesh for structural applications.

**9.36 When the American Plains states were settled, no trees existed for the construction of housing. Pioneers cut bricks from sodbasically, prairie soil as a matrix and grass and its root system as reinforcement. Explain why this worked. Also, if you were a pioneer, would you stack the bricks with the grass horizontally or vertically? Explain.**

When grass grows from the earth, it is the same effect as the straw in clay bricks (which was the first composite material used). If this type of brick was used in a wall, the orientation would be decided by the type and direction of loading. A wind load, for example, would subject a wall to bending. In this case, the grass should be oriented in the same direction as the applied bending moment.

**9.37 Compare the advantages and disadvantages of metal-matrix composites, reinforced plastics, and ceramic-matrix composites.**

There are many possible answers to this question, and students should be encouraged to develop their own answers. For example, students may compare these materials with each other, or they may compare them against other benchmarks such as carbon steel and other metals and alloys. Some answers are:

- Metal-matrix composites: Advantages are higher stiffness than reinforced plastics or unreinforced metals, good high-temperature performance as compared to polymers or reinforced polymers, and very high strength-to-weight ratios. Disadvantages are high cost, especially for small production runs, and difficulty in machining them into desired shapes.
- Reinforced plastics: Advantages include very high strength-to-weight and stiffness-to-weight ratios as compared to other materials, flexibility in manufacturing processes, ability to use continuous or discontinuous fibers, a wide variety of available matrix materials. Disadvantages include limited high-temperature performance, cost, and difficulty in machining.
- Ceramic matrix composites: Advantages are their high-temperature strength and stiffness. Disadvantages are associated with high cost and difficulty in machining.

**9.38 You studied the many advantages of composite materials in this chapter. What limitations or disadvantages do these materials have? What suggestions would you make to overcome these limitations?**

By the student. There are many disadvantages that could be suggested based on the student's experience. Two examples of disadvantages are anisotropy of properties and possible environmental attack of the fibers (especially water adsorption). Anisotropy of properties (which is not always undesirable) can be reduced by having a random dispersion of reinforcing materials. Environmental attack of the fibers would cause loss of fiber strength and possibly debonding from the matrix (see also Section 9.3 on p. 244). Applying a thin protective coating to the composite and selecting appropriate matrix and fiber materials can help reduce environmental attack.

**9.39** By incorporating small amounts of blowing agent, it is possible to manufacture hollow polymer fibers with gas cores. List applications for such fibers.

The benefits of a gas core are that the polymer is lighter than other polymers, and that the polymer will have a lower thermal conductivity. This has beneficial applications in the production of, for example, cold-weather clothing, which can be made simultaneously lightweight and insulating.

## QUANTITATIVE PROBLEMS

**9.40 Calculate the average increase in the properties of the plastics given in Table 7.1, as a result of their reinforcement, and describe your observations.**

The results are summarized below:

| Material | Unreinforced, ave. (MPa) | Reinforced, ave. (MPa) | Average increase (%) |
|---|---|---|---|
| ABS, UTS | 42 | 100 | 59 |
| *E* | 2100 | 7500 | 54 |
| Acetal, UTS | 63 | 135 | 73 |
| *E* | 2500 | 10,000 | 76 |
| Epoxy, UTS | 88 | 735 | 650 |
| *E* | 10,300 | 36,500 | 263 |
| Nylon, UTS | 69 | 140 | 71 |
| *E* | 2100 | 6000 | 39 |
| Polycarbonate, UTS | 63 | 110 | 48 |
| *E* | 2800 | 6000 | 33 |
| Polyester, UTS | 55 | 135 | 80 |
| *E* | 2000 | 10,200 | 82 |
| Polypropylene, UTS | 28 | 70 | 43 |
| *E* | 1000 | 4800 | 38 |

**9.41 In the example in Section 9.3, what would be the percentage of the load supported by the fibers if their strength is 1100 MPa and the matrix strength is 200 MPa? What if the fiber stiffness is doubled and the matrix stiffness is halved?**

A review of the calculations on pp. 229 indicates that the strength of the materials involved does not influence the results. Since the problem refers only to changes in strength, it is assumed that the moduli of elasticity are the same as in the original example.

Let's now consider the problem where the strengths are the same as in the original example, but the stiffness of the fiber is doubled (to 60 GPa) while that of the matrix is halved (to 5 GPa). The percentage of the load supported by the fibers can then be calculated as follows:

$$E_c = (0.2)(60) + (1 - 0.2)(5) = 12 + 4 = 16 \text{ GPa}$$

Also,

$$\frac{P_f}{P_m} = \frac{(0.20)(60)}{(0.8)(5)} = \frac{12}{4} = 3$$

or

$$P_c = P_f + P_f/3 = 1.33P_f$$

and thus

$$P_f = 0.75P_c$$

Thus, the fibers support 75% of the load in this composite material. As expected, this percentage is higher than the 43% in the sample calculations on pp. 247-248.

**9.42 Make a survey of the recent technical literature and present data indicating the effects of fiber length on such mechanical properties as the strength, the elastic modulus, and impact energy of reinforced plastics.**

By the student. There are several interesting topics that can be investigated. For example, research on the effect of whiskers on the fracture toughness of composites indicates that an optimum aspect ratio exists.

**9.43 Calculate the percent increase in the mechanical properties of reinforced nylon from the data shown in Fig. 9.4.**

As was given in the answer to Problem 9.40, The results are:

| | Unreinforced, ave. (MPa) | Reinforced, ave. (MPa) | Average increase (%) |
|---|---|---|---|
| UTS | 69 | 140 | 71 |
| $E$ | 2100 | 6000 | 39 |

**9.44 Plot $E/\rho$ and $E/\rho^{0.5}$ for the composite materials listed in Table 9.1 and make a comparison to the properties of the materials described in Chapters 4 through 8. (See also Table 9.2.)**

The plots are as follows:

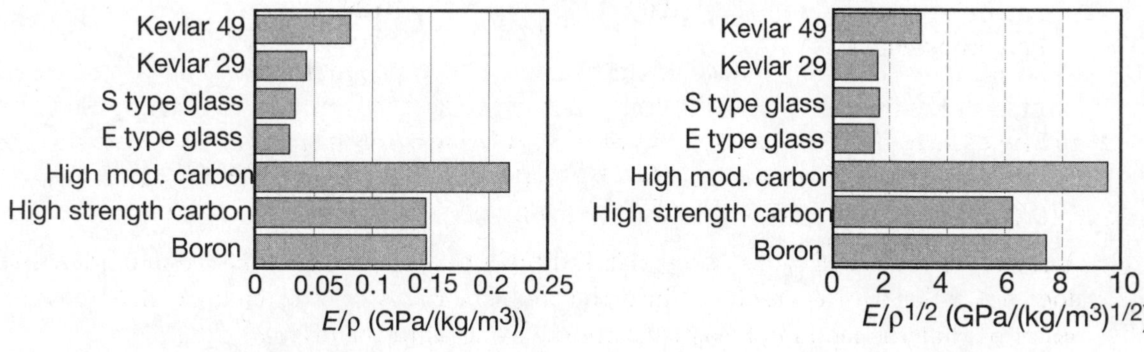

**9.45 Calculate the stress in the fibers and in the matrix for the Example in Section 9.3.1. Assume that the cross-sectional area is 0.1 in$^2$ and $P_c = 500$ lb**

If the total load is 500 lb., the fibers support 43% of this load, or 215 lb. The total cross-sectional area of the fibers is (0.2)(0.1 in$^2$)=0.02 in$^2$. The tensile stress in the fibers is then

$$\sigma_f = \frac{P_f}{A_f} = \frac{215 \text{ lb}}{0.02 \text{ in}^2} = 10.75 \text{ ksi}$$

The stress in the matrix is calculated in a similar manner. It is found that the load is 285 lb, the area is 0.08 in$^2$, and therefore the stress is 3.5 ksi.

**9.46 Repeat the calculations in the Example in Section 9.3.1 (a) if a high-modulus carbon fiber is used and (b) if Kevlar 29 is used.**

The difference between these two problems is the stiffness of the fibers. For high-modulus carbon fibers, $E = 415$ GPa, while for Kevlar 29, $E = 62$ GPa. Using the same approach as in the Example on p. 229, for high-modulus carbon fibers we have

$$E_c = (0.2)(415 \text{ GPa}) + (1 - 0.2)(100 \text{ GPa}) = 163 \text{ GPa}$$

and

$$\frac{P_f}{P_m} = 0.2\frac{(415)}{0.8(100)} = 1.075$$

Therefore, $P_f = 0.52P_c$. For the Kevlar, $E_c = 92.4$ GPa, $P_f/P_m = 0.155$, or $P_f = 0.13P_c$.

**9.47 Refer to the properties listed in Table 7.1. If acetal is reinforced with E-type glass fibers, what is the range of fiber content in glass-reinforced acetal?**

For E-type glass fibers, the elastic modulus is obtained from Table 9.2 on p. 224 as 73 GPa. Acetal has an elastic modulus between 1.4 and 3.5 GPa, while for reinforced acetal the modulus is listed as 10 GPa. If a composite is made with acetal and E-type glass fibers, its stiffness is given by Eq. (9.5) on p. 247, which can be solved for the volume fraction of fibers, $x$. For example, for the less stiff acetal:

$$E_c = 10 \text{ GPa} = xE_f + (1 - x)E_m = x(73 \text{ GPa}) + (1 - x)(1.4 \text{ GPa}) \quad \rightarrow \quad x = 0.12$$

or 12%. Using the same equation for stiff acetal, we have $x = 0.093$, or 9.3%.

9.48 **Plot the elastic modulus and strength of an aluminum metal-matrix composite with high-modulus carbon fibers, as a function of fiber content.**

The stiffness of high-modulus carbon fibers is 415 GPa (see Table 9.2 on p. 224), while the stiffness of aluminum is 69 GPa (Table 2.2 on p. 58). The stiffness is given by Eq. (9.5):

$$E_c = xE_f + (1 - x)E_m = x(415 \text{ GPa}) + (1 - x)(69 \text{ GPa}) = (246 \text{ GPa})x + 69 \text{ GPa}$$

The plot is shown below.

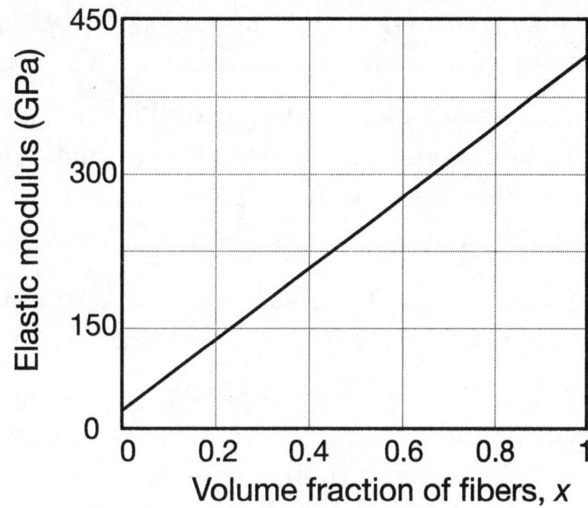


**9.49 For the data in the numerical example in Section 9.3.1, what should be the fiber content so that the fibers and the matrix fail simultaneously? Use an allowable fiber stress of 200 MPa and a matrix strength of 50 MPa.**

The stress in the fibers is given by $\sigma_f = P_f/A_f = P_f/(xA_c)$. The stress in the matrix is

$$\sigma_m = \frac{P_m}{A_m} = \frac{1}{1-x}\frac{P_m}{A_c}$$

Also, from Eq. (9.4) on p. 247:

$$P_f = \frac{A_f E_f}{A_m E_m} P_m = \frac{x A_c E_f}{(1-x) A_c E_m} P_m = \frac{x}{1-x}\frac{E_f}{E_m} P_m$$

Substituting into the equation for fiber stress gives

$$\sigma_f = \frac{P_f}{x A_c} = \frac{1}{1-x}\frac{E_f}{E_m}\frac{P_m}{A_c}$$

Substituting $E_f/E_m = 3$, $\sigma_f = 200$ MPa, and $\sigma_m = 50$ MPa yields two equations (for $\sigma_m$ and $\sigma_f$) and two unknowns ($x$ and $P_m/A_c$). These are solved numerically to give a value of $x = 0.57$.

## SYNTHESIS, DESIGN AND PROJECTS

**9.50 What applications for composite materials can you think of other than those listed in Section 9.4? Why do you think your applications are suitable for these materials?**

By the student. Other components that could benefit from the weight savings offered by graphite-epoxy reinforced plastics are landing-gear doors, fuselage doors, and cowl components of the engine.

**9.51 Using the information given in this chapter, develop special designs and shapes for new applications of composite materials.**

By the student. The approaches may include examining a particular component and reproducing the geometry using a composite material. Alternatively, one can select a particular aspect of composites (such as high strength-to-weight and stiffness-to-weight ratios) and design a product, such as a desk or sports equipment that is very lightweight.

**9.52 Would a composite material with a strong and stiff matrix and soft and flexible reinforcement have any practical uses? Explain.**

By the student. This type of composite probably will have a higher toughness than the matrix alone, since the soft and flexible reinforcement material could blunt a propagating crack. However, its usefulness would depend on whether or not it has a higher combination of strength and toughness than that of a composite with a ductile matrix and strong reinforcement.

**9.53 Make a list of products for which the use of composite materials could be advantageous because of their anisotropic properties.**

By the student. Some products where anisotropic properties of composites can be useful are: cables, packing tape (where the fiber is oriented to prevent boxes from opening and generates a circumferential reinforcement), pressure vessels, tubing, and tires (steel-belted radials).

**9.54 Inspect Fig. 9.1 and explain what other components of an aircraft, including parts in the cabin, could be made of composites.**

By the student. Other applications for composites in airplanes could be fuselage doors, seats, overhead storage compartments, and trays and their brackets.

**9.55 Name applications in which both specific strength and specific stiffness (Fig. 9.2) are important.**

By the student. Specific strength and specific modulus are important in applications where the material should be light and possess high strength and stiffness. A few possible applications are structural components for aircraft, helicopter blades, and automobile body panels.

**9.56 What applications for composite materials can you think of in which high thermal conductivity would be desirable?**

By the student. Composites with high thermal conductivity would be important for applications such as heat exchangers (such as car radiators) and heat extractors in nuclear reaction chambers.

**9.57 As with other materials, the mechanical properties of composites are obtained by preparing appropriate specimens and for testing in tension. Explain what problems you might encounter in preparing specimens for and in testing tension. Suggest methods for making appropriate specimens, including their shape and how they are clamped into the jaws of testing machines.**

By the student. Testing composite materials is challenging because of the potential for anisotropic behavior, which may lead to significant warpage during the test. Better approaches would involve measuring deformations in more than one direction (as opposed to conventional tests where typically only the longitudinal strain is measured). Traditional tensile specimens (see Fig. 2.1a on p. 66) can be used if no other strains are to be measured, or if the fiber orientation is known.

**9.58 Design and describe a test method to determine the mechanical properties of reinforced plastics in their thickness direction.**

By the student. This is a very difficult problem with many potential answers, but with no obvious answers. The mechanical properties in the thickness direction are very difficult to measure because of the small thickness as compared with the surface area of a specimen. An acceptable approach may be to derive the properties in the thickness direction by performing tests in the other principal directions, and then applying a known failure criterion.

**9.59 Developments are taking place in techniques for three-dimensional reinforcement of plastics. Describe (a) applications in which strength in the thickness direction of the composite is important and (b) your ideas on how to achieve this strength. Include simple sketches of the structure utilizing such reinforced plastics.**

The thickness direction is important in, for example, thick-walled pressure vessels. These thick-walled pipes are common for high-pressure service of hydraulic fluids, as well as for residential water service. Radial reinforcement can be imparted using properly oriented, discontinuous fibers.

**9.60 As described in this chapter, reinforced plastics can be adversely affected by environment - in particular by moisture, chemicals, and temperature variations. Design and describe test methods to determine the mechanical properties of composite materials subjected to these conditions.**

By the student. Even simple experiments, such as tension tests, are suitable if they are conducted in a controlled atmosphere. Chambers are commonly installed around test specimens for such environmentally-controlled testing.

**9.61 Comment about your observations on the design of the sailboard shown in Fig. 9.8.**

By the student. A number of observations are possible, including the use of a honeycomb structure for light weight and stiff performance, protected by an exterior skin. There are several layers in the surf board, each for different reasons, such as wear resistance, stiffness, and toughness.

**9.62 Describe the similarities and differences between ordinary corrugated cardboard and a honeycomb structure.**

By the student. This is an open-ended problem with many potential answers. The obvious similarities mainly lie in their common shape. The cross-section of corrugated cardboard is typically a repeating pattern of one-half of a hexagon. The differences are in the type and variety of the materials used; cardboard uses paper, and honeycomb structures use paper, polymers and/or metals in their construction.

**9.63 Suggest product designs in which corrugated cardboard can be used. Comment on the advantages and limitations.**

By the student. Corrugated cardboard can be used for a number of applications, including lightweight stage decorations (walls, ramps), moveable walls, and displays. Students should search for sources for corrugated paper, and determine the allowable loadings - corrugated paper is surprisingly strong. With proper cross-sectional dimensions, such materials can be used for walkways, seats, tabletops, etc.

**9.64 Suggest consumer-product designs that could utilize honeycomb structures. For example, an elevator can use a honeycomb laminate as a stiff and lightweight floor material.**

By the student. Honeycomb structures provide high stiffness at light weights. Any application where these features are desirable could find a practical use for them. Examples include wheelchair seats (supporting the padding), folding tables, lawn chairs, kennels for pet travel, and displays for trade shows.

**9.65 Make a survey of various sports equipment and identify the components made of composite materials. Explain the reasons for and the advantages of using composites in these specific applications.**

By the student. Examples include rackets for tennis, badminton, and racquetball; baseball and softball bats; golf clubs; fishing rods; and skis and ski poles. The main reason is the light weight of these materials, combined with high stiffness and strength, resulting in superior performance.

**9.66 Several material combinations and structures were described in this chapter. In relative terms, identify those that would be suitable for applications involving one of the following: (a) very low temperatures, (b) very high temperatures, (c) vibrations, and (d) high humidity.**

This is an open-ended problem with a large number of possible answers. Examples of acceptable answers are:

(a) At very low temperatures, most materials become brittle. One of the concerns with a composite material is the effect of thermal strains, which would suggest selecting a material with closely-matched thermal expansion coefficients for fiber and matrix (see Section 3.6 on p. 107).

(b) For very high temperatures, ceramic-matrix composites are the superior choice, as discussed in this chapter.

(c) In an environment where vibration is a concern, any composite is a good choice because of damping due to energy dissipation at the matrix-fiber interfaces.

(d) High humidity applications can utilize any of the materials described in this chapter, except for polymeric matrices, such as nylons, which are hygroscopic.

**9.67 Obtain a textbook on composite materials and investigate the effective stiffness of a continuous fiber-reinforced polymer. Plot the stiffness of such a composite as a function of orientation with respect to the fiber direction.**

The equations are fairly complex. For example, if the fibers are placed at an angle $\theta$ from the loading direction $x$, the stiffness in the $x$ direction is given by:

$$E_x = \frac{E_m}{\frac{E_m}{E_f}\left[\cos^2\theta\left(\cos^2\theta - \nu_m \sin^2\theta\right) + \sin^2\theta\left(\sin^2\theta - \nu_m\cos^2\theta\right)\right] + \frac{E_m}{G_m}\sin^2\theta\cos^2\theta}$$

This equation is plotted as follows:

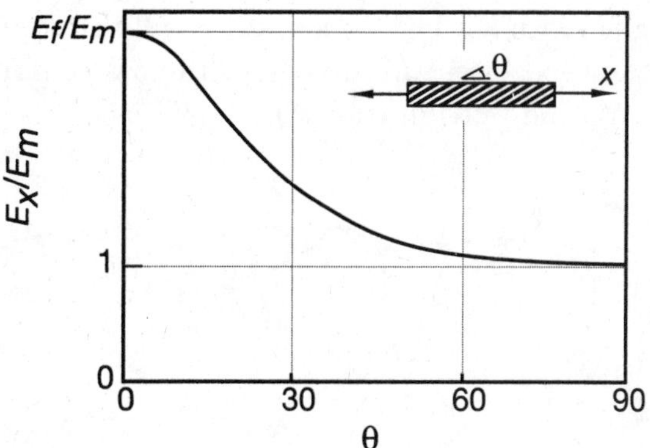


**9.68 Derive a general expression for the coefficient of thermal expansion for a continuous fiber-reinforced composite in the fiber direction.**

For this case, let the subscripts $m$ refer to the matrix and $f$ to the fiber. A temperature increase in the composite causes a strain of $\epsilon_c = \alpha_c \Delta T$; this strain is also the strain encountered by both the fiber and the matrix. We can then write:

$$\epsilon_f = \alpha_f \Delta T + P_t/A_f E_f$$

$$\epsilon_m = \alpha_m \Delta T + P_t/A_m E_m$$

where $P_t$ is an internal force which develops to ensure the fiber and matrix have the same strain. Since $\epsilon_f = \epsilon_m$, these equations can be equated to each other to obtain an expression for $P_t$:

$$\alpha_f \Delta T + \frac{P_t}{A_f E_f} = \alpha_m \Delta T + \frac{P_t}{A_m E_m} \quad \rightarrow \quad P_t = \frac{(\alpha_m - \alpha_f)\Delta T}{\left[\frac{1}{A_f E_f} - \frac{1}{A_m E_m}\right]}$$

Now, by equating $\epsilon_c$ to either $\epsilon_f$ or $\epsilon_m$ we obtain:

$$\alpha_c = \frac{A_m E_m \alpha_m - A_f E_f \alpha_f}{A_m E_m - A_f E_f}$$

**9.69 Instead of a constant cross-section, it is possible to make fibers or whiskers with a varying cross-section or a "wavy" fiber. What advantages would such fibers have?**

A common failure mode for fiber-reinforced polymers is the delamination of the fiber from the matrix. It is not uncommon for a relatively small stress to cause failure of the interface between the fiber and the matrix because of low adhesion between these two materials. By using wavy fibers, the strength of the fiber/matrix interface is increased by mechanical interference (locking) between the fibers and the matrix. There is also a larger interfacial area along which adhesion can take place, thus improving the interfacial strength.

**9.70 Describe how you can produce some simple composite materials using raw materials available around your home. Explain.**

By the student. For example, a composite material can be produced simply by mixing common household glue with sewing thread, or by gluing several layers of fabric together. Other examples include chocolate-chip cookies (with nuts), marbled rye bread, cement mixed with wire reinforcement, and putty mixed with small nails.

# Chapter 10

# Fundamentals of Metal Casting

## QUALITATIVE PROBLEMS

**10.15 Describe the stages involved in the contraction of metals during casting.**

The stages involved in the contraction of metals during casting are outlined in Section 10.5.2 on p. 274. The student is encouraged to elaborate further regarding these stages, also providing some data from the technical literature for purposes of comparison.

**10.16 Explain the reasons why heat transfer and fluid flow are important in metal casting.**

Heat transfer and fluid flow have a direct effect on the formation or suppression of defects in metal casting. Defects such as porosity (due to either shrinkage or gas), hot tears, and misruns (i.e., when the molten metal in a casting freezes before the mold is completely filled, shutting off that portion of the mold) are all controlled by these factors. Furthermore, the grain structure (hence properties such as strength and toughness of a metal casting) is dependent upon the rate and direction of heat transfer.

**10.17 We know that pouring metal at a high rate into a mold has certain disadvantages. Are there any disadvantages to pouring it very slowly?**

If a metal is poured too slowly it may solidify while it is still in the gating system or before completely filling the mold cavities. This will result in an incomplete or partial casting. This situation can be overcome by using a mold with a lower thermal conductivity or a preheated mold, but these lead to reduced mold life and longer cycle times.

**10.18 Describe the events depicted in Fig. 10.5.**

Due to a greater freezing range (see Eq. (10.1) on p. 264), gray cast iron forms an extensive dendritic structure and requires a considerable amount of time to solidify (Fig. 10.5a on p. 265). Steel, on the other hand, has a shorter freezing range and, thus. has a less extensive dendritic structure. As the carbon in the steel is increased, however, there is a greater tendency to form dendrites and hence the time to solidify increases. The effect of a chill mold is to greatly decrease the time for the metal to solidify, and this limit dendrite formation.

**10.19 Would you be concerned about the fact that parts of internal chills are left within the casting? What materials do you think chills should be made of and why?**

The fact that a part of the chill remains within the casting should be considered in the design of the part. The following factors should be taken into consideration:

(a) Any gas entrained in the molten metal when it contacts the chill may not readily escape; the chill could be a location where gas bubbles are in locally high concentration, and this can be a stress concentration.

(b) The chill may not fuse with the casting, developing regions of weakness.

(c) The material from which the chill is made should be compatible with the metal being cast, i.e., it should have approximately the same composition of the metal being poured.

If these factors are understood and provided for, the fact that a piece of the chill remains within the casting should generally not be a significant concern.

**10.20 What practical demonstrations can you offer to indicate the relationship of the solidification time to the volume and surface area?**

By the student. As an example, consider the following: If a swimming pool is filled with water and an equal volume of water is spread on a road were both subjected to a temperature below freezing, it is easy to see which would freeze first. Students should give other examples to illustrate this situation.

**10.21 Explain why you may want to subject a casting to various heat treatments.**

Heat treatments (described in Chapter 4) such as quenching and tempering, among others, are carried out to optimize the grain structure of metal castings, thereby controlling and enhancing mechanical properties. Heat treating can control microporosity, which is a main reason that castings are weak in tension.

**10.22 Why does porosity have detrimental effects on the mechanical properties of castings? Would physical properties (such as thermal and electrical conductivity) also be affected by porosity? Explain.**

Pores are, in effect, internal discontinuities that are prone to propagate under external stresses. Thus, the toughness of a material, for example, will decrease as a result of porosity. Furthermore, the presence of pores in a metal part under tension requires that the material around the pores support a greater load than if no pores were present; thus the strength and elastic modulus are also lowered. Considering thermal and electrical conductivity, porosity decreases both the thermal and electrical conductivity because of the presence of a vacuum or air.

**10.23 A spoked handwheel is to be cast in gray iron. In order to prevent hot tearing of the spokes, would you insulate the spokes or chill them? Explain.**

Referring to Table 10.1 on p. 275, we first note that gray iron undergoes an expansion up to 2.5% on solidification. Although this fact may suggest that hot tearing cannot occur (see Fig.

10.12 on p. 276), we should also consider contraction of the spokes during cooling. Since the hot tearing tendency will be reduced as the strength increases, it would be advisable to chill the spokes to develop this strength.

**10.24 Which of the following considerations is/are important for a riser to function properly? Must it: (a) have a surface area larger than the part being cast, (b) be kept open to atmospheric pressure, and/or (c) solidify first? Why?**

Both (a) and (c) would result in a situation contrary to a riser's purpose, that is, if a riser solidifies first, it cannot feed the mold cavity to avoid shrinkage in the part. Concerning (b), when the molten metal enters the mold cavity, the air which was in the mold has to be forced out. If a riser is not open to the atmosphere, either the gas will become dissolved into the metal (due to the increased pressure and depending on solubility), or sufficient pressure will build up which may crack the mold. Thus, a riser should be kept open to atmospheric pressure in order for it to function properly.

**10.25 Explain why the constant $C$ in Eq. (10.7) depends on mold material, metal properties, and temperature.**

The constant $C$ in Eq. (10.7) on p. 272 takes into account various factors such as the conductivity of the mold material and external temperature. For example, zircon sand (zirconium silicate) has a higher thermal conductivity than basic silica sand; as a result, a part cast in a zircon mold of equal volume and surface area to that of a part cast in silica will require less time to solidify.

**10.26 Are external chills as effective as internal chills? Explain.**

The answer depends on the location of the chills in the mold (see Fig. 10.14 on p. 278). That is, if a surface needs to be chilled (say, for example, to directionally solidify a casting), then an external chill is as effective as an internal chill. Often, however, chilling is required at some depth beneath the surface of a casting. For this condition an internal chill would be more effective.

**10.27 Explain why gray cast iron undergoes expansion rather than contraction during solidification, as shown in Table 10.1.**

As gray cast iron solidifies, a period of graphitization occurs during the final stages. This causes an expansion that counteracts the shrinkage of the metal during solidification, and results in an overall expansion.

**10.28 Referring to Fig. 10.11, explain why internal corners (such as A) develop a thinner skin than external corners (such as B) during solidification.**

We note in Fig. 10.11 on p. 273 that the internal corner A has a larger volume of material near to its surface area than does the external corner B . This situation can be visualized even better by assuming that the angles at A and B are less than 90°. Consequently, a point at a certain distance inward from corner A will remain at a higher temperature than a point at the same distance inward from corner B. Therefore, during the same time period, corner A will develop a thinner skin than will corner B. This can also be explained by considering heat flow directions, and noting that the volume in a corner will solidify most quickly because heat can be quickly extracted from this area; at an internal corner such as at A, the mold material cannot conduct as much heat as quickly.

**10.29 Note the shape of the two risers in Fig. 10.8, and discuss your observations with respect to Eq. (10.7).**

This is an open-ended problem, and a number of observations can be made. The side riser (at left in Fig. 10.8 on p. 268) has a greater volume than the top riser shown on the right. As a result and referring to Eq. (10.7) on p. 272, we would expect the side riser to require a longer solidification time than the top riser. This is, as one would expect, because the metal closest to the point of entry, i.e., sprue and runner, will be the hottest. The metal near the side riser should remain liquid longer than that near the top riser, thus requiring a larger riser because that portion of the casting is intended to be the last to solidify.

**10.30 Is there any difference in the tendency for shrinkage void formation for metals with short and long freezing ranges, respectively? Explain.**

Consider an alloy poured into a mold, where the exterior solidified and a solidification front progresses towards the casting center. In an alloy with a large freezing range, the presence of a large mushy zone is more likely to occur and, thus, the formation of microporosity. However, in an alloy with a short freezing range, the formation of gross shrinkage voids is more likely to occur near the center of the casting. The total porosity is the same in this case. With proper gating and riser design, the porosity for the short freezing range alloy is easier to eliminate or control.

**10.31 What is the influence of the cross-sectional area of the spiral channel in Fig. 10.9 on fluidity test results? What is the effect of sprue height? If this test is run with the test setup heated to elevated temperatures, would the test results be more useful? Explain.**

Referring to Fig. 10.9 on p. 272, we can make the following observations:

(a) The greater the cross-sectional area of the spiral channel, the further the metal will flow in the mold. Consider Eq. (10.7) on p. 272, which describes the solidification time.

(b) An increase in sprue height would increase the velocity of the metal that enters the spiral, thus allowing the metal to flow further into the spiral than for a lower sprue height.

(c) Tests can be, and are, conducted with the test setup used at elevated temperatures, showing the effect of a preheated mold on the fluidity of the molten metal. Such as test is especially useful for the investment or die-casting processes described in Sections 11.2.6 on p. 300 and 11.3.5 on p. 306, respectively.

**10.32 It has long been observed by foundrymen and ingot casters that low pouring temperatures (i.e., low superheat) promote formation of equiaxed grains over columnar grains. Also, equiaxed grains become finer as the pouring temperature decreases. Explain these phenomena.**

Equiaxed grains develop in castings near the mold wall where rapid cooling and solidification takes place by heat transfer through the relatively cool mold. With low pouring temperatures, cooling to the solidification temperature is faster because of the lower heat capacity of the molten metal. With a high pouring temperature, cooling to the solidification temperature is slower. The mold still dissipates the heat but the metal being poured remains molten for a longer period of time, thus producing columnar grains in the direction of heat conduction. As the pouring temperature is decreased, equiaxed grains become finer because the energy required to heat the mold is a larger fraction of the heat in the molten metal. Thus there is more rapid initial cooling as the mold temperature is increased.

**10.33 What would you expect to occur (in casting metal alloys) if the mold was agitated aggressively (vibrated) after the molten metal had been in the mold for a sufficient amount of time to form a skin?**

By the student. Several effects can occur. The most obvious is that any dendrites which may exist in the slushy phase will be broken up by the agitation. Also, agitation will aid in more rapid cooling, because of the increased contribution of convection and also because the mold/casting interface will have a lower thermal resistance.

**10.34 If you examine a typical ice cube, you will see pockets and cracks in the cube. However, some ice cubes are tubular in shape and do not have noticeable air pockets or cracks in their structure. Explain these phenomena.**

Note that this is not universally true; ice expands when it solidifies, and needs to be cooled sufficiently before stresses develop that crack the ice. The reason for this is that the ice cube first begins to solidify at its outside surfaces; the interior then contracts as it begins to cool. Since there is no riser or an equivalent means, the ice cube develops microcracks in the interior. The effect is actually less than for metals because water has a minimum specific volume at -4°C, whereas most metals shrink further while undergoing phase changes during solidification. Tubular ice pieces are formed by the exposure of water to copper tubes that have a refrigerant pumped through them. Thus, they solidify from the inside outward. The pockets are gases that are soluble in the water but have lower solubility in ice.

**10.35 How can you tell whether cavities in a casting are due to shrinkage or entrained air bubbles?**

The simplest method is observing them under a microscope. Air bubbles will have sufficient surface tension while the metal is liquid to form a spherical cavity, whereas shrinkage pores will be far more jagged because they are formed by localized fracture of the solidified metal. There are other tests that can be performed as well, for example, shrinkage cavities will theoretically be under a vacuum, whereas an air bubble will be filled with gas. Therefore, casting can be performed in the presence of a gas that can be traced, such as argon or helium. The casting can be remelted in vacuum and outgassing of argon or helium can be measured.

**10.36 Describe the drawbacks to having a riser that is (a) too large and (b) too small.**

A riser that is too large wastes material, adds to the solidification time and will require additional finishing operations. Also, a large riser can adversely affect the solidification pattern and lead to voids or cold shuts in the casting. In addition, large risers may be difficult to locate in the sand mold. On the other hand, a riser that is too small may not provide sufficient molten metal to compensate for solidification shrinkage in the casting. Also, it may solidify prematurely, so that it fails to serve as a riser; it may not influence the solidification front;

and it may require higher preheat levels, leading to more shrinkage pores and hence lower casting quality.

**10.37 What are the benefits and drawbacks to having a pouring temperature that is much higher than the metal's melting temperature? What are the advantages and disadvantages in having the pouring temperature remain close to the melting temperature?**

If the pouring temperature is much higher than that of the mold temperature, there is less danger that the metal will solidify in the mold and it is likely that even intricate molds can be fully filled. This situation makes runners, gates, wells, etc., easier to design because their cross-sections are less critical for complete mold filling. The main drawback is that there is an increased likelihood of shrinkage pores, cold shuts, and other defects associated with shrinkage, and an increased likelihood of entrained air since the viscosity will be lower at the higher pouring temperature. If the pouring temperature is close to the melting temperature, there will be less likelihood of shrinkage pores and entrained air. However, there is the danger of the molten metal solidifying in a runner before the mold cavity is completely filled; this may be overcome with higher injection pressures but clearly have a cost implication.

## QUANTITATIVE PROBLEMS

**10.38 Sketch a graph of specific volume versus temperature for a metal that shrinks as it cools from the liquid state to room temperature. On the graph, mark the area where shrinkage is compensated for by risers.**

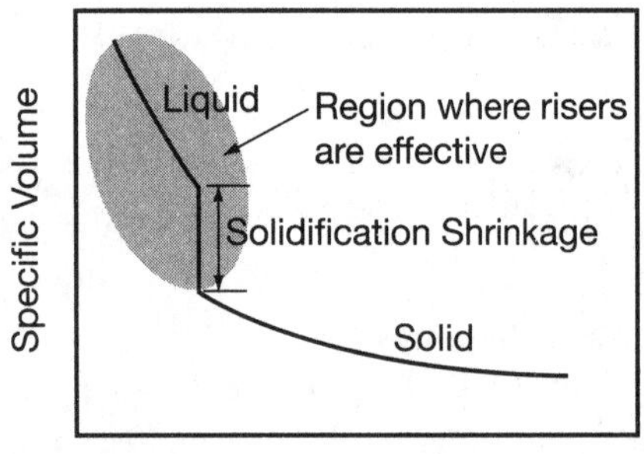


The graph for specific volume versus temperature is shown to the left, including compensation for shrinkage. The risers can compensate for shrinkage from the superheat temperature to solidification temperature, and also, if properly designed, for shrinkage associated with solidification.

**10.39 A round casting is 0.2 m (7.9 in.) in diameter and 0.5 m (19.7 in.) in length. Another casting of the same metal is elliptical in cross-section with a major to minor axis ratio of 2 and has the same length and cross-sectional area as the round casting. Both pieces are cast under the same conditions. What is the difference in the solidification times of the two castings?**

For the same length and cross-sectional area (thus the same volume), and same casting conditions, the same $C$ value should occur. The surface area and volume of the round casting is

$$A_{\text{round}} = 2\pi rl + 2\pi r^2 = 0.377 \text{ m}^2$$

$$V_{\text{round}} = 2\pi r^2 h = 0.031 \text{ in}^2$$

Since the cross-sectional area of the ellipse is the same as that for the cylinder, and it has a major and minor diameter of $a$ and $b$, respectively, where $a = 2b$, then

$$\pi ab = \pi r^2 \quad \rightarrow \quad 2b^2 = r^2 \quad \rightarrow \quad b = 0.071 \text{ m}$$

So that $a = 0.14$ m. The surface area of the ellipse-based part is (see a basic geometry text for the area equation derivations):

$$A_{\text{ellipse}} = 2\pi ab + 2\pi\sqrt{a^2 + b^2}h = 0.556 \text{ m}^2$$

The volume is still 0.031 in$^2$. According to Eq. (10.7) on page 250, we thus have

$$\frac{T_{\text{round}}}{T_{\text{ellipse}}} = \frac{(V/A_{\text{round}})^2}{(V/A_{\text{ellipse}})^2} = \left(\frac{A_{\text{ellipse}}}{A_{\text{round}}}\right)^2 = 2.17$$

**10.40 A 100-mm (4-in.) thick square plate and a right circular cylinder with a radius of 100 mm (4 in.) and a height of 50 mm each have the same volume. If each is to be cast using a cylindrical riser, will each part require the same size riser to ensure proper feeding? Explain.**

First note that it is important for the riser to solidify after the casting has solidified. A casting that solidifies rapidly would be expected to require a smaller riser than one that solidifies over a longer period of time. Let's now calculate the relative solidification times. For the cylindrical part, we have

$$V = \pi r^2 h = \pi(4)^2(2) = 100.5 \text{ in}^3$$

and

$$A = 2\pi r^2 + 2\pi rh = 2\pi(4)^2 + 2\pi(4)(2) = 150.8 \text{ in}^2$$

Thus

$$t_{\text{cylinder}} = C(100.5/150.8)^2 = 0.444C$$

For a square plate with sides $L$ and height $h$, we have

$$V = 100.5 = L^2 h = L^2(4), \text{ or } L = 5.0 \text{ in.}$$

and

$$A = 2L^2 + 4Lh = 130 \text{ in}^2$$

Thus

$$t_{\text{plate}} = C(100.5/130)^2 = 0.59C$$

Therefore, the cylindrical casting will take less time to solidify and hence will require a smaller riser.

**10.41 Assume that the top of a round sprue has a diameter of 3 in. (75 mm) and is at a height of 8 in. (200 mm) from the runner. Based on Eq. (10.5), plot the profile of the sprue diameter as a function of its height. Assume that the sprue wall has a diameter of 0.25 in. (6 mm) at the bottom.**

From Eq. (10.5) and substituting for the area, it can be shown that

$$\frac{d_1^2}{d^2} = \sqrt{\frac{h}{h_1}} \quad \rightarrow \quad d = \sqrt{d_1^2 \sqrt{\frac{h_1}{h}}} \quad \rightarrow \quad d = Ch^{-0.25}$$

The difficulty is that the reference location for height measurements is not known. The boundary conditions are that at $h = h_o$, $d = 0.25$ (where $h_o$ is the height at bottom of the sprue from the reference location) and at $h = h_o + 8$ in., $d = 3$ in. The first boundary condition yields $0.25 = C(h_o)^{-0.25}$; $h_o = 0.25C^{-4}$. The second boundary condition yields

$$3 = C(h_o + 8)^{-0.25} = C(0.25C^{-4} + 8)^{-0.25}$$

This equation is solved numerically as $C = 5.04$, so that $h_o = 0.000386$. These values are substituted into the expression above to get the plot shown below. Note that $h_o$ is the location of the bottom of the sprue and that the sprue is axisymmetric. The sprue shape based on this curve is shown to the right. Note that normally a pouring basin would be included in the design, and the sprue would either be tapped to the side or would sit on top of a well.

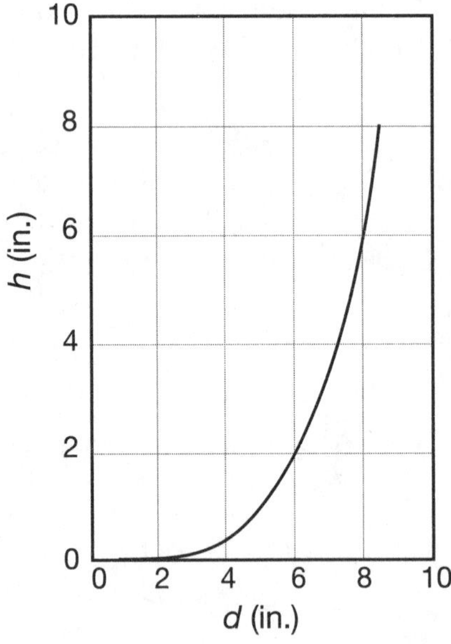


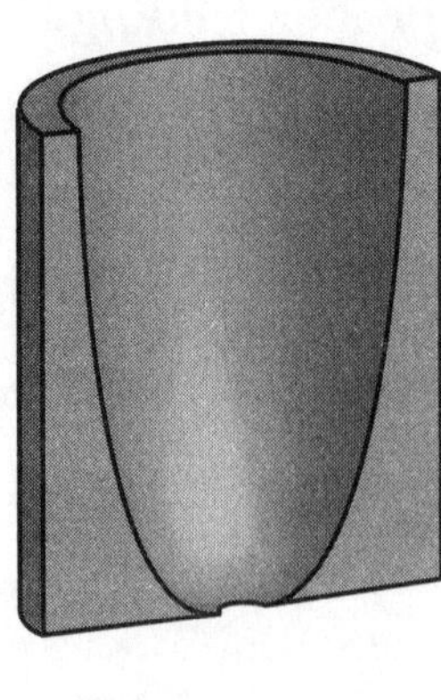

**10.42 Pure aluminum is poured into a sand mold. The metal level in the pouring basin is 8 in. above the metal level in the mold, and the runner is circular with a 0.5-in. diameter. What is the velocity and rate of flow of the metal into the mold? Is the flow turbulent or laminar?**

Equation (10.3) on page 268 gives the metal flow; assuming the pressure does not change appreciably in the channel and that there is no friction in the sprue, the flow is

$$h_1 + \frac{v_1^2}{2g} = h_2 + \frac{v_2^2}{2g}$$

Where the subscript 1 indicates the top of the sprue and 2 the bottom. If we assume that the velocity at the top of the sprue is very low (as would occur with the normal case of a pouring basin on top of the sprue with a large cross-sectional area), then $v_1 = 0$. Therefore, the velocity at the bottom of the sprue is

$$v_2^2 = 2g(h_1 - h_2) \quad \rightarrow \quad v_2 = \sqrt{2g\Delta h} = \sqrt{2(32.2 \text{ ft/s}^2)(12 \text{ in/ft})(8 \text{ in})} = 78.6 \text{ in./s}$$

If the opening is 0.5-in. in diameter, the flow rate is $Q = v_2 A = 15.4 \text{ in}^3\text{/s}$. Pure aluminum has a density of 2700 kg/m$^3$ (Table 3.1 on p. 103) and a viscosity that is comparable to water at room temperature ($0.15 \times 10^{-6}$ lb-s/in$^2$). The Reynolds number, from Eq. (10.6) on p. 270, is then

$$\text{Re} = \frac{vD\rho}{\eta} = \frac{(78.6 \text{ in./s})(0.5 \text{ in.})(2700 \text{ kg/m}^3)}{0.15 \times 10^{-6} \text{ lb-sec/in}^2} = 68,000$$

**10.43 A cylinder with a diameter of 1 in. and height of 3 in. solidifies in three minutes in a sand casting operation. What is the solidification time if the cylinder height is doubled? What is the time if the diameter is doubled?**

The surface area of the cylinder is given by

$$A = 2\left(\frac{\pi}{4}d^2\right) + \pi dh = \frac{\pi}{2}(1 \text{ in.})^2 + \pi(1)(3) = 3.5\pi \text{ in}^2$$

and the volume is

$$V = \frac{\pi}{4}d^2 h = \frac{\pi}{4}(1)^2(3) = 0.75\pi \text{ in.}^2$$

From Eq. (10.7), we can evaluate the constant $C$ as:

$$\text{Solidification time} = C\left(\frac{V}{A}\right)^2 \quad \rightarrow \quad 3 \text{ min} = C\left(\frac{0.75\pi \text{ in.}^3}{3.5\pi \text{ in}^2}\right)^2$$

or $C = 65.33 \text{ min/in}^2$. If the height is doubled, so that $h = 6$ in., then

$$A = 2\left(\frac{\pi}{4}d^2\right) + \pi dh = \frac{\pi}{2}(1 \text{ in.})^2 + \pi(1)(6) = 6.5\pi \text{ in}^2$$

$$V = \frac{\pi}{4}d^2 h = \frac{\pi}{4}(1)^2(6) = 1.5\pi \text{ in}^3$$

so that from Chvorinov's rule, we have

$$\text{Solidification time} = C\left(\frac{V}{A}\right)^2 = \left(65.33 \text{ min/in}^2\right)\left(\frac{1.5\pi \text{ in}^3}{6.5\pi \text{ in}^2}\right)^2 = 3.48 \text{ min}$$

which represents an increase of about 28 seconds. If the diameter is doubled to 6 in., then

$$A = 2\left(\frac{\pi}{4}d^2\right) + \pi dh = \frac{\pi}{2}(2 \text{ in.})^2 + \pi(2)(3) = 8\pi \text{ in}^2$$

$$V = \frac{\pi}{4}d^2 h = \frac{\pi}{4}(2)^2(3) = 3\pi \text{ in}^3$$

and

$$\text{Solidification time} = C\left(\frac{V}{A}\right)^2 = \left(65.33 \text{ min/in}^2\right)\left(\frac{3\pi \text{ in}^3}{8\pi \text{ in}^2}\right)^2 = 9.19 \text{ min}$$

Thus, the solidification time increases by more than six minutes.

**10.44 The volume flow rate of metal into a mold is 0.01 $m^3$/min. The top of the sprue has a diameter of 20 mm, and its length is 200 mm. What diameter should be specified at the bottom of the sprue to prevent aspiration? What is the resultant velocity and Reynolds number at the bottom of the sprue if the metal being cast is aluminum with a viscosity of 0.004 N.s/$m^2$?**

Note that the metal volume flow rate is $Q = 0.01\text{ m}^3/\text{min} = 1.667\times10^{-4}\text{ m}^3/\text{s}$. Again, let's use the subscripts 1 for the top and 2 for the bottom of the sprue. Since $d_1 = 20\text{ mm} = 0.02$ m,

$$A_1 = \frac{\pi}{4}d^2 = \frac{\pi}{4}(0.02\text{ m})^2 = 3.14\times10^{-4}\text{ m}^2$$

Therefore,

$$v_1 = \frac{Q}{A_1} = \frac{1.667\times10^{-4}\text{ m}^3/\text{s}}{3.14\times10^{-4}\text{ m}^2} = 0.531\text{ m/s}$$

Assuming no frictional losses and recognizing that the pressure at the top and bottom of the sprue is atmospheric, Eq. (10.3) gives

$$h_1 + \frac{v_1^2}{2g} = h_2 + \frac{v_2^2}{2g} \quad\rightarrow\quad 0.2\text{ m} + \frac{(0.531\text{ m/s})^2}{2(9.81\text{ m/s}^2)} = 0 + \frac{v_2^2}{2(9.81\text{ m/s}^2)}$$

or $v_2 = 1.45$ m/s. To prevent aspiration, the sprue opening should be the same as that required by flow continuity, or

$$Q = A_2v_2 = 1.667\times10^{-4}\text{ m}^3/\text{s} = A_2(1.45\text{ m/s}) \quad\rightarrow\quad A_2 = 1.150\times10^{-4}\text{ m}^2$$

hence $d = 12$ mm. To calculate the Reynolds number, we first note from Table 3.1 that the density of aluminum is 2700 kg/$m^3$. The density for molten aluminum will of course be lower, but not significantly so, so this value is sufficient for this problem. From Eq. (10.6),

$$\text{Re} = \frac{vD\rho}{\eta} = \frac{(1.45\text{ m/s})(0.012\text{ m})(2700\text{ kg/m}^3)}{0.004\text{ Ns/m}^2} = 11,745$$

As discussed on p. 270, this is typical and is a mixture of laminar and turbulent flow.

**10.45 A rectangular mold with dimensions 100 mm × 200 mm × 400 mm is filled with aluminum with no superheat. Determine the final dimensions of the part as it cools to room temperature. Repeat the analysis for gray cast iron.**

Note that the initial volume of the box is (0.100)(0.200)(0.400)=0.008 $m^3$. From Table 10.1 on p. 275, the volumetric contraction for aluminum is 6.6%. Therefore, the box volume will be

$$V = (1-0.066)(0.008\text{ m}^3) = 0.007472\text{ m}^3$$

Assuming the box has the same aspect ratio as the mold (1:2:4), and that warpage can be ignored, then we can calculate the dimensions of the box after solidification as 97.7 mm × 195.5 mm × 391 mm. From Table 3.1 on p. 103, the melting point of aluminum is 660°C, with a coefficient of thermal expansion of 23.6 $\mu$m/m°C. Thus, the total strain in cooling from 660°C to room temperature (25°C) is

$$\epsilon = \alpha\Delta t = (23.6\mu\text{m/m}^\circ\text{C})(660^\circ\text{C} - 25^\circ\text{C}) = 0.0150$$

So that the final box dimensions are 96.2 × 192.5 × 385 mm. For gray cast iron, the metal expands upon solidification. Assuming the mold will allow expansion, the volume after solidification is given by

$$V = (1.025)(0.008 \text{ m}^3) = 0.0082 \text{ m}^3$$

If the box has the same aspect ratio as the initial mold cavity, the dimensions after solidification are 100.8 × 201.7 × 403.3 mm. Using the data for iron in Table 3.1 on p. 103, the melting point is taken as 1537°C and the coefficient of thermal expansion is 11.5 $\mu$m/m°C. Therefore

$$\epsilon = \alpha \Delta t = (11.5 \mu\text{m/m}^\circ\text{C})(1537^\circ\text{C} - 25^\circ\text{C}) = 0.0174$$

So that the final dimensions are 99.0 × 198.1 × 396 mm. Note that even though the cast iron needed to cool off from a higher initial temperature, the box of cast iron is much closer to the mold dimensions than the aluminum.

**10.46 The constant $C$ in Chvorinov's rule is given as 3 s/mm$^2$, and is used to produce a cylindrical casting with a diameter of 75 mm and height of 125 mm. Estimate the time for the casting to fully solidify. The mold can be broken safely when the solidified shell is at least 20 mm. Assuming the cylinder cools evenly, how much time must transpire after pouring the molten metal before the mold can be broken?**

Note that for the cylinder

$$A = 2\left(\frac{\pi}{4}d^2\right) + \pi d h = 2\left[\frac{\pi}{4}(75)^2\right] + \pi(75)(125) = 38,290 \text{ mm}^2$$

$$V = \frac{\pi}{4}d^2 h = \frac{\pi}{4}(75)^2(12) = 5.522 \times 10^5 \text{ mm}^3$$

From Chvorinov's rule given by Eq. (10.7) on p. 272,

$$t = C\left(\frac{V}{A}\right)^2 = (3 \text{ s/mm}^2)\left(\frac{5.522 \times 10^5}{38,290}\right)^2 = 624 \text{ s}$$

or, just over ten seconds to solidify. The second part of the problem is far more difficult, and different answers can be obtained depending on the method of analysis. The solution is not as straightforward as it may seem initially. For example, one could say that the 20 mm wall is 53.3% of the thickness, so that 0.533(624)=333 seconds is needed. However, this would be insufficient because an annular section at an outside radius has more material than one closer to the center. It is reasonable and conservative to consider the time required for the remaining cylinder to solidify. Using $h$ = 85 mm and $d$ = 35 mm, the solidification time is found to be 21.8 seconds. Therefore, one still has to wait 602 seconds before the mold can be broken.

**10.47 Assume that you are an instructor covering the topics described in this chapter, and you are giving a quiz on the numerical aspects to test the understanding of the students. Prepare two quantitative problems and supply the answers.**

By the student. This is a good, open-ended question that requires considerable focus and understanding on the part of the students, and has, in the past, been found to be a very valuable homework problem.

## SYNTHESIS, DESIGN AND PROJECTS

**10.48 Can you devise fluidity tests other than that shown in Fig. 10.9? Explain the features of your test methods.**

By the student. As a suggestion, tests could involve convergent sections, moving walls, or gravity assistance. Note that the tests should allow for a competition between pressure-driven flow and cooling of the molten metal along the path.

**10.49 Figure P10.49 indicates various defects and discontinuities in cast products. Review each one and offer solutions to avoid them.**

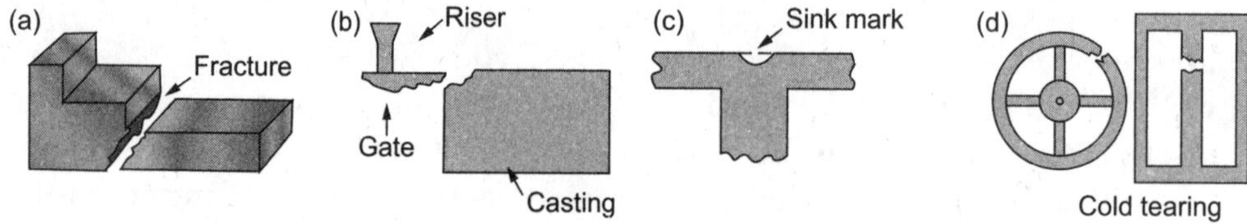


**FIGURE P10.49**

By the student. Some examples are:

(a) Notice that fracture occurred at one of the two steps in the casting, so that fracture is at stress riser. A better design would utilize a more gradual fillet radius.

(b) Fracture at the gate indicates this runner section is too narrow and will solidified first; this gate should be larger.

**10.50 The fluidity test shown in Fig. 10.9 only illustrates the principle of this test. Design a setup for such a test, showing the type of materials and the equipment to be used. Explain the method by which you would determine the length of the solidified metal in the spiral passage.**

By the student. This is an open-ended problem with a large number of potential solutions, automated or manual and made of different materials to accommodate different metals. Students should be encouraged to pursue their own creative solutions to this problem. Note that if the spiral pattern is known, an angular measurement can be converted to length.

**10.51 Utilizing the equipment and materials available in a typical kitchen, design an experiment to reproduce results similar to those shown in Fig. 10.11. Comment on your observations.**

By the student. For example, a simple experiment can be performed with melted chocolate and a coffee cup. If a parting agent (oil) is first sprayed inside the cup and then molten chocolate is poured into the cup, after a short while the molten center portion can be poured out of the cup, leaving a solidified shell. This effect can be made more pronounced by using cups that have been chilled in a freezer. It is also interesting to investigate object shapes with steps as those shown in Fig. 10.11.

**10.52 One method of relieving stress concentrations in a part is to apply a small, uniform plastic deformation to it. Make a list of your concerns and recommendations if such an approach is suggested for a casting.**

The plastic deformations, if tensile or flexural, need to be applied with great care on castings. The main reason is that castings are typically weak in tension, due to micropores which act as stress risers. While the intent may be to relieve residual stresses, the result may be to fracture the part.

**10.53 If a casting of a given shape is to be doubled in volume, describe the effects on mold design, including the required change in the size of risers, runners, chokes, and sprues.**

By the student. This is an open ended problem, and students may interpret this problem differently in their answer. Some of the considerations are:

- It must be realized that if the volume is doubled, with no changes in any other mold features, the molten metal still has to flow through the same sprues and at the same velocity for twice as long as the initial design. This may be accomplished without any changes in sprue, runner, etc., size at all if the original design had large features to begin with or if a high superheat is prescribed.
- Otherwise, these features will have to be increased in size, but not by a factor of two - Eqs. (10.3)-(10.5) give the design guidelines.
- Students may discuss the need for chills, or the use of vacuum casting or alternative processes to prevent entrained gases or shrinkage pores in larger castings.

**10.54 Small amounts of slag often persist after skimming and are introduced into the molten-metal flow in casting. Recognizing that the slag is much less dense than the metal, design mold features that will remove small amounts of slag before the metal reaches the mold cavity.**

There are several trap designs in use in foundries. An excellent discussion of dross trap design is given in J. Campbell, *Castings*, 1991, Reed Educational Publishers, pp. 53-55. A conventional and effective dross trap is the following design:

The design is based on the principle that a trap at the end of a runner will capture the first material through the runner and keep it away from the gates. The design shown above is a wedge-type trap. Metal entering the runner contacts the wedge, and the leading front of the metal wave is chilled and attaches itself to the runner wall, and thus it is kept out of the mold cavity. The wedge must be designed to avoid reflected waves that would recirculate the dross or slag.

The following design is a swirl trap, which is based on the principle that the dross or slag is less dense than the metal. The metal enters the trap off of the center, inducing a swirl in the molten metal as the trap is filled with molten metal. Since it is much less dense than the metal, the dross or slag remains in the center of the swirl trap. Since the metal is tapped from the outside periphery, dross or slag is excluded from entering the casting.

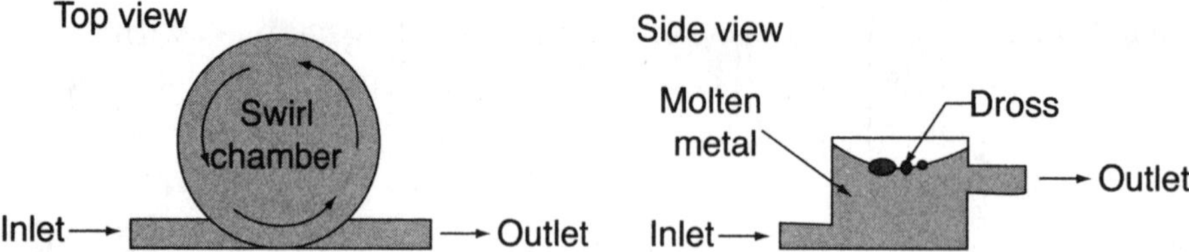


**10.55 Figure II.1 shows a variety of components in a typical automobile that are produced by casting. Think of other products, such as power tools and small appliances, and make a similar illustration as done in that figure.**

By the student. Among many possible solutions, the following is an example showing cast parts. Students should be encouraged to develop their own designs, based on disassembly of a product, which can be a challenging project.

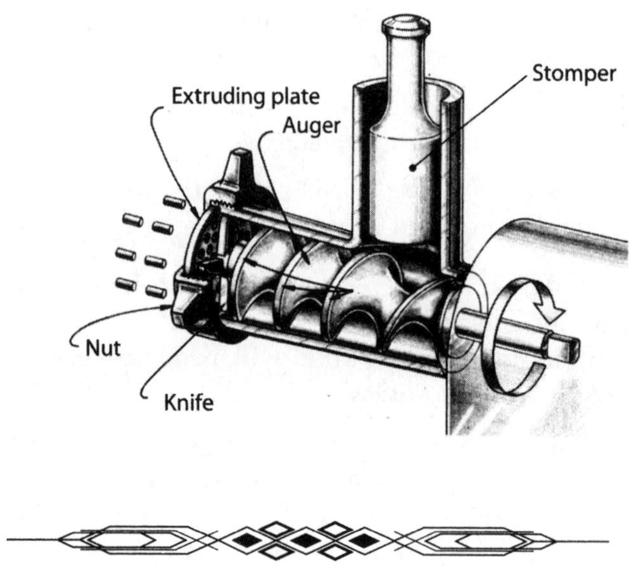

# Chapter 11

# Metal Casting Processes

## QUALITATIVE PROBLEMS

**11.17 If you need only a few units of a particular casting, which process(es) would you use? Why?**

By the student. This is an open-ended question, with many good answers, and the answer given will depend on the applications envisioned by the student. For example, are they considering a zinc die casting or a very large stainless steel part that must be sand cast? In general, the answer depends on the ability to create pattern or mold/die prototypes. If a rapid prototyping system is available (see Chapter 20), a wax blank can be produced relatively easily, and the lost-wax (investment casting) process can be used for small production runs. If a three-dimensional printing system is available, a sand mold can be prototyped directly for sand casting. If the part is too large for investment casting, a pattern plate can be produced for sand casting. If a CNC milling machine (see, for example, Fig. 24.17 on p. 740) is available, a foam or wax pattern can be produced and investment casting or the lost-foam method can be used. Otherwise, sand casting is perhaps the most economical because of the inherent low tooling costs involved.

**11.18 What are the reasons for the large variety of casting processes that have been developed over the years? Explain with specific examples.**

By the student. There are a large number of acceptable answers depending on the interpretation of the problem by the student. Students may approach this as processes have been application driven, material driven, or economics driven. For example, while investment casting is more expensive than sand casting, closer dimensional tolerances are possible and thus for certain parts, e.g., barrels for handguns, investment casting is preferable. Consider also the differences between the hot- and cold-chamber permanent-mold casting operations. While the hot-chamber process is more automated, thus reducing cost, there are certain disadvantages.

**11.19 Why does die casting produce the smallest cast parts?**

By the student. Note that because of the high pressures involved in die casting, wall thicknesses less than those attainable by other casting methods are possible.

**11.20 What differences, if any, would you expect in the properties of castings made by permanent mold vs. sand casting?**

This is an open-ended problem, and a large number of answers are acceptable. Most of the different answers are associated with the students' interpretation of the word 'properties', which can be restricted to mechanical properties or can incorporate design attributes. Examples of answers are that permanent-mold castings generally possess a better surface finish, closer dimensional tolerances, more uniform mechanical properties, and more sound thin-walled sections than sand castings. However, sand castings generally will be of more intricate shapes, larger overall sizes, and (depending upon the alloy) lower in cost than permanent-mold casting.

**11.21 Would you recommend preheating the molds used in permanent-mold casting? Would you remove the casting soon after it has solidified? Explain your reasons.**

Preheating the molds in permanent-mold casting is advisable in order to reduce the chilling effect of the metal mold, which could lead to low metal fluidity. Also, the molds are heated to reduce thermal damage (fatigue, shock) which may result from repeated contact with the molten metal. Considering casting removal, the casting should be allowed to cool in the mold until there is no danger of distortion or developing defects during shakeout. While this may be a very short period of time for small castings, large castings may require an hour or more.

**11.22 Referring to Fig. 11.3, do you think it is necessary to weigh down or clamp the two halves of the mold? Explain your reasons. Do you think that the kind of metal cast, such as gray cast iron vs. aluminum, should make a difference in the clamping force? Explain.**

Due to the force exerted on the cope portion of the mold by the molten metal, it is necessary to weigh down or clamp the two halves of the mold. Furthermore, a metal with higher density will exert a higher pressure on the cope; thus, the clamping force depends on the metal cast.

**11.23 Explain why squeeze casting produces parts with better mechanical properties, dimensional accuracy, and surface finish than do expendable-mold processes.**

The squeeze-casting process involves a combination of casting and forging. The pressure applied to the molten metal by the punch or the upper die keeps the entrapped gases in solution, and thus porosity generally is not found in these products. Also, the rapid heat transfer results in a fine microstructure with good mechanical properties. Due to the applied pressure and the type of die material used, good dimensional accuracy and surface finish are typically obtained for squeeze-cast parts.

**11.24 How would you attach the individual wax patterns on a "tree" in investment casting?**

Both the pattern and the tree are locally melted at the contact surface and held together; upon solidification, the surfaces fuse together. This is repeated for each pattern until the "tree" is completed.

**11.25 Describe the measures that you would take to reduce core shifting in sand casting.**

Core shifting is reduced in a sand mold by core prints, chaplets, or both. Core prints (see Fig. 11.6 on p. 292) are recesses in the pattern to support the core inside the mold. If excessive shifting occurs, chaplets may be used. Chaplets are small metal supports which act both as a spacer for the core to assure proper core location and as an added support to resist shifting.

**11.26 You have seen that even though die casting produces thin parts, there is a limit to how thin they can be. Why can't even thinner parts be made by this process?**

Because of the high thermal conductivity the metal dies exhibit, there is a limiting thickness below which the molten metal will solidify prematurely before completely filling the mold cavity.

**11.27 How are hollow parts with various cavities made by die casting? Are cores used? If so, how? Explain.**

Hollow parts and cavities are generally made using unit dies (see Fig. 11.19d on p. 309 and its definition at the bottom of p. 308), although cores also can be used. Core setting occurs mechanically, e.g., for an aluminum tube, as the die closes. A rod, which extends the length of the cavity, is pushed into the mold and the molten metal is then injected. This "core" must be coated with an appropriate parting agent or lubricant to ensure easy ejection of the part without damaging it.

**11.28 It was stated that the strength-to-weight ratio of die-cast parts increases with decreasing wall thickness. Explain why.**

Because the metal die acts as a chill for the molten metal, the molten metal chills rapidly, forming a fine-grained hard skin (see, for example, Fig. 10.3 on p. 263) with higher strength. Consequently, the strength-to-weight ratio of die-cast parts increases with decreasing wall thickness.

**11.29 How are risers and sprues placed in sand molds? Explain with appropriate sketches.**

Risers and sprues are usually created from plastic or metal shapes which are produced specifically for this purpose. Thus, a metal sprue is machined to duplicate the desired shape in the mold. This sprue model is then affixed to the pattern plate before the flask is filled with sand. The sand mold is prepared as discussed in the chapter (see Fig. 11.8 on p. 294). When the pattern plate is removed, the riser and sprue patterns are removed at the same time.

**11.30 In shell-mold casting, the curing process is critical to the quality of the finished mold. In this part of the process, the shell-mold assembly and cores are placed in an oven for a short period of time to complete the curing of the resin binder. List probable causes of unevenly cured cores or of uneven core thicknesses.**

In the production of shell molds and cores, lack of temperature control is often the most probable cause of problems. Unevenly cured cores or uneven core thicknesses are usually caused by furnace- or temperature-control related problems, such as:

(a) Insufficient number of burners or inoperative burners in the curing furnace.

(b) One-half of the core box is higher in temperature that the other half.

(c) Mixture of low- and high-temperature melting-point sands that were improperly blended, thus causing different parts of the core to cure differently.

(d) Temperature controllers not functioning properly.

(e) The core was removed too slowly from the furnace, allowing some of it to be heated longer.

**11.31 Why does the die-casting machine shown in Fig. 11.17 have such a large mechanism to close the dies? Explain.**

As discussed in the text, the molten metal in die casting is introduced into the mold cavity under great pressure. This pressure has thus a tendency to separate the mold halves, resulting in large flash and unacceptable parts. The large clamp is therefore needed to hold the mold together during the entire casting cycle.

**11.32 Chocolate is available in hollow shapes, such as bunnies. What process is used to make these candies?**

Thin shells are typically and easily made through slush casting (see Fig. 10.11 on p. 273, and also slush molding, top of p. 555), using split molds. This can be verified by obtaining such a chocolate and breaking it, and observing the interior surface is rather coarse and shows no evidence of having contacted a mold.

**11.33 What are the benefits and drawbacks to heating the mold in investment casting before pouring in the molten metal?**

The benefits to heating the mold include: Greater fluidity for detailed parts (in that the molten metal will not solidify as quickly), a possible reduction in surface tension and in viscous friction in the mold, and slower cooling. The main drawbacks to heating the mold are that the mold may not have as high a strength at the elevated temperature, and the metal may be less viscid and becomes turbulent as discussed in Chapter 10. Also, the solidification time will be larger with increased mold preheat, and this can adversely affect production time and process economics as a result.

**11.34 The slushy state of alloys refers to that state between the solidus and liquidus temperatures, as described in Section 10.2. Pure metals do not have such a slushy state. Does this mean that pure metals cannot be slush cast? Explain.**

The "slushy" state in alloy solidification refers to an intermediate state between liquid and solid. Slush casting involves casting an alloy where the molten metal is poured into the mold, allowed to begin to solidify. The molten portion of the metal is then poured out of the mold, leaving a shell behind. This can be done using pure metals as well as alloys.

**11.35 Can a chaplet also be a chill? Explain.**

While, in theory, a chaplet can serve as a chill, in practice chaplets rarely do so. Chaplets are intended to support a core or a section of mold. If they are placed in a position to support the core, they may not be in a location that requires a chill. Chaplets have a large footprint, and this helps to transfer heat to the core. However, heat transfer to the core is not an option for faster cooling of the casting; heat instead must be conducted outside of the mold. Therefore, the chaplet cannot usually be considered a chill.

**11.36 Rank the casting processes described in this chapter in terms of their solidification rate. That is, which processes extract heat the fastest from a given volume of metal?**

There is, as expected, some overlap between the various processes, and the rate of heat transfer can be modified when desired. However, a general ranking in terms of rate of heat extraction is as follows: Die casting (cold chamber), squeeze casting, centrifugal casting, slush casting, die casting (hot chamber), permanent mold casting, shell mold casting, investment casting, sand casting, lost foam, ceramic-mold casting, and plaster-mold casting.

## QUANTITATIVE PROBLEMS

**11.37 Estimate the clamping force for a die-casting machine in which the casting is rectangular with projected dimensions of 125 mm x 175 mm (5 in. x 7 in.). Would your answer depend on whether it is a hot-chamber or cold-chamber process? Explain.**

The projected area is 35 in$^2$. For the hot-chamber process and using an average pressure of 2,000 psi, the force is 2,000 x 35 = 70,000 lb. For the cold-chamber process and using a pressure of 6,000 psi, the force is 210,000 lb. Thus, the force depends on the process as well as shape complexity.

**11.38 The blank for the spool shown in Figure P11.38 is to be sand cast out of A-319, an aluminum casting alloy. Make a sketch of the wooden pattern for this part, and include all necessary allowances for shrinkage and machining.**

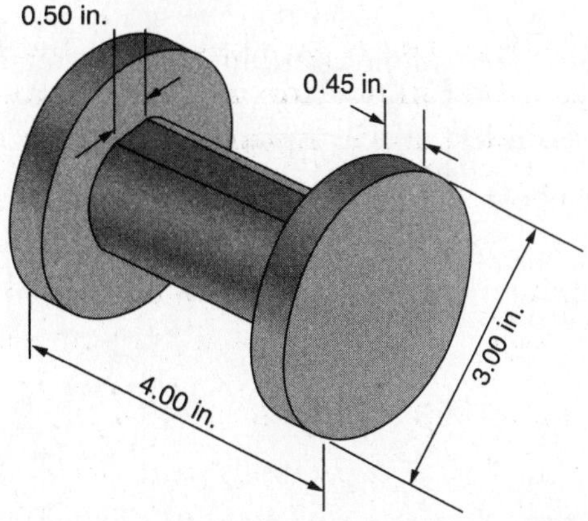


The sketch for a typical green-sand casting pattern for the spool is shown below. A cross-sectional view is also provided to clearly indicate shrinkage and machining allowances, as well as the draft angles (see p. 326 for the required information). The important elements of this pattern are as follows (dimensions in inches):

(a) Two-piece pattern.

(b) Locating pins will be needed in the pattern plate to make sure these features align properly.

(c) Shrinkage allowance = 5/32 in./ft.

(d) Machining allowance = 1/16 in.

(e) Draft = 3°.

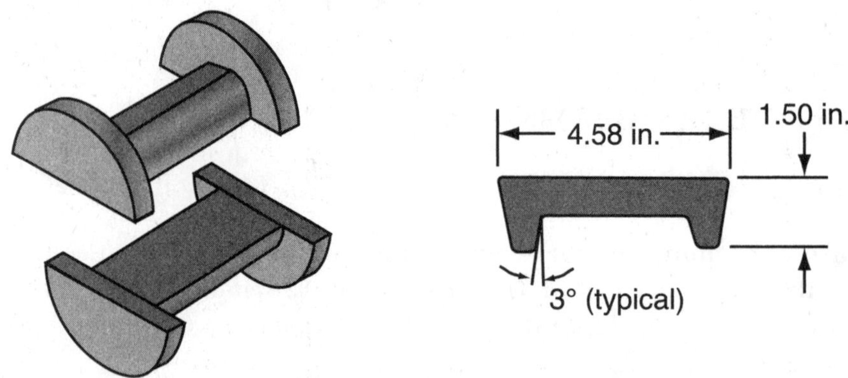


**11.39 Repeat Problem 11.38 but assume that the aluminum spool is to be cast using expendable-pattern casting. Explain the important differences between the two patterns.**

A sketch for a typical expandable-pattern casting is shown below. A cross-sectional view is also provided to clearly show the differences between green-sand (from Problem 11.38) and evaporative-casting patterns. There may be some variation in the patterns produced by students depending on which dimensions are assigned a machining allowance. The important elements of this pattern are as follows (dimensions in inches.):

(a) One-piece pattern, made of polystyrene.

(b) Shrinkage allowance = 5/32 in./ft

(c) Machining allowance = 1/16 in.

(d) No draft angles are necessary.

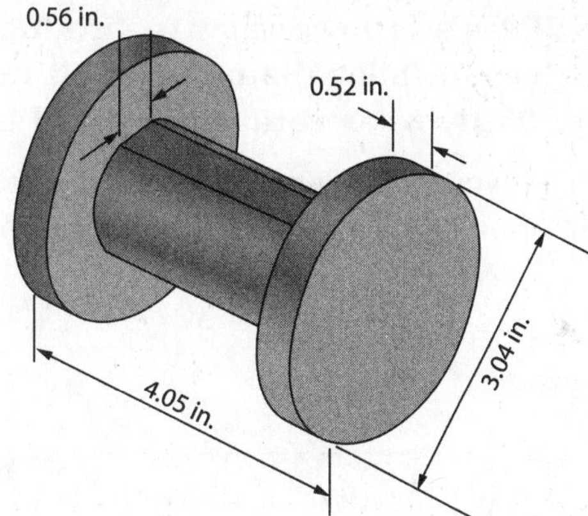


**11.40 In sand casting, it is important that the cope mold half be weighted down with sufficient force to keep it from floating when the molten metal is poured in. For the casting shown in the figure below, calculate the minimum amount of weight necessary to keep the cope from floating up as the molten metal is poured in. (Hint: The buoyancy force exerted by the molten metal on the cope is dependent on the effective height of the metal head above the cope.)**

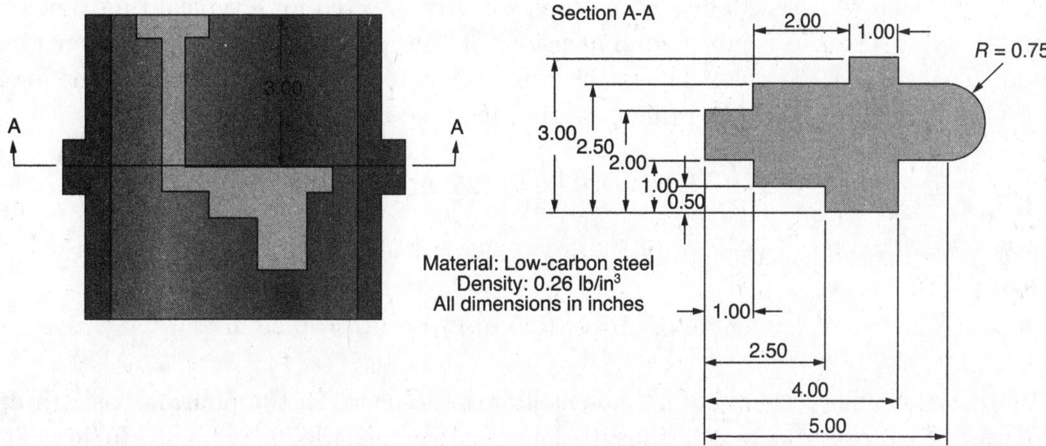


The cope mold half must be heavy enough or be weighted sufficiently to keep it from floating when the molten metal is poured into the mold. The buoyancy force, $F$, on the cope is exerted by the metallostatic pressure (caused by the metal in the cope above the parting line) and can be calculated using the formula

$$F = pA$$

where $p$ is the pressure at the parting line and $A$ is the projected area of the mold cavity. The pressure is

$$p = wh = (0.26 \text{ lb/in}^3)(3.00 \text{ in.}) = 0.78 \text{ psi}$$

The projected mold-cavity area can be calculated from the dimensions given on the right figure in the problem, and is found to be 10.13 in$^2$. Thus the force $F$ is

$$F = (0.78)(10.13) = 7.9 \text{ lb}$$

**11.41 If an acceleration of 100 g's is necessary to produce a part in true centrifugal casting, and the part has an inner diameter of 10 in., a mean outer diameter of 14 in., and a length of 25 ft, what rotational speed is needed?**

The angular acceleration is given by $\alpha = \omega^2 r$. Recognizing that the largest force is experienced at the outside radius, this value for $r$ is used in the calculation:

$$\alpha = \omega^2 r = 100 \text{ g} = 3220 \text{ ft/s}^2$$

Therefore, solving for $\omega$,

$$\omega = \sqrt{\alpha / r} = \sqrt{\left(3220 \text{ ft/s}^2\right) / (0.583 \text{ ft})} = 74 \text{ rad/s} = 710 \text{ rpm}$$

**11.42 A jeweler wishes to produce twenty gold rings in one investment casting operation. The wax parts are attached to a wax central sprue of 0.5 in. diameter. The rings are located in four rows, each 0.5 in. from the other on the sprue. The rings require a 0.125-in. diameter, 0.5-in. long runner to the sprue. Estimate the weight of gold needed to completely fill the rings, runners, and sprues. The specific gravity of gold is 19.3.**

The particular answer will depend on the geometry selected for a typical ring. Let's approximate a typical ring as a tube with dimensions of 1 in. outer diameter, 5/8 in. inner diameter, and 3/8 in. width. The volume of each ring is then 0.18 in$^3$, and a total volume for 20 rings of 3.6 in$^3$. There are twenty runners to the sprue, so this volume component is

$$V = 20 \left(\frac{\pi}{4} d^2\right) L = 20 \left(\frac{\pi}{4} (0.125 \text{ in.})^2\right) (0.5 \text{ in.}) = 0.123 \text{ in}^3$$

The central sprue has a length of 1.5 in., so that its volume is

$$V = \frac{\pi}{4} d^2 L = \frac{\pi}{4} (0.5 \text{ in.})^2 (1.5 \text{ in.}) = 0.29 \text{ in}^3$$

The total volume is then 4.0 in$^3$, not including the metal in the pouring basin, if any. The specific gravity of gold is 19.3, thus its density is 19.3(62.4 lb/ft$^3$) = 0.697 lb/in$^3$. Therefore, the jeweler needs 2.79 lb. of gold.

**11.43 Assume that you are an instructor covering the topics in this chapter, and you are giving a quiz on the numerical aspects to test the understanding of the students. Prepare two quantitative problems and supply the answers.**

By the student. This is a challenging, open-ended question that requires considerable focus and understanding on the part of the students, and has been found to be a very valuable homework problem.

## SYNTHESIS, DESIGN, AND PROJECTS

**11.44 Make a list of the mold and die materials used in the casting processes described in this chapter. Under each type of material, list the casting processes that are employed, and explain why these processes are suitable for that particular mold or die material.**

- Sand: Used because of its ability to resist very high temperatures, availability, and low cost. Used for sand, shell, expanded-pattern, investment, and ceramic-mold casting processes.
- Metal: Such as steel or iron. Result in excellent surface finish and good dimensional accuracy. Used for die, slush, pressure, centrifugal, and squeeze-casting processes.
- Graphite: Used for conditions similar to those for metal molds; however, lower pressures are tolerable for this material. Used in pressure- and centrifugal-casting processes.
- Plaster of paris: Used in the plaster-mold casting process in the production of small components, such as fittings and valves.

**11.45 The optimum shape of a riser is spherical to ensure that it cools more slowly than the casting it feeds. However, spherically-shaped risers are difficult to cast. (a) Sketch the shape of a blind riser that is easy to mold, but also has the smallest possible surface area-to-volume ratio. (b) Compare the solidification time of the riser in part (a) to that of a riser shaped like a right circular cylinder. Assume that the volume of each riser is the same and that, for each, the height is equal to the diameter. (See the example in Section 10.3.4.)**

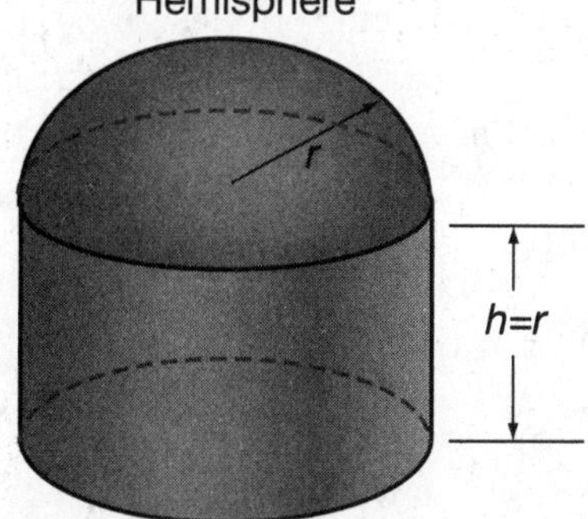


A sketch of a blind riser that is easy to cast is shown above, consisting of a cylindrical and a hemispherical portion. Note that the height of the cylindrical portion is equal to its radius (so that the total height of the riser is equal to its diameter). The volume, $V$, of this riser is

$$V = \pi r^2 h + \left(\frac{1}{2}\right)\left(\frac{4\pi r^3}{3}\right) = \left(\frac{5\pi r^3}{3}\right)$$

Letting $V$ be unity, we have $r = (3\pi/5)^{1/3}$. The surface area $A$ of this riser is

$$A = 2\pi rh + \pi r^2 + (1/2)(4\pi r^2) = 5\pi r^2 = 5\pi(3\pi/5)^{2/3} = 5.21$$

Thus, from Eq. (10.7) on p. 272, the solidification time, $t$, for the blind riser will be

$$t = C(V/A)^2 = C(1/5.21)^2 = 0.037C$$

From Example 10.1 on p. 274, we know that the solidification time for a cylinder with a height equal to its diameter is $0.033C$. Thus, the blinder riser in (a) will cool a little slower.

**11.46 Sketch an automated casting line consisting of machienry, conveyors, robots, sensors, etc., that could automatically perform the expendable-pattern casting process.**

By the student. Several designs for an automated casting line could be developed. The student should consider the proper sequence of operations and place the required machinery in a logical and efficient order, including material handling capability.

**11.47 Which of the casting processes would be most suitable for making small toys? Why?**

Small toys, such as metal cars, are produced in large quantities so that the mold cost is spread over many parts. Referring to Table 11.1 on page 262, to produce the intricate shapes needed at large quantities reduces the options to investment casting and die casting. Since the parts are nonferrous, die casting is the logical choice.

**11.48 Describe the procedures that would be involved in making a large bronze statue. Which casting process(es) would be suitable? Why?**

By the student. Very large statues, such as those found in parks and museums, are produced in a number of methods. One is by first manufacturing or sculpting a blank from wax and then using investment casting. Another involves producing a plaster mold from a wax or wooden blank, which is closely related to plaster mold and investment casting.

**11.49 Write a brief report on the permeability of molds and the techniques that are used to determine permeability.**

By the student. Good sources for such a literature search are machine tool design handbooks and texts on casting operations. Permeability suggests that there is a potential for material to penetrate into the porous mold material. This penetration can be measured through a number of experimental setups, such as using a standard sized slug or shape of sand, and applying a known pressure to one side and measuring the flow rate through the sand.

**11.50 Light metals are commonly cast in vulcanized rubber molds. Perform a literature search and describe the mechanics of this process.**

By the student. The basic mechanics are that an elastomer in a container is used along with a blank of the desired part. The elastomer is compressed against the blank, the container is clamped against the part and then the elastomer is vulcanized (see Section 7.9 on p. 214) and maintains its shape. This is restricted to light metals because the rubber molds would chemically degrade at the casting temperatures for other metals. A complete description is given in Gonicberg, J.A., and Ritch, M.L., *Principles of Centrifugal Rubber Mold Casting*, Providence, A.J. Oster Co., 1980.

**11.51 It is sometimes desirable to cool metals more slowly than they would if the molds were maintained at room temperature. List and explain methods you woulod use to slow down the cooling process.**

The cooling process can be slowed, first by cooling the mold in a room at elevated temperature. This is similar to the single-crystal casting technique shown in Fig. 11.30 on page 290. In addition, one could place a container, such as a steel drum, around the mold to slow the convected heat transfer to the ambient air. One could also reheat the mold at some stage during the cooling cycle, perhaps even with a simple approach as with a gas torch.

**11.52 The part shown below is a hemispherical shell used as an acetabular (mushroom shaped) cup in a total hip replacement. Select a casting process for this part and provide a sketch of all the patterns or tooling needed if it is to be produced from a cobalt-chrome alloy.**

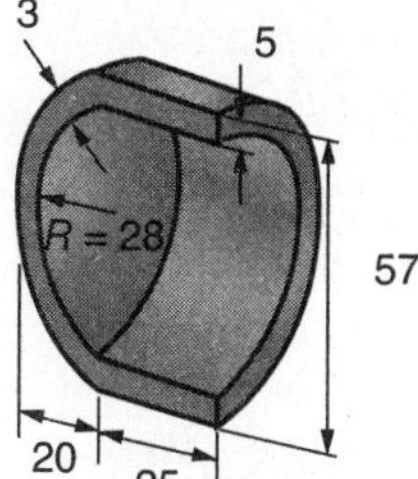


By the student. Various answers are possible, depending on the student's estimates of production rate and equipment costs. In practice, such a part would be produced through an investment-casting operation, where the individual parts with runners are injection molded and then attached to a central sprue. The tooling that would be needed include:

(a) A mold for injection molding of wax into the cup shape.

(b) Templates for placement of the cup shape onto the sprue, in order to assure proper spacing for evenly controlled cooling.

(c) Machining fixtures. It should also be noted that the wax pattern will be larger than the desired casting, because of shrinkage as well as the incorporation of a shrinkage allowance.

**11.53** Porosity developed in the boss of a casting is illustrated in the figure below. Show that this problem can be eliminated by simply repositioning the parting line of this casting.

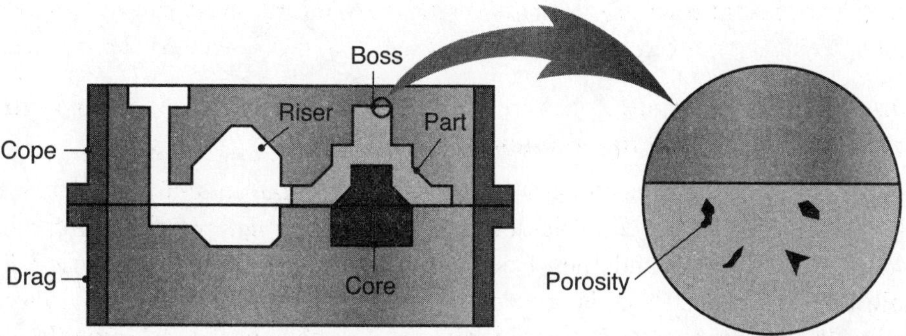


Note in the figure below that the boss is at some distance from the blind riser; consequently, the boss can develop porosity as shown because of a lack of supply of molten metal from the riser. The sketch below shows a repositioned parting line that would eliminate porosity in the boss. Note that the boss can now be supplied with molten metal as it begins to solidify and shrink.

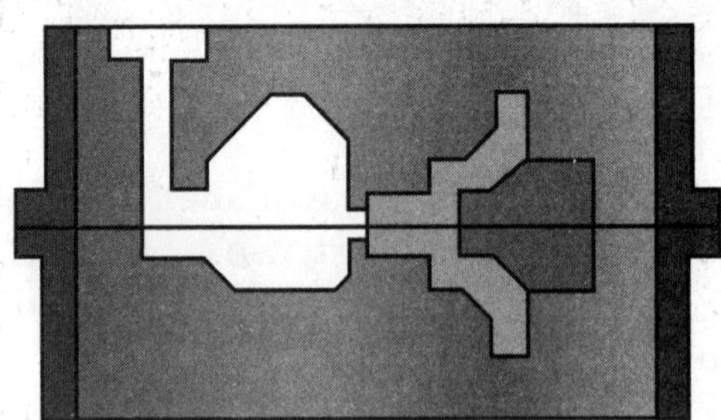

# Chapter 12

# Metal Casting: Design, Materials, and Economics

## QUALITATIVE PROBLEMS

**12.12 Describe the procedure you would follow to determine whether a defect in a casting is a shrinkage cavity or a porosity caused by gases.**

Evidence of which type of porosity is present (gas or shrinkage) can be gained by studying the location and shape of the cavity. If the porosity is near the mold surface, core surface, or chaplet surface, it is most likely to be gas porosity because the air bubbles rise to the surface due to buoyancy, whereas large shrinkage pores are more likely in the casting's bulk. However, if the porosity occurs in an area considered to be a hot spot in the casting, it is most likely shrinkage porosity. Furthermore, gas porosity generally has smooth surfaces and is often, though not always, spherical in shape (inspect, for example, the holes in Swiss cheese and observe how shiny they are). Shrinkage porosity has a more textured and jagged surface and is generally irregular in shape.

**12.13 Explain how you would go about avoiding hot tearing.**

Hot tearing can be avoided by two methods: (a) change the mold design to decrease the tensile stress that arises upon contraction during solidification, and/or (b) change the mold composition, such that the mold and cores are collapsible under the resulting pressure on them during shrinkage.

**12.14 Describe your observation concerning the design changes shown in Fig. 12.1.**

Several observations can be made regarding this figure. Figure 12.1a is further emphasized in Fig. 12.2 on p. 326, and shows that hot spots can develop where the section thickness changes abruptly or where corners exist. Figure 12.2b shows how deep cavities should be located on one side of the casting to greatly simplify pattern design as well as removal of the pattern from the sand mold. Due to large temperature gradients (which may form along flat surfaces during cooling) warping may occur. The design of a mold with ribs and serrations shown in Fig. 12.1d can reduce this effect and result in a more sound (not warped) casting. Ribs may be used, for example, on steel flanges at the recessed portion in order to avoid warping of both surfaces with which it is in contact.

**12.15 If you need only a few castings of the same design, which three processes would be the most expensive per piece cast?**

Die casting, shell-mold casting, and centrifugal casting would be the three most expensive processes per piece because these processes involve high equipment costs and a high degree of automation. Both of these factors require large production runs to justify their high cost. The high tooling cost can be mitigated somewhat by rapid tooling technologies, as discussed in Section 20.5 on p. 594. As an interesting comparison, refer to the answer to Problem 11.17 for a discussion regarding the most cost-effective means of producing only a few cast parts.

**12.16 Do you generally agree with the cost ratings in Table 12.6? If so, why?**

The cost ratings given in Table 12.6 on p. 337 are based on initial investment (die and equipment) and the labor required to run the processes. The labor cost depends on the extent of process automation. Thus, die casting has a low labor cost (highly automated) and investment casting has a high labor cost (little automation).

**12.17 Add more examples to those shown in Fig. 12.2.**

By the student. A wide variety of potential examples can be presented. The main consideration is maintaining a uniform section thickness and eliminating corners in order to avoid hot spots. Students should be encouraged to sketch designs that involve varying cross-sections, but also to place chills as an alternative to modifying the shape of the casting. Some examples of these rules are shown in Fig. 12.1c and 12.1e. Some additional designs that attempt to maintain section thickness are shown below:

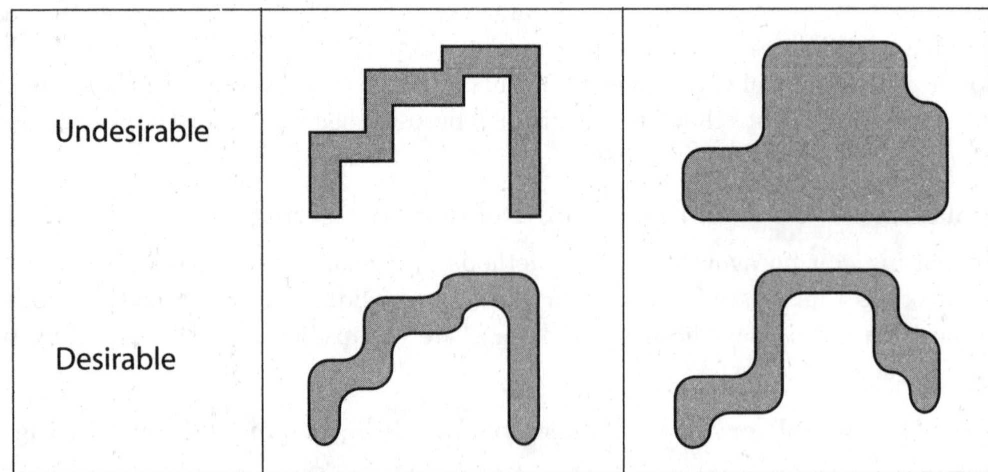


**12.18 Explain how ribs and serrations are helpful in casting flat surfaces that otherwise may warp. Give a specific illustration.**

Due to large temperature gradients which may develop along flat surfaces during cooling, warping may be a problem. The design of a mold with ribs and serrations can reduce this effect and result in a more sound (unwarped) casting because these increase the stiffness of the casting and reduce the strain associated with a residual stress. Ribs may be used, for example, on steel flanges at the recessed portion in order to avoid warping of both surfaces with which it is in contact. An illustration of a situation where a rib is beneficial is given in Fig. 12.1d on p. 325.

**12.19 Describe the nature of the design changes made in Fig. 12.3. What general principles do you observe in this figure?**

Several observations can be made regarding Fig. 12.3 on p. 331, and students are encouraged to think creatively in analyzing these design features. Some of the observations that can be made are:

- In (a), the "poor" design would result in a very thin wall next to the counterbore (which may lead to potential failure), whereas the "good" design eliminates this thin wall.
- In (b), a large flat area may not be acceptable because of casting defects or warpage. The surface can be made much more aesthetically pleasing by incorporating featuers such as serrations and stripling.
- In (c), a radius makes the part much easier to cast; the likelihood of a large pore near the corner is reduced and the mold integrity is improved. Furthermore, a sharp inner corner may create difficulties durign assembly with components that may eb isnerted into the cavity.
- In (d), the "poor" design is difficult to machine (hence costly) into a die; the "good" design is much easier to produce.
- In (e), The "poor" design requires a sharp, knife edge in the die, which could reduce die life. The "good" design eliminates the need for a knife edge in the die.
- In (f), when casting threaded inserts in place, it is good practice to have a length of shank exposed before the threaded section so that the cast metal does not compormise the threads and interfere with their function.

**12.20 Note in Fig. 12.4 that the ductility of some cast alloys is very low. Do you think this should be a significant concern in engineering applications of castings? Explain.**

The low ductility of some cast alloys shown in Fig. 12.4 on p. 333 should certainly be taken into consideration in engineering applications of the casting. Low ductility will adversely affect properties such as toughness (since the area under the stress-strain curve will be much smaller) and fatigue life. This is particularly significant in applications where the casting is subjected to impact forces.

**12.21 Do you think there will be fewer defects in a casting made by gravity pouring versus one made by pouring under pressure? Explain.**

When an external pressure is applied, defects such as gas porosity, poor surface finish, and surface porosity are reduced or eliminated. Since gravity pouring does not exert as much pressure as pouring under pressure, gravity pouring generally will produce more defects.

**12.22 Explain the difference in the importance of drafts in green-sand casting versus permanent-mold casting.**

Draft is provided in a mold to allow the removal of the pattern from the mold without damaging the mold (see, for example, Fig. 11.5 on p. 292). If the mold material is sand and the pattern has no draft (taper), the mold cavity can be damaged upon pattern removal due to the low strength of the sand mold. However, a die made of high-strength steel, which is typical for permanent-mold casting, is not likely to be damaged during the removal of the part; thus smaller draft angles can be employed.

**12.23 What type of cast iron would be suitable for heavy-machine bases, such as presses and machine tools? Why?**

Because of its relatively high strength and excellent castability (which generally means low cost), a pearlitic gray cast iron would probably be most suitable for this application. Note that, as no significant ductility is required for this application, the low ductility of gray irons is of little consequence. An important further advantage is the damping capacity of these cast irons, especially for machine tools (see Section 25.4 on p. 770).

**12.24 Explain the advantages and limitations of sharp and rounded fillets, respectively, in casting design.**

Sharp corners and fillets should be avoided in casting design because of their tendency to cause cracking and tearing of the casting during solidification. Fillet radii should be large enough to avoid stress concentrations and yet small enough to avoid a low rate of cooling and hot spots that can cause shrinkage cavities in the casting.

**12.25 Explain why the elastic modulus, $E$, of gray cast iron varies so widely, as shown in Table 12.4.**

Because the shape, size, and distribution of the second phase, i.e., the graphite flakes, vary greatly for gray cast irons, there is a large corresponding variation of properties attainable. The elastic modulus is one property which is affected by this factor.

**12.26 Why are risers not as useful in die casting as compared to sand casting?**

The main reasons are the size of typical cast parts and the solidification times involved. Die cast parts generally have smaller sections than sand cast parts; a riser used in die casting will not provide molten metal to the casting because the thin sections solidify and block the flow of molten metal to the remainder of the mold. The solidification rates are important as well; to provide molten metal to the cast shape, the flow rates have to be very high because the casting solidifies so rapidly. Thus, even if a riser is provided in a die casting, the pressure is insufficient to get molten metal to flow where it is needed.

**12.27** Describe the drawbacks to having a riser that is (a) too large and (b) too small.

The main drawbacks to having too large of a riser are:

(a) The material in the riser is eventually scrapped and recycled, representing a material loss;

(b) the riser has to be removed, and a larger riser will cost more to machine;

(c) a very large riser increases the solidification time;

(d) the riser may interfere with solidification elsewhere in the casting; and

(e) the extra molten metal may cause buoyancy forces sufficient to separate the mold halves unless they are properly weighted or clamped.

The drawbacks to having too small a riser are mainly associated with defects in the casting, either due to insufficient feeding of liquid metal to compensate for solidification shrinkage, and the development of shrinkage pores because the solidification front is not uniform.

**12.28 Why can blind risers be smaller than open-top risers?**

Risers are used as reservoirs for a casting in regions where shrinkage is expected to occur, i.e, areas which are the last to solidify. Thus, risers must be made large enough to ensure that they are the last to solidify. If a riser solidifies before the part (it is to feed) does, it is useless. Consequently, an open riser (which is in contact with air) must be larger to ensure it will not solidify first. A blind riser is less prone to this phenomenon, as it is in contact with the mold on all surfaces. Thus, it is slower to cool since the mold increases in temperature and the riser can be located in an area that will cool more slowly; thus, a blind riser may be made smaller.

**12.29 If you were to incorporate lettering or numbers on a sand-cast part, would you make them to protrude from the surface or recess them into the surface? What if the part were to be made by investment casting? Explain your answer.**

The answer depends on the casting process used. In both processes, letters are commonly machined, and it is easiest to machine recessed letters. In sand casting, a pattern will be machined; the recessed pattern letters will produce sand molds of protruding letters. The parts will then have recessed letters. In investment casting (see Section 19.3 on p. 544), the mold will likely be machined directly; the parts will then have protruding letters.

**12.30 The general design recommendations for a well in sand casting (see Fig. 11.3) are that (a) its diameter should be at least twice the exit diameter of the sprue and (b) its depth should be approximately twice the depth of the runner. Explain the consequences of deviating from these guidelines.**

(a) Regarding this rule, if the well diameter is much smaller than twice the exit diameter, then the liquid will not fill the well (see Fig. 11.3 on p. 290), and aspiration of the molten metal will result. If the diameter is much larger than twice the exit diameter, the metal may solidify in the well because of longer time there.

(b) If the depth of the well is not greater than that of the runner, turbulent metal that first splashed into the well is immediately fed into the casting, leading to aspiration and defects. If the depth is much greater, then the liquid metal stays too long in the well and thus it can solidify prematurely.

**12.31 The heavy regions of parts typically are placed in the drag in sand casting and not in the cope. Explain why.**

Heavy parts are placed in the drag (see Fig. 11.3 on p. 290) so that the buoyancy force on the cope is reduced. If the buoyancy force becomes high enough, the cope can separate from the drag, resulting in excessive flash in the casting. This requires expensive removal operations such as machining or cropping (see Fig. 14.8 on p. 378 for a similar example).

# QUANTITATIVE PROBLEMS

**12.32 When designing patterns for casting, patternmakers use special rulers that automatically incorporate solid shrinkage allowances into their designs. For example, a 12-in. patternmaker's ruler is longer than one foot. How long should a patternmaker's ruler be for making patterns for (a) aluminum castings and (b) high-manganese steel?**

Referring to Table 12.1 on p. 326, we note that the shrinkage allowance for the two metals are: (a) aluminum alloy = 1.3% and (b) high-manganese steel = 2.6%. From the formula below,

$$L_f = L_o(1 + \text{shrinkage})$$

we find that for aluminum we have

$$L_f = (12.000)(1.013) = 12.156 \text{ in.}$$

and for high-manganese steel

$$L_f = (12.000)(1.026) = 12.312 \text{ in.}$$

**12.33 Using the data given in Table 12.2, develop approximate plots of (a) castability versus weldability and (b) castability versus machinability for at least five of the materials listed in the table.**

The plots are as follows:

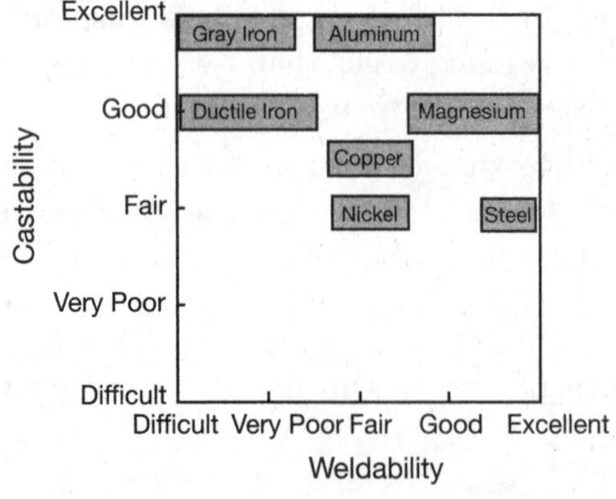


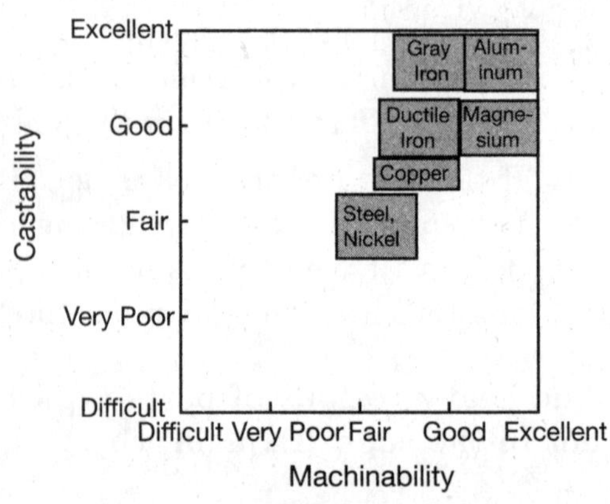

## SYNTHESIS, DESIGN, AND PROJECTS

**12.34 List casting processes that are suitable for making hollow parts with (a) complex external features, (b) complex internal features, and (c) both external and internal features. Explain your choices.**

By the student. The answers depend on the size of the part under consideration and the materials used. Students should be encouraged to develop solutions based on their experience and training. Although complex features are always difficult to cast, sometimes they can be accomodated. For example, for complex external features:

- Within limits, a pattern plate can create intricate patterns in a sand mold, so sand casting could be suitable.
- Investment casting can utilize any pattern that allows metal to flow into and fill the cavity; these can be rapid prototyped or carved by hand, and can have very intricate external features.
- Shell molding has similar capabilities as sand casting with respect to external features.
- Die casting can produce complex features as long as they do not interfere with ejection of parts from the dies.

Internal features are more difficult to produce; however, the following are possible:

- In sand casting, a core with complex features can be used when necessary.
- In investment casting, internal features can be produced as long as they can be reproduced on the pattern.

When both are featuers are required, sand or investment casting may be suitable.

**12.35 Small amounts of slag and dross often persist after skimming and are introduced into the molten metal flow in casting. Recognizing that slag and dross are less dense than the molten metal, design mold features that will remove small amounts of slag before the metal reaches the mold cavity.**

There are several trap designs in use in foundries. An excellent discussion of dross trap design is given in J. Campbell, *Castings*, 1991, Reed Educational Publishers, pp. 53-55. A conventional and effective dross trap is the following design:

The design is based on the principle that a trap at the end of a runner will capture the first material through the runner and keep it away from the gates. The design shown above is a wedge-type trap. Metal entering the runner contacts the wedge, and the leading front of the metal wave is chilled and attaches itself to the runner wall, and thus it is kept out of the mold cavity. The wedge must be designed to avoid reflected waves that would recirculate the dross or slag.

The following design is a swirl trap, which is based on the principle that the dross or slag is less dense than the metal. The metal enters the trap off of the center, inducing a swirl in the molten metal as the trap is filled with molten metal. Since it is much less dense than the metal, the dross or slag remains in the center of the swirl trap. Since the metal is tapped from the outside periphery, dross or slag is excluded from entering the casting.

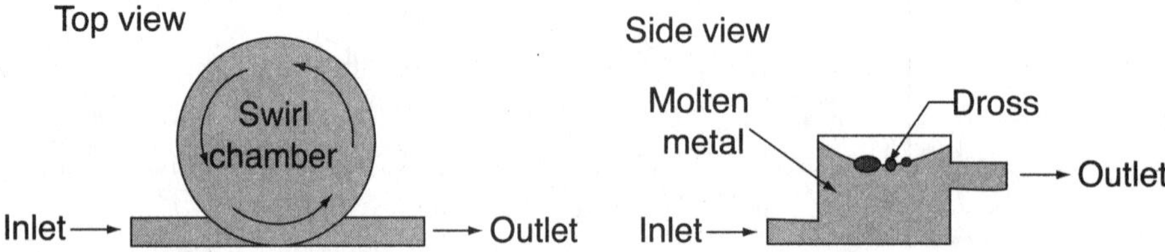


**12.36 For the cast metal wheel illustrated in Figure P12.36, show how (a) riser placement, (b) core placement, (c) padding, and (d) chills may be used to help feed molten metal and eliminate porosity in the isolated hub boss.**

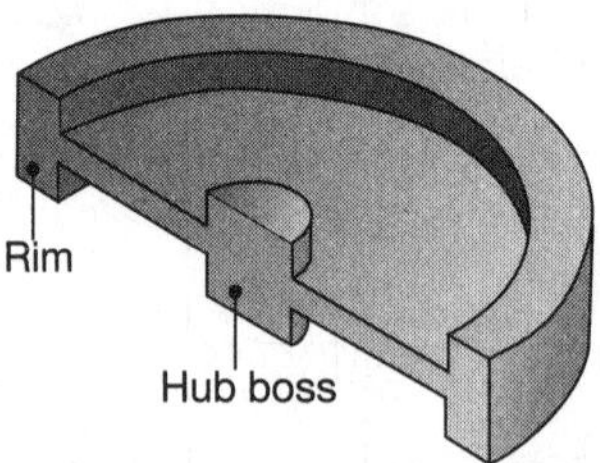


Four different methods are shown below.

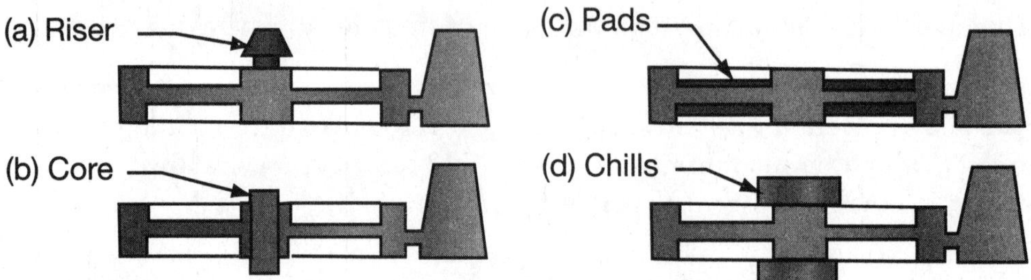


**12.37 Assume that the introduction to this chapter is missing. Write a brief introduction to highlight the importance of the topics covered in it.**

By the student. The most challenging aspect of this problem is to make the introduction sufficiently brief.

**12.38 In Fig. P12.38, the original casting design shown in (a) was modified to the design shown in (b). The casting is round and has a vertical axis of symmetry. As a functional part, what advantages do you think the new design has over the old one?**

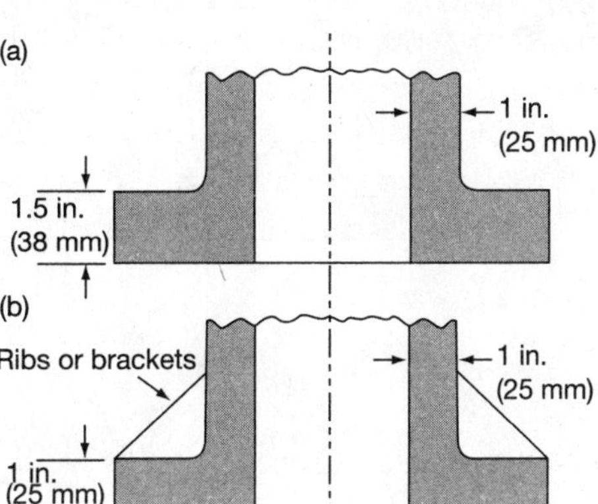


By the student. There are a number of advantages, including the fact that the part thickness is more uniform, so that large shrinkage porosity is less likely, and the ribs will control warpage due to thermal stresses as well as increase joint stiffness. This redesign illustrates the recommendations given in Figs. 12.1 and 12.2 on pp. 325-326.

**12.39 An incorrect and a correct design for casting are shown Fig. P12.39. Review the changes made and comment on their advantages.**

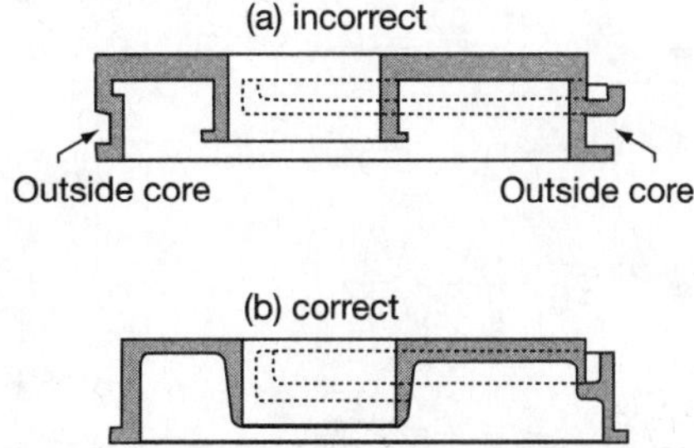


By the student. The main advantage of the new part is that it can be easily cast without using an external core. The original part requires two such cores because the shape is such that it cannot be obtained in a sand mold without using cores.

**12.40 Three sets of designs for die casting are shown in Fig. P12.40. Note the changes made to die design 1 and comment on the reasons.**

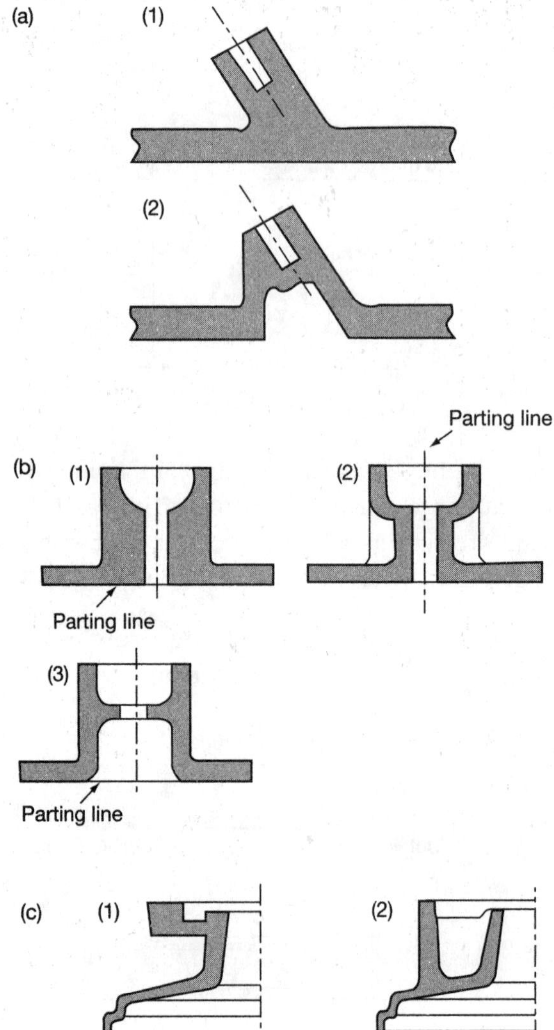


By the student. There are many observations, usually with the intent of minimizing changes in section thickness, eliminating inclined surfaces to simplify mold construction, and to orient flanges so that they can be easily cast.

# Chapter 13

# Rolling of Metals

## QUALITATIVE PROBLEMS

**13.14 Explain why the rolling process was invented and developed.**

By the student. Machinery, structures, bridges, boilers, pressure vessels, etc. typically require metal plates or sheets. Consequently, there was urgent need for developing the rolling process which could economically deliver large amounts of the necessary plate. Note in Table I.2 on p. 5 that the word rolling first appears in the 1500s.

**13.15 Flat rolling reduces the thickness of plates and sheets. It is possible, instead, to reduce their thickness by simply stretching the material. Would this be a feasible process? Explain.**

By the student. Although stretching reduces the thickness of materials, there are several limitations associated with it as compared to rolling. Stretching process is a batch process and it cannot be continuous as it is in rolling. The reduction in thickness is limited by necking of the sheet, depending on its strain-hardening exponent, $n$ (see Section 2.2 on p. 65). Furthermore, as the sheet is stretched, the surface finish becomes dull due to the orange-peel effect. Stretching the sheet requires some means of clamping the material at its ends which, in turn, will leave marks on the sheet.

**13.16 Explain how the residual stress patterns shown in Fig. 13.9 become reversed when the roll radius or reduction-per-pass is changed.**

As shown in Fig. 13.9a on p. 357, with small rolls and/or small reductions, the workpiece is deformed, as expected, at its surfaces more than it is in the bulk. With large rolls and/or large reductions, the reverse is true. The large roll-strip contact area develops a situation similar to that shown in Fig. 13.9b, namely, that the material flows more along the inside while the surfaces are more constrained.

**13.17 Explain whether it would be practical to apply the roller-leveling technique shown in Fig. 13.7 to thick plates.**

It is doubtful that the roller-leveling process, shown in Fig. 13.7 on p. 356, can be applied to plates. In this process, the strip is flattened by repeatedly flexing it in opposite directions. To do the same with a plate would require much higher forces in order to develop stresses that are of the same magnitude at the plate surface as they are in sheet. Also, unless it is sufficiently ductile, the plate may develop cracks if bent to small radii.

**13.18 Describe the factors that influence the magnitude of the roll force, $F$, in Fig. 13.2c.**

By the student. As can be deduced by observing the equations on pp. 350-351, the roll force, $F$, is influenced by the roll radius, strip width, draft (hence the roll-strip contact area), coefficient of friction, and the strength of the material at the rolling temperature. If the material is strain-rate sensitive (i.e., high $m$ value), the rolling speed would also influence the roll force; this is particularly important in hot rolling.

**13.19 Explain how you would go about applying front and back tensions to sheet metals during rolling. How would you go about controlling these tensions?**

Front tensions are applied and controlled by the take-up reel of a rolling mill (see Fig. 13.11 on page 359). The greater the torque to this reel, the greater the front tension. Back tension is applied by the pay-off reel of the rolling mill, whereby increasing the brake force on the pay-off reel increases the back tension.

**13.20 We noted that rolls tend to flatten under roll forces. Describe the methods by which flattening can be reduced. Which property or properties of the roll material can be increased to reduce flattening?**

Flattening is elastic deformation of the roll and results in a larger contact length in the roll gap; therefore, the elastic modulus of the roll should be increased, for example, by making it from materials with high modulus of elasticity, such as carbides (see Tables 2.1 on p. 65, 2.2 on p. 67, and 22.1 on p. 649). Roll flattening also can be reduced by (a) decreasing the reduction per pass and (b) reducing friction at the roll-sheet interface.

**13.21 It was stated that spreading in flat rolling increases with (a) decreasing width-to-thickness ratio of the entering material, (b) decreasing friction, and (c) decreasing ratio of the roll radius to the strip thickness. Explain why.**

See the bottom of p. 353. (a) If the width-to-thickness ratio is small, the material in the roll bite is less restrained by the frictional force in the width direction and, as a result, spreading increases. (b) The lower the friction, the lower the resistance to relative motion between the rolls and the workpiece and, hence, the greater the spreading. (c) If the roll radius is large as compared to the strip thickness, there will be lower frictional resistance in the rolling direction than across it, and thus the material will flow more in the longitudinal direction, hence spreading will decrease.

**13.22 As stated in this chapter, flat rolling can be carried out by front tension only, using idling rolls (Steckel rolling). Since the torque on the rolls is now zero,**

**where, then, is the energy coming from to supply the work of deformation in rolling?**

The energy for work of deformation in Steckel rolling (p. 352) is supplied by the front tension required to pull the strip through the roll gap between the idling rolls. The product of tension and exiting strip velocity is power supplied in rolling. This power is provided by the coil winder or draw bench.

**13.23 What is the consequence of applying too high a back tension in rolling?**

If the back tension is too high, the rolls will begin to slip and no reduction in thickness will take place. An analogy would be the slipping of the wheels of an automobile while pulling a heavy trailer.

**13.24 Note in Fig. 13.3d that the driven rolls (powered rolls) are the third set from the work roll. Why isn't power supplied through the work roll itself? Is it even possible? Explain.**

We note in Fig. 13.3 on p. 352 that the diameter of the rolls increases as we move away from the work (smallest) roll. The reason why power cannot be supplied through the work roll is that the significant power required for this rolling operation will subject the work roll to a high torque. Since its diameter is small, the torsional stresses on the roll would be too high; the roll will either fracture or undergo permanent twist. With the setup shown in the figure, the power is applied to a larger-diameter roll, which can support a large torque.

**13.25 Describe the importance of controlling roll speeds, roll gaps, temperature, and other process variables in a tandem-rolling operation, as shown in Fig. 13.11. Explain how you would go about determining the distance between the stands.**

Referring to the tandem rolling operation shown in Fig. 13.11 on p. 359, we note that mass continuity has to be maintained during rolling. Thus, if the roll speed is not synchronized with the strip thickness in a particular stand, excessive tensions or slack may develop between the stands; some rolls may slip. Also, if the temperature is not controlled properly, strip thickness will change, thus affecting reduction per pass and, consequently, the roll forces involved. This, in turn, will also affect the actual roll gap and roll deflections. Complex control systems have been developed for monitoring and controlling such operations at high rolling speeds.

**13.26 In Fig. 13.9a, if you remove the top compressive layer by, say, grinding, will the strip remain flat? If not, which way will it curve and why?**

We can model the residual stresses in the strip in Fig. 13.9a on p. 357 by three horizontal and parallel springs: compression spring (top), tension spring (middle), and compression spring (bottom). Note that the top layer is in compression, and when we remove the top spring, the balance of internal moment and internal horizontal forces will be disturbed. The strip will thus distort, in a manner that it will hold water, i.e., like cupping your hand. The remaining residual stresses in the strip will rearrange themselves to ensure balancing of the internal moment and internal horizontal forces.

**13.27 Name several products that can be made by each of the operations shown in Fig. 13.1.**

By the student. Examples of parts from cold rolled strip are car bodies and aluminum foil for food packaging. Examples of plate are tractor and machinery frames and warship hulls. Rolled shapes include architectural beams and railroad rails.

**13.28 List the possible consequences of rolling at (a) too high of a speed and (b) too low a speed.**

There are advantages and disadvantages to each. Rolling at high speed is advantageous in that production rate is increased, but it has disadvantages as well, including:

- The lubricant film thickness entrained will be larger, which can reduce friction and lead to a slick mill condition where the rolls slip against the workpiece. This can lead to a damaged surface finish on the workpiece.
- The thicker lubricant film associated with higher speeds can result in significant oil peel, or surface roughening.
- Because of the higher speed, chatter may occur, compromising the surface quality or process viability.
- There is a limit to speed associated with the motor and power source that drive the rolls.

Rolling at low speed is advantageous because the surface roughness in the workpiece can match that of the rolls (which can be polished). However, rolling at too low a speed has consequences such as:

- Production rate will be low, and thus the cost per unit weight will be higher.
- Because a thick lubricant film cannot be developed and maintained, there is a danger of transferring material from the workpiece to the roll (pickup), thus compromising surface finish.
- The workpiece may cool excessively before contacting the rolls. This is because a long billet that is rolled slowly loses some of its heat to the environment and also through conduction through the roller conveyor.

**13.29 Describe your observations concerning Fig. 13.12.**

By the student. Several observations may be made regarding the rolls arrangements and noting the result from each of the six steps shown in the figure.

## QUANTITATIVE PROBLEMS

**13.30 Using simple geometric relationships and the inclined-plane principle for friction, prove Eq. (13.1).**

Referring to the figure below and note that $x = h_o - h_f$, called draft. Note that a common mistake is to take $x/2 = h_o - h_f$, but this is clearly not true since the triangle shown is for the top roll only, and an identical geometry exists for the bottom roll. For small $\alpha$, $z = R\sin\alpha$. Also, realizing that for small angles $x/2 = z\sin\alpha/2$, and therefore $x = z\sin\alpha$, we have $x = R\sin^2\alpha$. At small angles the sine and tangent functions are approximately equal, hence $x = h_o - h_f = R\tan^2\alpha$. The inclined-plane principle for friction suggests $\alpha = \tan^{-1}\mu$, or $\mu = \tan^{-1}\alpha$. Substituting, we have $h_o - h_f = R\mu^2$.

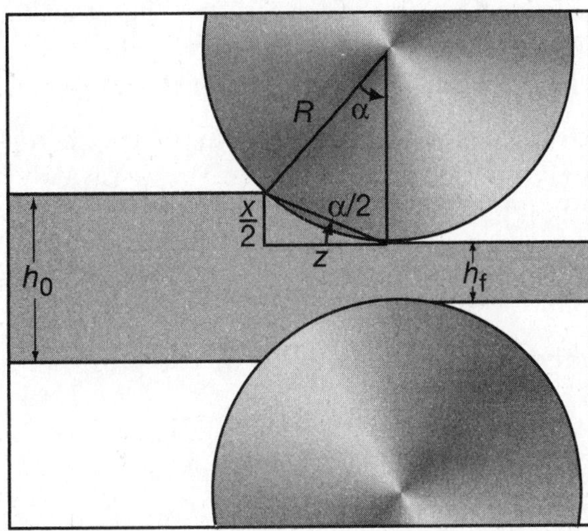


**13.31 Estimate the roll force, $F$, and the torque for AISI 1020 carbon-steel strip that is 200 mm wide and 10 mm thick and rolled to a thickness of 7 mm. The roll radius is 200 mm, and it rotates at 200 rpm.**

The roll force is given by $F = LwY_{\text{avg}}$, where $L$ is the roll-strip contact length, $w$ is the strip width, and $Y_{\text{avg}}$ is the average stress during the operation. As discussed in Example 13.1 on p. 351, $L$ is given by

$$L = \sqrt{R\Delta h} = \sqrt{(0.2 \text{ m})(0.01 \text{ m} - 0.007 \text{ m})} = 0.0245 \text{ m}$$

The true strain for this operation is

$$\epsilon = \ln(10/7) = 0.36$$

and the average flow stress, $Y_{\text{avg}}$, is given by

$$Y_{\text{avg}} = \frac{K\epsilon^n}{n+1}$$

For AISI 1020 carbon steel (from Table 2.3 on p. 72), $K = 530$ MPa and $n = 0.26$; therefore

$$Y_{\text{avg}} = 323 \text{ MPa}$$

and thus the roll force, $F$, is

$$F = LwY_{\text{avg}} = (0.0245)(0.2)(323) = 1.58 \text{ MN}$$

and the required torque, $T$, is

$$T = FL/2 = (1.58)(0.0245)/2 = 0.019 \text{ MN-m}$$

**13.32 In Example 13.1, calculate the roll force and the power for the case in which the workpiece material is 1100-O aluminum and the roll radius $R$ is 10 in.**

As discussed in Example 13.1 on p. 351, the roll-strip contact length, $L$, is given by

$$L = \sqrt{R\Delta h} = \sqrt{(10)(1.00 - 0.8)} = 1.414 \text{ in.}$$

or $L = 0.118$ ft. Referring to Fig. 2.6 on p. 72 we find that for 1100-O aluminum the yield stress is about 8,000 psi, and that at a true strain of 0.223, the true stress (flow stress) is about 16,000 psi. Thus the average stress $Y_{\text{avg}}$ is 12,000 psi, and the roll force, $F$, is

$$F = (1.41)(9)(12,000) = 153,000 \text{ lb}$$

and the power is given by Eq. (13.4) on page 350 as:

$$P = \frac{2\pi FLN}{33,000 \text{ hp}} = \frac{2\pi(153,000)(0.18)(100)}{33,000} = 524 \text{ hp}$$

**13.33 Calculate the individual drafts in each of the stands in the tandem-rolling operation shown in Fig. 13.11.**

The answers are:

- Stand 5: 2.25 - 1.45 = 0.80 mm, or 36%.
- Stand 4: 1.45 - 0.90 = 0.55 mm, or 38%.
- Stand 3: 0.90 - 0.56 = 0.34 mm, or 38%.
- Stand 2: 0.56 - 0.34 = 0.22 mm, or 39%.
- Stand 1: 0.34 - 0.26 = 0.08 mm, or 24%.

**13.34 Assume that you are an instructor covering the topics described in this chapter, and you are giving a quiz on the numerical aspects to test the understanding of the students. Prepare two quantitative problems and supply the answers.**

By the student. This is a challenging open-ended question and requires considerable focus and understanding on the part of the students, and has been found to be a very valuable homework problem.

## SYNTHESIS, DESIGN, AND PROJECTS

**13.35 A simple sketch for a four-high mill stand is shown in Fig. 13.3a. Make a survey of the technical literature and present a more detailed sketch for such a stand, showing the major components.**

By the student. The results will vary widely depending on the age of the machine, the material, and the size of the plates rolled. For example, a fully automated aluminum rolling mill will have a complex system of sensors and controls, whereas a specialty jewelry manufacturer may have a manually powered (hand crank) four-high rolling mill for producing gold foil.

**13.36 Obtain a piece of soft, round rubber eraser, such as that at the end of pencils, and duplicate the process shown in Fig. 13.18b. Note how the central portion of the eraser will begin to erode away, producing a hole.**

By the student. This is an interesting project, but is a little tricky to perform and may need several tries. Also, the hole needs to have the eroded material from the center removed periodically, such as by brisk blowing, to make a well-defined hole.

**13.37 If you repeat the experiment in Problem 13.36, but with a harder eraser, such as that used for erasing ink, you will note that the whole eraser will begin to crack and crumble. Explain why.**

By the student. The main reason for this behavior is that with an ordinary (tougher) eraser, the deterioration of the material starts at the center of the eraser and grows outward at a slow rate. With a hard eraser (typically containing small abrasive particles such as fine sand), the crack growth is very fast, and fracture occurs before any noticeable cavity is formed.

**13.38 Design a set of rolls to produce cross-sections other than those shown in Fig. 13.12.**

By the student. There are several possible designs, such as the following for producing railroad rails:

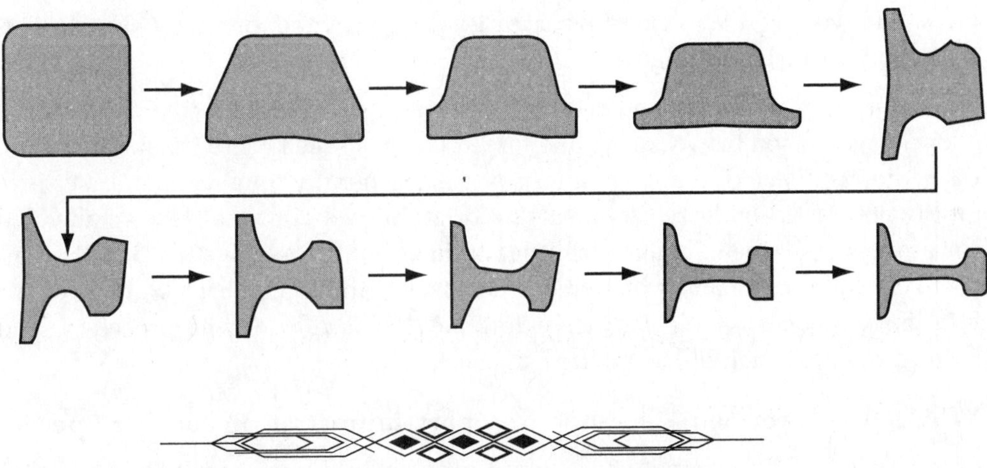

# Chapter 14

# Forging of Metals

## QUALITATIVE PROBLEMS

**14.11 How can you tell whether a certain part is forged or cast? Explain the features that you would investigate.**

Numerous nondestructive and destructive tests (see Sections 36.10 and 36.11) are available to allow identification between cast and forged parts. Forged parts generally exhibit greater ductility when subjected to a tension test, and are generally tougher than cast parts. Depending on the processes and heat treatments used, grain size will usually be smaller in forgings, and the grains will have undergone deformation in specific directions (preferred orientation). Cast parts, on the other hand, will be more isotropic than forged parts. Surface characteristics are also likely to be non-uniform, depending on the specific casting processes used and factors such as the condition of the mold or die surfaces.

**14.12 Why is the intermediate shape of a part important in forging operations?**

Clearly it is the final shape that is important from a design standpoint, and the intermediate shapes have no direct design implications. However, the intermediate shape is important for achieving a reasonable die life. To control die wear, it is highly desirable to control the sliding and the pressures involved in each section of the die. The contact stresses should pereferably be low when the sliding distance is large, or that the sliding distance be small when the stresses are high. Refer to Fig. 14.7a on p. 377 and note that the edging and blocking stages involve significant deformation, but the part thickness is large so that the die pressures are relatively low. In the finishing stage, there is significant flash, so the pressures will be high. See also the discussion on preforming operations on pp. 376-377. The result is that the selection of an intermediate shape results in controlled pressure and sliding in the cavities of a forging die, and when properly selected can lead to low wear and long die life.

**14.13 Explain the functions of flash in impression-die forging.**

In impression-die forging (Section 14.3 on p. 376), it is desirable to impart a specific shape to a workpiece, hence the name of the process. The flash is excess metal which is squeezed out from the die cavity into the space between the two dies. The flash cools faster than the material in the cavity due to the high $a/h$ ratio and the more intimate contact with the relatively cool dies. Consequently, the flash has higher strength than the hotter workpiece in the die cavity and, with higher frictional resistance in the flash gap, provides greater resistance to material flow outward through the flash gap. Thus, the flash allows filling of complex cavities.

**14.14 Why is control of the volume of the blank important in closed-die forging?**

If too large a billet is placed into the dies in a closed-die forging operation, presses can jam and thus not be able to complete their stroke. In turn, this would cause high loads to the press structure. Numerous catastrophic failures in presses have been attributed to such excessive loads. If, on the other hand, the blank is too small, obviously the desired shape will not be completely imparted onto the workpiece.

**14.15 Why are there so many types of forging machines? Describe the capabilities and limitations of each.**

By the student. Each type of forging machine (see Section 14.8 on p. 390) has its own advantages, each being ideally suited for different applications. The factors involved in equipment selection may be summarized as follows: (a) Force and energy requirements, (b) force-stroke characteristics, (c) length of ram travel, (d) production-rate requirements, (e) strain-rate sensitivity of the workpiece material, and (f) cooling of the workpiece in the die in hot forging and its consequences regarding die filling and forging forces.

**14.16 What are the advantages and limitations of (a) a cogging operation and (b) isothermal forging?**

Since the contact area in cogging is relatively small compared to the workpiece size (see Fig. 14.4a on p. 374) large cross-sections of bars can be reduced at low loads, thus requiring lower-capacity machinery, which is an economic advantage. Furthermore, various cross-sections can be produced along the length of the bar by varying the stroke during cogging steps. Note that the process is similar to what a blacksmith does in making various wrought-iron shapes and ornamental objects. A corresponding disadvantage is the time and large number of strokes required to shape long workpieces, as well as the difficulty in controlling straightness, flatness, and deformation with sufficient dimensional accuracy. The advantages to isothermal forging (see p. 383) are that (a) the workpiece has better formability because of elevated temperatures, and (b) the temperatures are maintained because the hot tooling doesn't conduct heat from the workpiece. The limitations of this process are somewhat low life of costly dies (which require high-temperature strength and wear resistance) because of the elevated temperatures involved and difficulties in properly lubricating isothermal forging operations.

**14.17 Describe your observations concerning Fig. 14.16.**

By the student. Figure 14.16 on p. 386 clearly shows the importance of properly planning all stages of an impression-die forging operation, and shows how laps, cracks, and shuts can develop in forging.

**14.18 What are the advantages and limitations of using die inserts?**

Die inserts (see Fig. 14.6 on p. 377 and text on p. 376) are useful because they allow stronger and wear-resistant materials to be placed in locations where wear is most critical. They can be inexpensively and easily replaced when worn or broken, and thus avoid the necessity of replacing entire dies. Furthermore, inserts reduce die production costs because of the possibility of modular die construction.

**14.19 Review Fig. 14.5d and explain why inner draft angles are larger than outer angles. Is this also true for permanent-mold casting?**

Draft angles (shown in Fig. 14.5 on p. 376) are necessary to assist in part removal from dies. Hot forgings will shrink radially (inward in the figure) and longitudinally upon cooling. Therefore, larger angles or tapers are required on the surfaces which will oppose the shrinkage. By definition, these are the inner surfaces. On the other hand, the workpiece shrinks away from the outer surfaces, and thus outer surfaces do not need as large a draft angle as do inner surfaces. This is also true for permanent-mold castings; see the discussion of drafts in castings on p. 326 and p. 330.

**14.20 Comment on your observations regarding the grain flow pattern in Fig. 14.12.**

The type of information obtained from Fig. 14.12 on p. 381 would be important in situations where certain regions of a forged part are to be subjected to, for example, high loads, excessive wear, and impact. In such cases, every attempt should be made so that the part is forged in such a way that those regions acquire the desired final properties. The student is encouraged to give examples of products where such considerations would be important.

**14.21 Describe your observations concerning the control of final tube thickness in Fig. 14.15.**

By the student. It is difficult to control the final tube thickness in Fig. 14.15a on p. 385 without a mandrel because the compressive action of the swaging machine results in radial, circumferential (hoop), or axial strains; these strains will vary depending on the particular workpiece and die geometry, as well as lubrication. To accurately control the final tube thickness, a mandrel as shown in Fig. 14.15b is needed, but this can be problematic for long workpieces or closed-ended workpieces such as the baseball bat shown in the middle of Fig. 14.14d.

**14.22 By inspecting some forged products, (such as a pipe wrench) you can see that the lettering on them is raised rather than sunk. Offer an explanation as to why they are made that way.**

By the student. It is much easier and economical to produce cavities in a die (thus producing lettering on a forging that are raised from its surface) than producing protrusions (thus producing lettering that are like impressions on the forged surface). See also answer to Problem 12.29. Various conventional and unconventional methods of producing dies are described in Section 14.7 on p. 388 and in Part IV of the text.

**14.23 Describe the difficulties involved in precisely defining the term "forgeability."**

By the student. Forgeability is a relative term (see Section 14.5 on p. 384), and various tests have been developed to define it. The fundamental problem is that, in view of the numerous parameters involved, it is difficult to develop a specific forgeability test that will simulate material's performance in an actual forging operation.

**14.24 Identify casting design rules (described in Section 12.2) that can also be applied to forging.**

By the student. Note that there are several rules that apply equally well to casting and forging, including the following:

- Corners, angles, and fillets should be avoided.
- Large flat areas should be avoided.
- A small draft angle (taper) is useful for removing a cast part from a mold, and for removing a forged part from a die.
- Lettering in a casting should be raised because it is easier to machine the design into a mold, and in a forging because it is easier to machine into a die.

The student is encouraged to observe other design features that are common among the various casting and forging processes.

## QUANTITATIVE PROBLEMS

**14.25 Calculate the forging force for a solid, cylindrical workpiece made of 1020 steel, that is 3.5 in. high and 5 in. in diameter and is to be reduced in height by 30%. Let the coefficient of friction be 0.2.**

The forging force for a cylindrical workpiece is given by Eq. (14.1) on p. 375:

$$F = Y_f \pi r^2 \left(1 + \frac{2\mu r}{3h}\right)$$

(a) Forging force to initiate yielding in the material: $Y = 42.6$ ksi as obtained from Table 5.2 on p. 159 (assuming that the workpiece is annealed), $r = 2.5$ in, $h = 3.5$ in., and hence

$$F = Y_f \pi r^2 \left(1 + \frac{2\mu r}{3h}\right) = (42.6 \text{ ksi})\pi(2.5 \text{ in.})^2 \left[1 + \frac{2(0.2)(2.5 \text{ in.})}{3(3.5 \text{ in.})}\right] = 916 \text{ kip}$$

(b) Forging force at end of stroke: The true strain is

$$\epsilon = \ln(0.7) = -0.36$$

However, we need only consider the absolute value of the strain for determination of the mean stress. Therefore, let's take $\epsilon = 0.36$, whereby we find from Fig. 2.6 on

p. 72 that, approximately, $Y_f = 70,000$ psi. Since the reduction in height is 30%, $h = (0.70)(3.5 \text{ in.}) = 2.45$ in. The value of the radius $r$ is determined through volume constancy. Thus,

$$\pi r_1^2 h_1 = \pi r_2^2 h_2 \quad \rightarrow \quad r_2 = \sqrt{\frac{r_1^2 h_1}{h_2}} = \sqrt{\frac{(2.5 \text{ in.})^2(3.5 \text{ in.})}{(2.45 \text{ in.})}} = 3.0 \text{ in.}$$

and therefore,

$$F = Y_f \pi r^2 \left(1 + \frac{2\mu r}{3h}\right) = (70 \text{ ksi})\pi(3 \text{ in.})^2 \left[1 + \frac{2\mu(3 \text{ in.})}{3(2.45 \text{ in.})}\right] = 2300 \text{ kip}$$

**14.26 Using Eq. (14.2), estimate the forging force for the workpiece in Problem 14.25, assuming that it is a complex forging and that the projected area of the flash is 40% greater than the projected area of the forged workpiece.**

The forging force is given approximately by $F = kY_f A$, where $k$ is taken as 12 because of the complex forging, $Y_f$ is taken as 70,000 psi (see Problem 14.30), and $A = (1.4)(\pi)(3.0)^2 = 39.6$ in$^2$. Therefore,

$$F = (12)(70,000)(39.6) = 33 \times 10^6 \text{ lb}$$

**14.27 Take two solid, cylindrical specimens of equal diameter but different heights and compress them (frictionless) to the same percent reduction in height. Show that the final diameters will be the same.**

Let's identify the shorter cylindrical specimen with the subscript $s$ and the taller with $t$, and their original diameter as $D$. Subscripts $f$ and $o$ indicate final and original, respectively. Because both specimens undergo the same percent reduction in height, we can write

$$h_{tf}/h_{to} = h_{sf}/h_{so}$$

and from volume constancy,

$$h_{tf}/h_{to} = (D_{to}/D_{tf})^2$$

and

$$h_{sf}/h_{so} = (D_{so}/D_{sf})^2$$

Because $D_{to} = D_{so}$, we find that $D_{tf} = D_{sf}$.

**14.28 In Example 14.1, calculate the forging force, assuming that the material is 1100-O aluminum and that the coefficient of friction is 0.2.**

All conditions being the same, for 1100-O aluminum we have, from Fig. 2.6 on p. 72, a flow stress $Y_f = 140$ MPa. Thus,

$$F = Y_f \pi r^2 \left(1 + \frac{2\,ur}{3h}\right) = (140 \text{ MPa})\pi(0.106 \text{ m})^2 \left[1 + \frac{2(0.2)(0.106 \text{ m})}{3(0.050 \text{ m})}\right] = 6.3 \text{ MN}$$

**14.29 Using Eq. (14.1), make a plot of the forging force, $F$, as a function of the radius, $r$, of the workpiece. Assume that the flow stress, $Y_f$, of the material is constant. Remember that the volume of the material remains constant during forging, thus as $h$ decreases, $r$ increases.**

The curve for an initial $r/h$ of unity is given below.

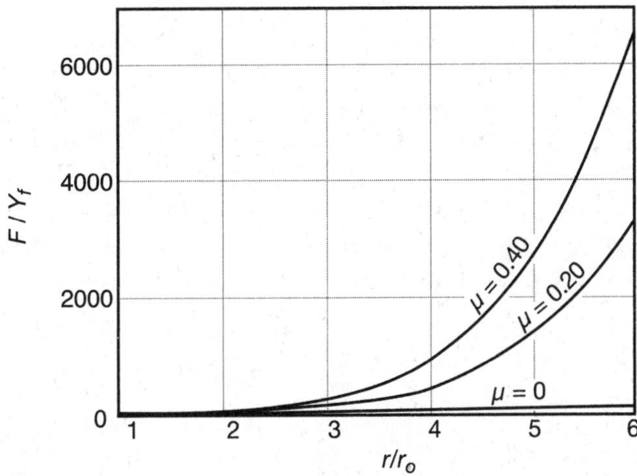


**14.30 How would you go about calculating the punch force required in a hubbing operation, assuming that the material is mild steel and the projected area of the impression is 0.5 in$^2$? Explain clearly. (Hint: See Section 2.6 on hardness.)**

We note on p. 381 that the piercing force involves a stress level that is the same as the hardness of the material. We also note from p. 82 in Section 2.6 that UTS is related to the hardness. From Fig. 2.16 on p. 85 we estimate the HB for mild steel to be 130. Thus,

$$\text{UTS} = (500)(130) = 65,000 \text{ psi}$$

and hence the punch force, $F$, would be

$$F = (65,000)(0.5) = 32,500 \text{ lb}$$

**14.31 A mechanical press is powered by a 30-hp motor and operates at forty strokes per minute. It uses a flywheel, so that the crankshaft speed does not vary appreciably during the stroke. If the stroke is 6 in., what is the maximum constant force that can be exerted over the entire stroke length?**

Assume that the press stroke is at a constant velocity. Although this is a poor approximation, it does not affect the answer because a constant force is assumed later. In reality, both the force and velocity will vary. At forty strokes per minute, with a 6-in. stroke, we would require a velocity of

$$V = (40 \text{ rpm})(12 \text{ in./rev})/60 \text{ min/s}) = 8 \text{ in./s}$$

The power exerted is the product of force and velocity; therefore

$$P = 30 \text{ hp} = 198,000 \text{ in-lb/s} = FV = F(8 \text{ in./s}) \quad \rightarrow \quad F = 24.75 \text{ kip}$$

**14.32 For the same mechanical press as in Problem 14.31, to what thickness can a cylinder of 5052-O aluminum 3 in. in diameter and 2 in. high be forged to before the press stalls?**

Based on Problem 14.31, the maximum force that can be exerted is 24.75 kip. For 5052-O, the yield strength is 90 MPa=13 ksi (from Table 6.3 on p. 171). Thus using Eq. (14.1) on p. 375,

$$F = 24,750 \text{ lb} = Y_f \pi r^2 \left(1 + \frac{2\mu r}{3h}\right) = (13 \text{ ksi})\pi(r^2)\left[1 + \frac{2(0.2)r}{3h}\right]$$

Also, from volume constancy, $r^2 h = r_o^2 h_o$. Substituting this into the above equation and solving it yields $r = 0.74$ in, or a diameter of about 1.5 in.

**14.33 Assume that you are an instructor covering the topics described in this chapter, and you are giving a quiz on the numerical aspects to test the understanding of the students. Prepare two quantitative problems and supply the answers.**

By the student. This is a challenging open-ended question and requires considerable focus and understanding on the part of the students, and has been found to be a very valuable homework problem.

## SYNTHESIS, DESIGN, AND PROJECTS

**14.34 Devise an experimental method whereby you can measure only the force required for forging the flash in impression-die forging.**

By the student. An experimental method to determine the forces required to forge only the flash (for an axisymmetric part) would involve making the die (see Fig. 14.5c on p. 376) in two concentric pieces, each with its own load cell to measure forces. The central die would only cover the projected area of the part itself, and the outer die (ring shaped) would cover the projected area of the circular flash. During forging, the load cells are monitored individually and thus the loads for the part and the flash, respectively, can be measured independently. Students are encouraged to devise other possible and practical methods.

**14.35 Assume that you represent the forging industry and that you are facing a representative of the casting industry. What would you tell that person about the merits of forging processes?**

By the student. Forgings have the advantages of better strength, toughness, surface finish, and dimensional accuracy. Forgings have the advantages of economic viability (depending on lot size), good mechanical properties, and the ability to produce complex parts with good surface finish. Forgings are available in a wide variety of sizes and materials, and the equipment for forging is widespread in industry.

**14.36 Figure P14.36 shows a round impression-die forging, made from a cylindrical blank as shown on the left. As described in this chapter, such parts are made**

**in a sequence of forging operations. Suggest a sequence of intermediate forging steps to make this part and sketch the shape of the dies needed.**

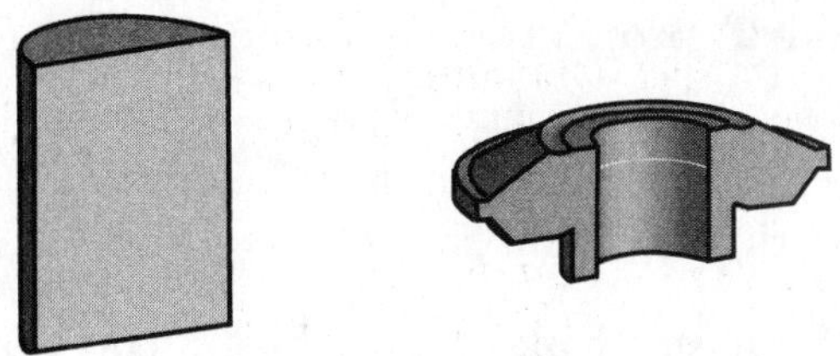

By the student. A possible set of intermediate forging steps is shown in the figure below. Note how the hole is produced by first piercing the blank in stage (c) then punching out the slug, as shown in stage (d). Other similar set of forming steps are also possible.

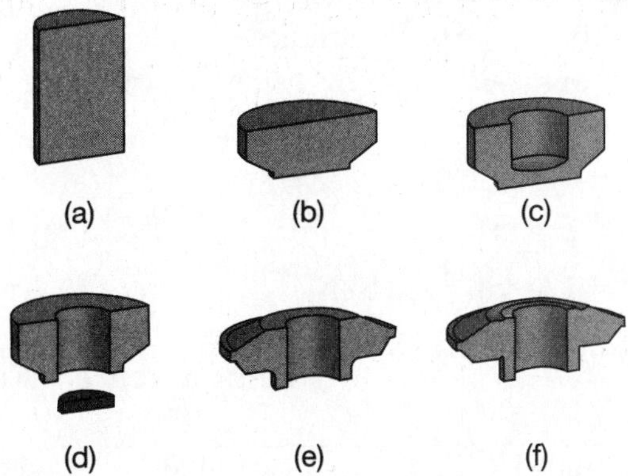


**14.37 Gears can be made by forging, especially bevel gears. Make a survey of the technical literature and describe the sequence of manufacturing steps involved. Comment on the quality of such a gear as compared to one made by the casting processes described in Chapter 11.**

By the student. The forging operations can be conventional or orbital, for example. There is usually a machining operation after forging to obtain final dimensional tolerances and surface finish. There is an advantage to forged gears over cast gears (depending on the materials involved) due to improved ductility and better fatigue and wear performance.

**14.38 Forging is one method of producing turbine blades for jet engines (in addition to casting or machining). Study the design of such blades and the relevant technical literature in the Bibliography, then prepare a step-by-step procedure to produce such blades by forging. Comment on the possible difficulties that may be encountered and offer solutions.**

By the student. A typical sequence would include cutting off a blank from bar stock, block forging, rough forging, finish forging, flash removal, inspection, finishing, and cleaning. There may be additional operations such as heat treating, depending on the material and desired properties. Difficulties that can be encountered include lubrication issues, control of workpiece and die heating, the need for correction if a part is oversized and material handling problems.

**14.39 In comparing forged parts with those that are cast, we have noted that the same part may be made by either process. Comment on the pros and cons of each process, considering factors such as part size and shape complexity, design flexibility, mechanical properties developed, and performance in service.**

By the student. Typical answers may address cost issues (forging will be expensive for short production runs), performance (castings may lack ductility and have lower strength-to-weight ratios), fatigure performance, grain flow, etc.

**14.40 From the data given in Table 14.3, obtain the approximate value of the yield strength of these materials at hot-forging temperatures. Plot a bar chart showing the maximum diameter of a hot-forged part produced on a press with a 60 ton capacity as a function of the material.**

By the student. The particular answers will vary widely depending on the particular strengths and temperatures considered; this is especially the case because alloys have not been designated in Table 14.3 on p. 386. Examples of calculations are included in the table below, where the diameter was calculated by using $\mu = 0$ in Eq. (14.1) to obtain the maximum diameter:

$$d = 2r = 2\sqrt{\frac{F}{\pi Y_f}}$$

where $F = 60$ tons $= 120$ kip $= 534$ kN.

| Material | Temperature (°C) | Flow Stress (MPa) | Diameter (m) |
|---|---|---|---|
| Aluminum (pure) | 400 | 18 | 0.19 |
| | 500 | 8 | 0.29 |
| C15 Steel | 1100 | 200 | 0.058 |
| Rene 88 (a nickel superalloy) | 1070 | 41 | 0.13 |

**14.41 Obtain a number of bolts, nails, and screws of different sizes. Measure the volume of the heads and calculate the original unsupported length-to-diameter ratio for these parts. Discuss these numbers with respect to the discussion in the text.**

By the student. The answers will of course depend on the specific bolt chosen. The typical unsupported length-to-diameter ratio is around 2:1 (which is in agreement with the limit of less than 3:1 as stated on page 380). Special fasteners and fasteners of extremely small or large size will give more extreme values.

**14.42 Review the sequence of operations in the production of the stepped pin shown in Fig. 14.13. If the conical upsetting step is not performed, what would be the consequences on the final part?**

By the student. The sequence shown in Fig. 14.13b on p. 382 is a revised version of the sequence that previously had led to excessive defects. When the conical upsetting step was not included, the heading process that produced the flange with the largest diameter would fail, with the workpiece cracking at the outside diameter.

**14.43 Perform simple cogging operations on pieces of clay using a flat piece of wood and make observations regarding the spread of the pieces as a function of the original cross-sections of the clay specimens (for example, square, or rectangular with different thickness-to-width ratios).**

By the student. If the part has a low height to width ratio, the spread will be minimal. However, as the height and width approach each other (i.e., square cross-section), the spread will be extensive. Other observations also can be made, including the shape of thecross-sections developed after cogging.

**14.44 Discuss the possible environmental concerns regarding the operations described in this chapter.**

By the student. The environmental concerns are mostly associated with metalworking and cleaning fluids used in the forging process and the finishing operations involved, as well as other exhausts such as fumes from furnaces. For example, forged parts are routinely coated in a phosphate soap (see conversion coatings on p. 1054), which may or may not be environmentally benign. Scrap from forging, such as trimmed flash, can be recovered and recycled.

# Chapter 15

# Extrusion and Drawing of Metals

## QUALITATIVE PROBLEMS

**15.16 Explain why extrusion is a batch or a semicontinuous process. Do you think it can be made into a continuous process? Explain.**

By the student. Extrusion is a batch process because the chamber size and the hydraulic ram stroke are limited. Also, the material is subjected to compression while it is in the chamber, and the high compressive forces required are difficult to develop continuously with means other than hydraulic rams. Hydrostatic extrusion can be regarded as a continuous process when reducing the small-diameter coiled stock which can be placed in the chamber of the setup.

**15.17 Explain the different ways by which changing the die angle affects the extrusion process.**

Some of the effects of die angle on the extrusion process are:

- Increasing the die angle restricts lubricant flow into the die.
- A larger die angle increases the redundant work.
- A dead metal zone may develop at large die angles.
- For a given reduction in area, friction forces may be lower with high die angles. This is because the friction force is proportional to the area of contact, and this area is reduced at higher die angles.

**15.18 Glass is a good lubricant in hot extrusion. Would you use glass for impression-die forging also? Explain.**

Glass, in various forms, is used as a lubricant in hot forging operations because of its superior properties at elevated temperatures (see p. 408). However, in impression-die forging thick lubricant films can prevent the workpiece from acquiring the die cavity shape and quality, and may prevent forging of desired shapes because of the glass being trapped in corners of the die. Also, one of the purposes of the lubricant is to ease part removal. This is impeded if the glass solidifies at the end of the forging cycle. Removing the lubricant from the part, and especially from the dies, is much more difficult with glass than with other liquid lubricants.

**15.19 How would you go about avoiding center-cracking defects in extrusion? Explain why your methods would be effective.**

Centerburst defects are attributed to a state of hydrostatic tensile stress at the centerline of the deformation zone in the die. The two major variables affecting hydrostatic tension are the die angle and extrusion ratio. Centerburst defects can be reduced or eliminated by lowering the die angles, because this increases the contact length for the same reduction, and thereby increases the deformation zone. Similarly, higher extrusion ratios also increase the size and depth of the deformation zone, and thus will reduce or eliminate these cracks.

**15.20 What is the purpose of a stripper plate in impact extrusion?**

As stated in the caption to Fig. 15.14 on p. 412, the stripper plate is needed because the parts tend to stick to the punch. This is especially important in presses that operate at high speed, and an effective means of removing the parts are essential.

**15.21 Table 15.1 gives temperature ranges for extruding various metals. Describe the possible consequences of extruding at a temperature (a) below and (b) above these ranges.**

If you extrude at below the temperatures given in Table 15.1 on p. 406, the yield stress will be higher and ductility will be reduced. If you extrude at higher temperatures, you risk greater oxide formation (resulting in poor surface finish) and less strain hardening and thus lower strength. Furthermore, temperature affects the performance of the lubricant, as viscosity and other lubricant characteristics will change. Die wear also will be affected by temperature and lubricant effectiveness.

**15.22 Will the force in direct extrusion vary as the billet gets shorter? If so, why?**

Yes; the force in direct extrusion is a function of the length of the billet still in the chamber (see Fig. 15.4 on p. 403). The initial force is high because the billet is at its full length. As extrusion progresses, the billet becomes shorter and hence the frictional force is lower, thus lowering the extrusion force.

**15.23 Comment on the significance of grain-flow patterns, such as those shown in Fig. 15.6.**

Grain-flow pattern has a major effect on the properties of the material, and in possible initiation of cracks within the part. Note in Fig. 15.6 on p. 404 that, depending on processing parameters, there is severe internal deformation in extrusion. The extruded material undergoes much higher strains and much less homogeneous deformation with increasing dead-metal zone, which invariably leads to higher residual stresses and internal defects (see Section 15.5 on p. 413). Materials whose strength increases rapidly with decreasing temperature will have larger dead-metal zones because of cooling of billet surfaces; the material in the center of the billet remains at a higher temperature and thus deforms much more readily.

**15.24 In which applications could you use the type of impact-extruded parts shown in Fig. 15.15?**

By the student. As described in Section 15.4.1 on p. 412, typical parts are for collapsible tubes, automotive parts, light fixtures, and small pressure vessels. Note that the process is generally confined to nonferrous metals, hence their use for structural strength is limited.

**15.25 Can spur gears be made by (a) drawing and (b) extrusion? Can helical gears? Explain.**

Spur gears can be made by drawing and/or extrusion (see, for a similar example, Fig. 15.2b on p. 401). One would extrude or draw a part with the cross-section identical to a spur gear, and then slice the extruded part to the proper thickness. Helical gears, with their spiraling cross-section, can also be extruded or drawn in this manner using appropriate dies.

**15.26 We have seen in Chapter 13 that applying back tension in rolling reduces the roll force. What advantages, if any, would applying back tension in rod or wire drawing have? Explain.**

The effect is similar to that for back tension in rolling. The benefit is that there are lower stresses on the dies, leading to less wear.

**15.27 How would you prepare the end of a wire so as to be able to feed it through a die so that a drawing operation can commence?**

A round rod may be machined to produce a point, which is then fed through the die and clamped for drawing to start. For smaller diameter rods, it is common practice to rotary swage the end of the rod or wire (see bottom of p. 383 and Fig. 14.14), thereby producing a pointed end that can be fed through the drawing die.

**15.28 What is the purpose of a dummy block in extrusion?**

A dummy block (see Fig. 15.3a on p. 402) is needed in extrusion to make sure that the entire billet is forced out the die. This is advantageous because the dummy block need not be as expensive of an alloy as the workpiece material; this ensures that the desired material is utilized fully while relegating the scrap to a less expensive alloy. The dummy block also protects the punch or ram tip against the high temperature of the billet.

**15.29 Describe your observations concerning Fig. 15.8.**

By the student. Note, for example, that the dies are complex, expensive to manufacture, and require proper maintenance. They are balanced, in that there is an equal number of ports on one side of the die compared to the other. The various components must be well supported.

**15.30 Occasionally, steel wire drawing will take place within a sheath of a soft metal, such as copper or lead. Why would this sheath be useful?**

The soft metal will act as a solid lubricant and reduce the friction stresses at the die-wire interfaces (see top of pp. 419 and 1054), especially if other lubricants are not effective. Thus technique is also useful in drawing metals that are reactive; the coating prevents contamination with the environment or with the die material itself (see also jacketing or canning on top of p. 408).

**15.31 What are the advantages to bundle drawing?**

As discussed on p. 417, bundle drawing has the advantage of higher production rates and therefore lower production cost when drawing very small diameter wire. One can appreciate the difficulties in drawing wire with diameters as small as 4 $\mu$m if they are drawn individually. Furthermore, dies may be difficult to produce and die life may be critical.

**15.32 Under what circumstances is backwards extrusion preferable to direct extrusion?**

Comparing Figs. 15.1 and 15.3 it is obvious that the main difference is that in backwards extrusion the billet is stationary, and in direct extrusion it is moving relative to the container walls. The main advantage becomes clear if a glass pillow is used to provide lubricant between the workpiece and the die. On the other hand, if there is significant friction between the workpiece and the chamber, then energy losses associated with friction are avoided in backwards extrusion (because of lack of movement between the bodies involved).

**15.33 Why is lubrication detrimental when extruding with a porthole die?**

These types of dies are shown in Fig. 15.8 on p. 407. It is important to note that any lubricant present at the interfaces within the die can interfere with the rewelding of the workpiece before it exits the die. (See explanation in the last paragraph on p. 406.)

**15.34 What is the purpose of a container liner in direct extrusion? (See Fig. 15.1.)**

The container liner is used as a sacrificial wear part, similar to the pads used in an automotive disk brake. When worn, it is far less expensive to replace a liner than to replace the entire container. Clearly, wear of the chamber surface is important because the clearance increases and the billet could conceivably extrude backwards.

## QUANTITATIVE PROBLEMS

**15.35 Estimate the force required in extruding 70-30 brass at 700 °C, if the billet diameter is 125 mm and the extrusion ratio is 20.**

From Fig. 15.5 on p. 403, $k$ for copper at 700 °C is approximately 180 MPa. Noting that $R$ is 20 and $d_o = 125$ mm $= 0.125$ m, and using Eq. (15.1) on p. 403, we find that

$$F = (\pi/4)(0.125)^2(180)(\ln 20) = 6.62 \text{ MN}$$

**15.36 Assuming an ideal drawing process, what is the smallest final diameter to which a 100-mm diameter rod can be drawn?**

As we read in the first paragraph on p. 416, the ideal maximum reduction per pass is 63%. For an original area of $A_o = \pi(100)^2/4$, or 7850 mm$^2$, this means that the final area is (1-0.63)(7850) $= 2900$ mm$^2$. Thus the final diameter is 60.8 mm.

**15.37 If you include friction in Problem 15.36, would the final diameter be different? Explain.**

If we include friction in the calculations in Problem 15.36, the stresses required to draw the material through the dies for a given reduction will increase because of the frictional work involved. As a result, the tensile stress in the wire will be higher and therefore the maximum reduction per pass will be less than 63%. Hence, the wire diameter will be larger than 60.8 mm.

**15.38 Calculate the extrusion force for a round billet 200 mm in diameter, made of stainless steel, and extruded at 1000 °C to a diameter of 50 mm.**

From Fig. 15.5 on p. 403, $k$ for stainless steel at 1000 °C is approximately 400 MPa. The extrusion ratio is

$$R = \frac{200^2}{50^2} = 16$$

Using Eq. (15.1) and noting that $d_o = 0.20$ m, we have

$$F = \left(\frac{\pi}{4}\right)(0.202)(400)(\ln 16) = 35 \text{ MN}$$

**15.39 Show that, for a perfectly plastic material with a yield stress $Y$, and under frictionless conditions, the pressure, $p$, in direct extrusion is**

$$p = Y \ln\left(\frac{A_o}{A_f}\right)$$

For a perfectly plastic material, the energy dissipated per unit volume is the area under the true stress-true strain curve (see Figs. 2.5 and 2.6 on pp. 71-72). It is given by $u = Y\epsilon$, where $\epsilon$ is the strain, defined as

$$\epsilon = \ln\left(\frac{A_o}{A_f}\right)$$

The work done is product of the energy per volume and the part volume. Note also that the work is also the product of the extrusion force and the billet length. Thus, $W = FL_o$, or $W = pA_oL_o$ where $p$ is the extrusion pressure and $A_o$ is the billet cross-sectional area. Therefore, we can write

$$W = pA_oL_o = A_oL_oY \ln\left(\frac{A_o}{A_f}\right) \quad \rightarrow \quad p = Y \ln\left(\frac{A_o}{A_f}\right)$$

**15.40 Show that, for the same conditions stated in Problem 15.39, the drawing stress, $\sigma_d$, in wire drawing is**

$$\sigma_d = Y \ln\left(\frac{A_o}{A_f}\right)$$

The derivation is similar to the problem above. For a perfectly plastic material, the energy dissipated per unit volume is the area under the stress-strain curve, and is $u = Y\epsilon$, where $\epsilon$ is the strain, given by

$$\epsilon = \ln\left(\frac{A_o}{A_f}\right)$$

Thus, the work done is $W = FL_f$, or $W = \sigma_d A_f L_f$, where $F$ is the drawing force, $\sigma_d$ is the drawing stress, and $A_f$ is the cross-sectional area of the drawn wire. Therefore, we can write

$$W = \sigma_d A_f L_f = A_f L_f Y \ln\left(\frac{A_o}{A_f}\right) \quad \rightarrow \quad \sigma_d = Y \ln\left(\frac{A_o}{A_f}\right)$$

**15.41 Plot the equations given in Problems 15.39 and 15.40 as a function of the percent reduction in area of the workpiece. Describe your observations.**

Note that the reduction is given by %red $= (A_o - A_f)/A_f$. Therefore, $A_o/A_f = 1/(1 - \%\text{red})$. Also note that both Problems 15.39 and 15.40 give the same equation; the plot is shown below.

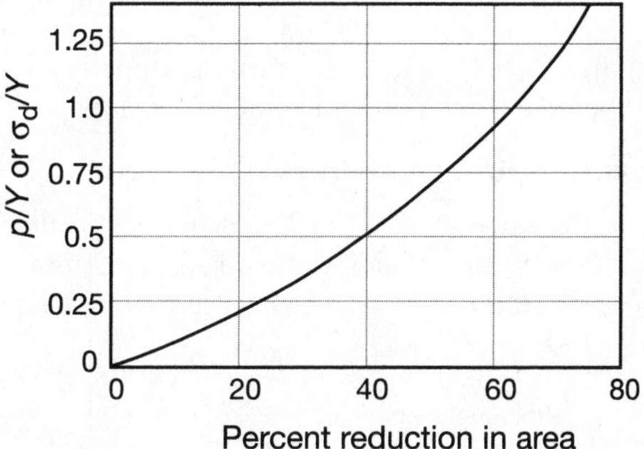


**15.42 A planned extrusion operation involves steel at 1000 °C with an initial diameter of 120 mm and a final diameter 20 mm. Two presses, one with capacity of 20 MN and the other with a capacity of 10 MN, are available for the operation. Is the smaller press sufficient for this operation? If not, what recommendations would you make to allow the use of the smaller press?**

For steel at 1000°C, $k = 325$ MPa (From Fig. 15.5 on p. 403). The initial and final areas are 0.0113 m$^2$ and $3.14 \times 10^{-4}$ m$^2$, respectively. From Eq. (15.1), the extrusion force required is

$$F = A_o k \ln\left(\frac{A_o}{A_f}\right) = (0.0113\ \text{m}^2)(325\ \text{MPa}) \ln\left(\frac{0.0113}{3.14 \times 10^{-4}}\right) = 13.2\ \text{MN}$$

Thus, the smaller and easier to use press is not suitable for this operation. However, if the extrusion temperature can be increased or if friction can be reduced (see Section 33.4 on p. 1043), it may then be possible to reduce the extrusion force sufficiently to make the use of this machine possible.

**15.43 A round wire made of a perfectly-plastic material with a yield stress of 30,000 psi is being drawn from a diameter of 0.1 in. to 0.07 in. in a draw die of 15°. Let the coefficient of friction be 0.1. Using both Eqs. (15.3) and (15.4), estimate the drawing force required. Comment on the difference in your answer.**

In this problem, $d_o = 0.1$ in, so that the initial cross-sectional area is

$$A_o = \frac{\pi}{4}d_o^2 = \frac{\pi}{4}(0.1 \text{ in.})^2 = 0.00785 \text{ in}^2$$

Similarly, since $d_f = 0.07$ in., $A_f = 0.00385$ in$^2$. From Eq. (15.3), the force required for drawing is

$$F = Y_{\text{avg}} A_f \ln\frac{A_o}{A_f} = (30,000)(0.00385)\ln\left(\frac{0.00785}{0.00385}\right) = 82.3 \text{ lb}$$

For $\mu = 0.1$ and $\alpha = 15° = 0.262$ radians, Eq. (15.4) yields

$$\begin{aligned} F &= Y_{\text{avg}} A_f \left[\left(1+\frac{\mu}{\alpha}\right)\ln\left(\frac{A_o}{A_f}\right) + \frac{2}{3}\alpha\right] \\ &= (30,000)(0.00385)\left[\left(1+\frac{0.1}{0.262}\right)\ln\left(\frac{0.00785}{0.00385}\right) + \frac{2}{3}(0.262)\right] \end{aligned}$$

or $F = 133$ lb. Note that Eq. (15.3) does not include friction or redundant work effects. Both of these factors will increase the forging force, and this is reflected by these results.

**15.44 Use Problem 15.43, but for 304 stainless steel (see Table 2.3).**

The approach here is the same as that for Problem 15.43, but the avereage yield strength has to be calculated. The cross-sectional areas are $A_o = 0.00785$ in$^2$ and $A_f = 0.00385$ in$^2$ as calculated in Problem 15.43. Note that the strain in this case is

$$\epsilon = \ln\frac{A_o}{A_f} = \ln\frac{0.00785}{0.00385} = 0.712$$

From Table 2.3 on p. 72, $K = 1275$ MPa and $n = 0.45$ for 304 stainless steel (a similar result can be obtained graphically using Fig. 2.6). The average yield stress is then

$$Y_{\text{avg}} = \frac{1}{\epsilon_f}\int_0^{\epsilon_f} \sigma d\epsilon = \frac{1}{\epsilon_f}\int_0^{\epsilon_f} K\epsilon^n = \frac{K\epsilon_f^n}{1+n} = 754 \text{ MPa} = 110 \text{ ksi}$$

Therefore, Eq. (15.3) gives

$$F = Y_{\text{avg}} A_f \ln\frac{A_o}{A_f} = (110,000)(0.00385)\ln\left(\frac{0.00785}{0.00385}\right) = 302 \text{ lb}$$

and Eq. (15.4) yields

$$\begin{aligned} F &= Y_{\text{avg}} A_f \left[\left(1+\frac{\mu}{\alpha}\right)\ln\left(\frac{A_o}{A_f}\right) + \frac{2}{3}\alpha\right] \\ &= (110,000)(0.00385)\left[\left(1+\frac{0.1}{0.262}\right)\ln\left(\frac{0.00785}{0.00385}\right) + \frac{2}{3}(0.262)\right] \end{aligned}$$

or $F = 488$ lb.

**15.45 Assume that you are an instructor covering the topics described in this chapter, and you are giving a quiz on the numerical aspects to test the understanding of the students. Prepare two quantitative problems and supply the answers.**

By the student. This is a challenging open-ended question and requires considerable focus and understanding on the part of the students, and has been found to be a very valuable homework problem.

## SYNTHESIS, DESIGN, AND PROJECTS

**15.46 Assume that you are the technical director of trade associations of (a) extruders and (b) rod and wire drawing operations. Prepare a technical leaflet for potential customers stating all the advantages of these processes, respectively.**

By the student, based on the subjects covered in this chapter. This is a good project for students to demonstrate their knowledge of the advantages (as well as limitations) of these processes. Students should be encouraged to obtain graphics from the Internet and to tabulate material properties and process capabilities.

**15.47 Assume that the summary to this chapter is missing. Write a one-page summary of the highlights to the wire-drawing process.**

By the student. This is a valuable exercise and a challenging task. The major difficulty is in highlighting the main points in one page.

**15.48 Review the technical literature and make a detailed list of the manufacturing steps involved in the manufacture of common metallic hypodermic needles.**

By the student. There are many manufacturers of hypodermic needles, and while each one uses a slightly different process for production, the basic steps remain the same, including needle formation, plastic component molding, piece assembly, packaging, labeling, and shipping. The basic steps are as follows:

(a) Making the needle. The needle is produced from extruded and drawn tubular steel, which is passed through a die designed to meet the size requirements of the needle. The wire is appropriately cut to form the needle. Some needles are significantly more complex and are produced directly from a die casting. Other metal components on the needle are also produced in this manner.

(b) Making the barrel and plunger. There are various ways that the syringe tube can be fashioned, depending on the design needed and the raw materials used. One method of production is extrusion molding. The plastic or glass is supplied as granules or powder and is fed into a large hopper. The extrusion process involves a large spiral screw, which forces the material through a heated chamber and makes it a thick, flowing mass. It is then forced through a die, producing a continuous tube that is cooled and cut.

(c) For pieces that have more complex shapes like the ends, the plunger, or the safety caps, injection molding is used. In this process the plastic is heated, converting it into a liquid. It is then forcibly injected into a mold that is the inverse of the desired shape. After it cools, it solidifies and maintains its shape after the die is opened. Although the head of the plunger is rubber, it can also be manufactured by injection molding. Later, the head of the plunger is attached to the plunger handle.

(d) Assembly and packaging. When all of the component pieces are available, final assembly can occur. As the tubes travel down a conveyor, the plunger is inserted and held into place. The ends that cap the tube are affixed. Graduation markings may also be printed on the main tube body at this point in the manufacturing process. The machines that print these markings are specially calibrated to ensure they print measurements on accurately. Depending on the design, the needle can also be attached at this time, along with the safety cap.

(e) After all of the components are in place and printing is complete, the hypodermic syringes are put into appropriate packaging. Since sterility of the device is imperative, steps are taken to ensure they are free from disease-causing agents. They are typically packaged individually in airtight plastic. Groups of syringes are packed into boxes, stacked on pallets, and shipped to distributors.

**15.49 Figure 15.2 shows examples of discrete parts that can be made by cutting extrusions into individual pieces. Name several other products that can be made in a similar fashion.**

By the student. Examples include cookies, pasta, blanks for bearing races, and support brackets of all types. Case Study 14.2 on p. 394 shows a support bracket for an automobile axle that was made in this manner. Using the Internet, the students should have no difficulty in obtaining numerous other examples.

**15.50 Survey the technical literature and explain how external vibrations can be applied to wire drawing to reduce friction. Comment also on the possible directions of vibration, such as longitudinal or torsional.**

By the student. It is not clear whether or not this is advantageous. Some research suggests that the energy input to drive the vibration source is roughly the same energy saved from lower friction. See J.A. Schey, *Tribology in Metalworking*, ASM International, 1984, pp. 374-376.

**15.51 A popular child's toy is a miniature extrusion press using a soft dough or a putty to make various shapes. Obtain such a toy and demonstrate the surface defects that may develop.**

By the student. Bambooing or fir-tree defects (see Section 15.5 on p. 413), for example, are easy to demonstrate, especially when (a) the putty is cold or dry and (b) the extrusion ratio is small. Different shapes of die opening should also be used. Another effect is curving of the exiting material. The experiments can also include the use of talcum powder as a dry lubricant, prior to inserting the billet into the chamber.

**15.52 In Case Study 14.2 on suspension uprights in Chapter 14, it was stated that there was a significant cost improvement with forgings when compared to extrusions. List and explain the reasons why you think these cost savings were possible.**

Comparing the optimized forging design in Fig. 14.20d on p. 395 and the extrusion design in Fig. 14.20b, it is obvious that the extrusion design has many more components than the forging design. There are costs that are associated with each part, each needing different tooling and equipment to manufacture the parts. Also, there is clearly more assembly cost involved with the extrusion design.

**15.53 It was stated that in bundle drawing the wires produced were more polygonal in cross-section than round. Produce some thin pieces of round clay or obtain cooked spaghetti, bundle them together, and compress them radially in a suitable fixture - in a manner similar to tightening one's belt. Comment on the shapes produced.**

By the student. If performed carefully, one can demonstrate that the close-packed structure of circular cross-sections become more polygonal as the circular cross-section deform to fill the voids when pressure is applied.

# Chapter 16

# Sheet-Metal Forming Processes

## QUALITATIVE PROBLEMS

**16.20 Outline the differences that you have observed between products made of sheet metals and those made by casting and forging.**

By the student. The most obvious difference between sheet-metal parts and those that are forged or cast is the difference in cross-section or thickness. Sheet-metal parts typically have large surface area-to-thickness ratios and are less stiff, hence easier to distort or flex. Sheet-metal parts are rarely for structural uses unless they are loaded in pure tension because they otherwise would buckle at relatively low compressive loads. Sheet-metal parts generally have a smoother surface than forgings or castings unless a finishing operation has been performed. Forged and cast structural parts can be subjected to various combinations of loads.

**16.21 Describe the cutting process that takes place when a pair of scissors cuts through aluminum foil.**

By the student. Note that scissors cut by a shearing process, which is why they are sometimes referred to as shears. The material is subjected to shear stresses at the intersection of the two blades of the scissors. Because shearing takes place in a small localized region, low forces are required to cut with scissors. The shearing process involves surface cracks propagating through the material until separation occurs (see Fig. 16.2 on p. 427). The clearance between the two blades is important or else the material may merely be pulled into the gap between the two blades.

**16.22 Identify the material and process variables that influence the punch force in shearing and explain how each of these affects this force.**

The punch force, $P$, is basically the product of the shear strength of the sheet metal and the cross-sectional area being sheared. However, friction between the punch and the workpiece can substantially increase this force. An approximate empirical formula for calculating the maximum punch force is given by

$$P = 0.7(\text{UTS})(t)(L)$$

where UTS is the material's ultimate tensile strength, $t$ is part thickness, and $L$ is the total length of the sheared edge.

**16.23 Explain why springback in bending depends on yield stress, elastic modulus, sheet thickness, and bend radius.**

Plastic deformation (such as in bending processes) is unavoidably followed by elastic recovery. For a given elastic modulus, a higher yield stress results in greater springback because the elastic strain is greater. A high modulus of elasticity with a given yield stress will result in less elastic strain, hence less springback. Equation (16.6) on p. 443 gives the relation between radius and thickness; thus, increasing the radius increases the springback and increasing the sheet thickness reduces the springback.

**16.24 What is the significance of the size of the circles in the grid patterns shown in Fig. 16.15? What is the significance of the thickness of the lines?**

Circles in the plane of the sheet which undergoing deformation will become ellipses (see, for example, Fig. 16.15 on p. 439). The major axis of the ellipse as compared to the original circle diameter will indicate the major engineering strain, and the minor axis as compared to the original diameter will give the minor engineering strain. The smaller the circle diameter, the more one can concentrate in a narrow region of the formed sheet-metal part. Thus, better accuracy is obtained in calculating the strains involved and in the use of forming-limit diagrams. The significance in the thickness of lines lies in the fact that the thicker the lines, the less accurate will be the measurements.

**16.25 Explain why cupping tests may not predict well the formability of sheet metals in actual forming processes.**

The difficulty with cupping tests is that deformations are axisymmetric, that is, they are the same in all directions. Sheet-metal forming operations, on the other hand, rarely take place in an axisymmetric state of strain. However, cupping tests are easy to perform on the shop floor and will give some approximate indication of formability.

**16.26 It was stated that the thicker the sheet metal, the higher the curves in Fig. 16.14b become. Why do you think this effect occurs?**

In the forming-limit diagrams (see p. 438), increasing sheet thickness tends to raise the curves because the material is capable of greater elongations since there is more material available. With a thicker sheet, the characteristic length in the thickness direction is larger, and as a result necking and fracture are delayed.

**16.27 Identify the factors that influence the deep-drawing force, $F$, in Fig. 16.32b, and explain why they do.**

Referring to p. 453 and to Eq. (16.9), the blank diameter affects the force because the larger the diameter, the greater the circumference, and therefore the greater the volume of material to be deformed. The clearance, $c$, between the punch and die directly affects the force because at smaller clearances, ironing begins to take place, thus increasing the force. The yield strength and strain-hardening exponent, $n$, of the workpiece affect the force, because as these parameters increase, higher forces will be required to cause deformation. Blank thickness also increases the area of the volume deformed, and therefore increases the force. The blankholder force and friction affect the punch force because they restrict the flow of the material into the die.

**16.28 Why are the beads in Fig. 16.36b placed in those particular locations?**

By the student. Beads are placed to restrict metal flow in regions where it flows most easily. Note in Fig. 16.36b on p. 456 that the sheet metal will obviously flow into the die cavity more easily along the edges of the die rather than at the corners.

**16.29 A general rule for dimensional relationships for successful drawing without a blankholder is given by Eq. (16.14). Explain what would happen if this limit were exceeded.**

By the student. If this limit is exceeded, one can expect the walls of the drawn part to buckle or wrinkle.

**16.30 Section 16.2.1 stated that the punch stripping force is difficult to estimate because of the many factors involved. Make a list of these factors with brief explanations about why they would affect the stripping force.**

By the student. Punch stripping force is difficult to estimate because of factors such as:

- The sheared surfaces contact the punch, leading to friction, which is difficult to estimate.
- Temperatures generated at interfaces can lead to distortion and adhesion between workpiece and punch.
- Anisotropy in the workpiece, causing nonuniform contact stresses between the workpiece and punch.
- Lubricants on the punch can be depleted during the operation.

**16.31 Is it possible for the forming-limit diagram shown in Fig. 16.14b to have a negative major strain? Explain.**

Because sheet-forming operations always involve stretching of the sheet in at least one direction, it is not possible for the forming-limit diagram to have a negative major strain.

**16.32 Inspect Fig. 16.14b and explain clearly whether in a sheet-forming operation you would like to develop a state of strain that is in the left half or in the right half of the forming-limit diagram.**

By the student. Note in Fig. 16.14b on p. 438 that the safe zone (area under the individual curves) is larger for the left side of the diagram than for the right side. Consequently, the state of strain developed should be to the left of the diagram, that is, the minor strain should be negative. Thus, in sheet-forming operations the material should be encouraged to develop a minor negative strain, such as by modifying die design and controlling lubrication.

**16.33 Is it possible to have ironing take place in an ordinary deep-drawing operation? What is the most important factor?**

Recall that ironing refers to a thinning of the can wall. If the clearance in a deep-drawing operation is large, the walls of the cup will be thicker at the rim than at the base of the cup (see Fig. 16.32 on p. 453); this is because more and more material has to be reduced in diameter as the cup is being drawn. If the clearance is controlled, such as by reducing it, the wall thickness of the cup, after a certain stroke, will become equal to the clearance. In practice, ironing during deep drawing is relatively minor, and deep drawing is often approximated as a process with a constant sheet thickness.

**16.34 Note the roughness of the periphery of the flanged hole in Fig. 16.25c and comment on its possible effects when the part is used in a product.**

The quality of the sheared edge (see Fig. 16.3 on p. 428) is important in subsequent forming operations, especially in subsequent operations such as stretch flanging (see, for example, Fig. 16.25c on p. 447). Depending on the notch sensitivity of the sheet material, a rough periphery can cause cracks to initiate. In service, this can cause additional problems such as decreased fatigue life of the part, as well as crevice corrosion.

**16.35 What recommendations would you make in order to eliminate cracking of the bent piece shown in Fig. 16.17c? Explain your reasons.**

By the student. We have seen that formability of materials depends not only on the inherent ductility of the material (which is a function of temperature and material quality) but also on factors such as surface finish of the sheet metal and direction of its roughness (if any), planar anisotropy, and strain rate. One or more of these factors should be considered in bending if cracking is a problem. Although not practical to perform, such cracks also can be eliminated by bending under high hydrostatic pressure (see also Section 2.2.8 on p. 76).

**16.36 As you can see, the forming-limit diagram axes pertain to engineering strains given as a percentage. Describe your thoughts about whether the use of true strains, as in Eq. (2.7), would have any significant advantage.**

In formability tests, circle distortions on sheets are easily measured in terms of percent elongation, hence engineering strain (see Fig. 16.15 on p. 439). There would be no significant advantage in using true strains (a) as long as it is specified that engineering strains have been used, and (b) because the two strains are rather close for small deformations, as can also be deduced by comparing Eqs. 2.2 and 2.7 on pp. 67 and 70, respectively. For example, an engineering strain of 0.5 in tension represents a true strain of 0.4 (see also Problem 2.18).

**16.37 It has been stated that the drawability of a material is higher in the hydroform process than in the deep-drawing process. Explain why.**

By comparing Fig. 16.32 on p. 453 and Fig. 16.40 on p. 460, we note that in the hydroform process the inner surface of the cup being formed is pressed against the cylindrical surface of the punch by the pressure in the forming chamber. This situation allows the cup to move with the punch, whereby the tensile stresses (that could eventually lead to cup tearing) are reduced due to the friction between the cup and the punch.

**16.38 Give several specific examples from this chapter in which friction is desirable and several in which it is not desirable.**

By the student. For example, high friction in sheet-metal forming can result in high localized strain and thus lowers formability. In ironing, high friction increases press forces. Friction is desirable, for example, with draw beads to improve their effectiveness and in clamps to secure blanks.

**16.39 As you can see, some of the operations described in this chapter produce considerable scrap. Describe your thoughts regarding the reuse, recycling, or disposal of this scrap. Consider its size, its shape, and its contamination by metalworking fluids during processing.**

By the student. The scrap is usually relatively easy to recycle because it is from the same known raw material used for the product, thus it can be easily sorted and recycled. Although not desirable, contaminants such as residual lubricants are not a major concern since most of these contaminants are removed during melting of the scrap metal.

**16.40 In the manufacture of automotive body panels from carbon-steel sheet, stretcher strains (or Lüders bands) are observed, which can detrimentally affect surface finish. How can these be eliminated?**

The stretcher strains are a concern, typically for some carbon steels. A common method of controlling these objectionable marks is to subject the sheet to a rolling reduction of 0.5 to 1.5% a short time prior to the forming operations (see *yield-point elongation* on p. 436 for details).

**16.41 A coil of sheet metal is taken to a furnace and annealed in order to improve its ductility. It is found, however, that the sheet has a lower limiting drawing ratio than it had before annealing. Explain why this effect has occurred.**

First note the effect of annealing the sheet. A cold worked sheet is highly anisotropic, whereas an annealed sheet will be isotropic. From Eq. (16.11) on p. 454, if a material is completely isotropic, the expected value of $R$ is 1. If it is anisotropic it will be greater than one (see also Table 16.4 on p. 454). Reviewing Fig. 16.34 on p. 455, the LDR increases with increasing $R$. Therefore, a fully annealed coil, which should be isotropic, will have lower formability than one with a higher anisotropy.

**16.42 Through changes in clamping or die design, it is possible for a sheet metal to undergo a negative minor strain. Explain how this effect can be advantageous.**

From the forming-limit diagram shown in Fig. 16.14b on p. 438, note that much larger major strains can be achieved with a negative minor strain. If through a change, such as in clamping or die design, a minor strain is allowed, then the safe zone in the diagram is larger and thus a reduction in part cracking can be achieved.

**16.43 How would you produce the part shown in Fig. 16.41b other than by tube hydroforming?**

Hydroforming has become very popular for producing these parts. Prior to the development of hydroforming, these parts had to be simpler in design and were typically made by bending tube segments and welding them together. Hydroforming eliminates this requirement, combines all of the bending operations into one step, and thus allows more elaborate designs. Consequently, it provides improved flexibility of operation while simultaneously reducing costs.

## QUANTITATIVE PROBLEMS

**16.44 Calculate $R_{avg}$ for a metal where the $R$ values for the 0°, 45°, and 90° directions are 0.9, 1.6, and 1.75, respectively. What is the limiting drawing ratio (LDR) for this material?**

From Eq. (16.12) on p. 454 we have

$$R = \frac{R_o + 2R_{45} + R_{90}}{4} = \frac{0.9 + 3.2 + 1.75}{4} = 1.46$$

The limiting drawing ratio (LDR) is defined as the maximum ratio of blank diameter to punch diameter that can be drawn without failure, i.e., $D_o/D_p$. From Fig. 16.34 on p. 455, we estimate the LDR for this steel to be approximately 2.5.

**16.45 Calculate the value of $\Delta R$ in Problem 16.44. Will any ears form when this material is deep drawn? Explain.**

From Eq. (16.13) on p. 455 we have

$$\Delta R = \frac{R_o - 2R_{45} + R_{90}}{2} = \frac{0.9 - 3.2 + 1.75}{2} = -0.55$$

Ears will not form if $\Delta R = 0$. Since this is not the case here, ears will form.

**16.46 Estimate the limiting drawing ratio for the materials listed in Table 16.4.**

Using the data in Table 16.4 on p. 454, and referring to Fig. 16.34 on p. 455, we estimate the following values for LDR:

| Material | LDR |
|---|---|
| Zinc | 1.8 |
| Hot-rolled steel | 2.3-2.4 |
| Cold-rolled rimmed steel | 2.3-2.5 |
| Cold-rolled aluminum-killed steel | 2.5-2.6 |
| Aluminum | 2.2-2.3 |
| Copper and brass | 2.3-2.4 |
| Titanium | 2.9-3.0 |

**16.47 Prove Eq. (16.4).**

Referring to Fig. 16.16 on p. 441 and letting the bend allowance length, i.e., length of the neutral axis, be $l_o$, we note that

$$l + o = (R + T/2)\alpha$$

and the length of the outer fiber is

$$l_f = (R + T)\alpha$$

where the angle $\alpha$ is in radians. The engineering strain for the outer fiber is

$$e_o = (l_f - l_o)/l_o = (l_f/l_o) - 1$$

Substituting the values of $l_f$ and $l_o$, we obtain

$$e_o = \frac{1}{(2R/T) + 1}$$

**16.48 Regarding Eq. (16.4), it has been stated that (in bending) actual values of the strain in the outer fibers (i.e., in tension) are higher than those on the inner fibers (in compression), the reason being that the neutral axis shifts during bending. With an appropriate sketch, explain this phenomenon.**

By the student. The subject of shifting of the neutral axis in bending is described in mechanics of solids texts. Briefly, the outer fibers in tension shrink laterally due to the Poisson effect, and the inner fibers expand. The student can demonstrate this phenomenon by simply bending a soft rectangular eraser and noting that the cross-section is no longer rectangular but has the shape of a trapezoid. The neutral axis has to shift in order to satisfy the equilibrium equations regarding balancing of forces in bending. This is sketched below.

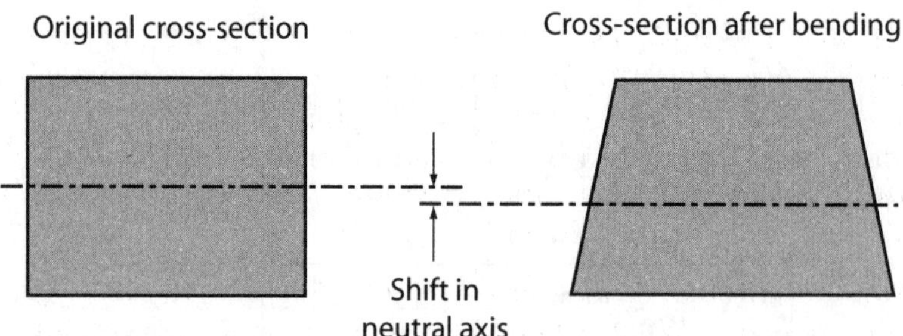


**16.49 Using Eq. (16.15) and the $K$ value for TNT, plot the pressure as a function of weight ($W$) and $R$, respectively. Describe your observations.**

Note that, as expected, the pressure increases with increasing weight of the explosive, $W$, but decays rapidly with increasing standoff distance, $R$. A plot for TNT in water is shown below.

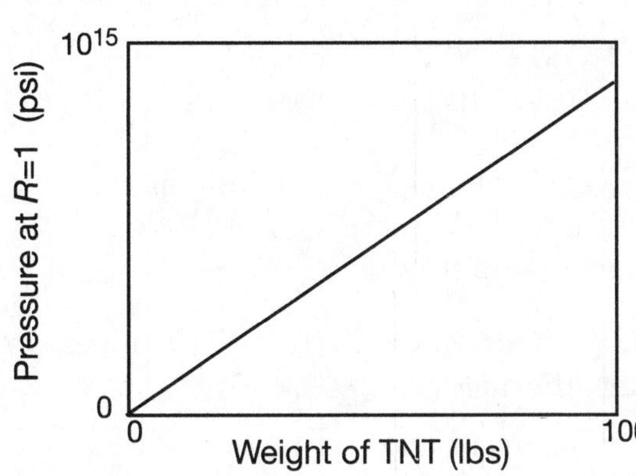


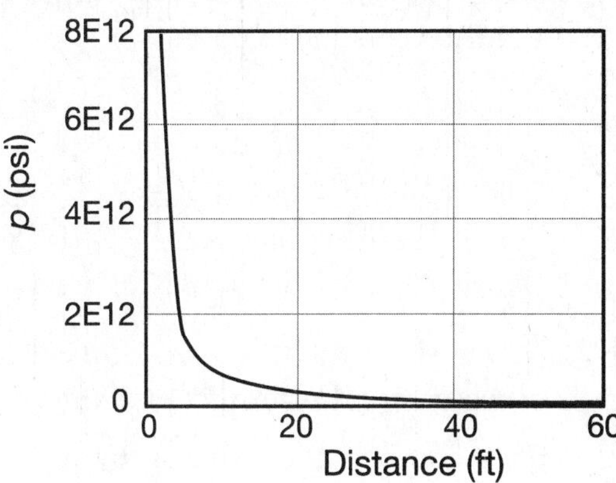


**16.50 Section 16.5 states that the $k$ values in bend allowance depend on the relative magnitudes of $R$ and $T$. Explain why this relationship exists.**

The bend allowance is based on the length of the neutral axis. As described in texts on mechanics of solids, the neutral axis can shift in bending depending on the dimensions of the cross-section and the bend radius. Consequently, the $k$ values will vary.

**16.51 In explosive forming, calculate the peak pressure in water for 0.3 lb of TNT at a standoff distance of 3 ft. Comment on whether or not the magnitude of this pressure is sufficiently high to form sheet metals.**

Using Eq. (16.15) on p. 466, we find that

$$p = 21,600\left(\frac{\sqrt[3]{0.2}}{3}\right)^{1.15} = 3300 \text{ psi}$$

This level of pressure would be sufficiently high for forming sheet metal, particularly thin sheet of relatively low strength. This can be proven by using examples such as expansion of thin-walled spherical or cylindrical shells by internal pressure, $p$, using yield criteria.

**16.52 Why is the bending force, $P$, proportional to the square of the sheet thickness, as seen in Eqs. (16.7) and (16.8)?**

This is obvious from observations in the study of mechanics of solids. The bending stress formula in beams is $\sigma = Mc/I$, where $I$ is the moment of inertia (and is proportional to $T^3$) and $c = T/2$. Thus, for a material with a certain strength, $\sigma$, the bending moment, hence the bending force, $P$ , is proportional to $T^2$.

**16.53 In Fig. 16.14a, measure the respective areas of the solid outlines and compare them with the areas of the original circles. Calculate the final thicknesses of the sheets, assuming that the original sheet is 1 mm thick.**

For the example on the left of Fig. 16.14a on p. 438, the original diameter is about 7 mm, and the ellipse has major and minor axes of 13 and 4.5 mm, respectively. Therefore, the strains in this plane are $\epsilon_{\text{maj}} = \ln(13/7) = 0.619$ and $\epsilon_{\text{min}} = \ln(4.5/7) = -0.44$. The strain in the thickness direction is then:

$$\epsilon_1 + \epsilon_2 + \epsilon_3 = 0 \quad \rightarrow \quad \epsilon_{\text{thickness}} = -0.619 + 0.44 = -0.177$$

Since $\epsilon_t = \ln(t/1\text{mm})$, the new thickness is 0.84 mm. For the ellipse on the right of the figure, the new dimensions are 13 mm and 9 mm, giving strains of 0.619 and 0.25, so that the thickness strain is -0.87, giving a new thickness of 0.42 mm.

**16.54 With the aid of a free-body diagram, prove the existence of compressive hoop stresses in the flange in a deep-drawing operation.**

This can be shown simply by a free-body diagram of an element in the flange, as shown below. Note the radial tensile stress and the compressive hoop stresses to balance the forces on the element. Note also that friction between the blank and the die and the blankholder also contributes to the increase in the tensile stress.

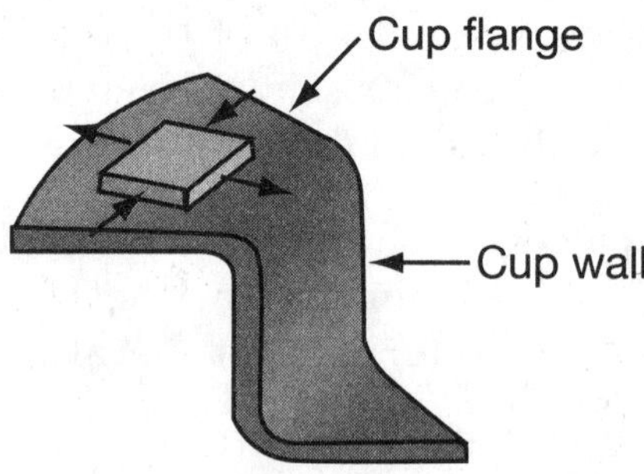


**16.55 Plot Eq. (16.6) in terms of the elastic modulus, $E$, and the yield stress, $Y$, of the material, and describe your observations.**

By the student. The plot of Eq. (16.6) on p. 443 is shown below:

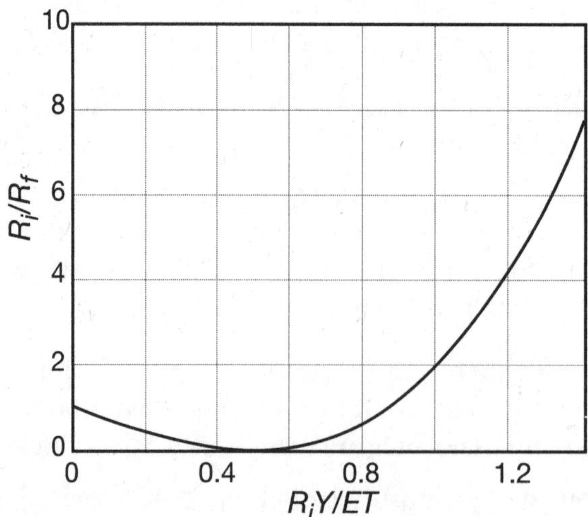

**16.56 What is the minimum bend radius for a 2-mm thick sheet metal with a tensile reduction of area of 30%? Does the bend angle affect your answer? Explain.**

In Eq. (16.5) on p. 442, the value of $r$ is now 30 and $T = 2$ mm. Thus, we have

$$R = 2\left[\left(\frac{50}{30}\right) - 1\right] = 1.33 \text{ mm}$$

The bend angle has no effect on the answer because it is not a factor in the strains involved in bending, as can be seen in Eq. (16.4) on p. 442.

**16.57 When a round sheet-metal blank is deep drawn, it is found that it does not exhibit any earing. Its $R$ values in the 0° and 90° directions to rolling are 1.4 and 1.8, respectively. What is the $R$ value in the 45° direction?**

Since no earing occurs and using the data given, Eq. (16.12) on p. 454 can now be written as

$$0 = \frac{1.4 - 2R_{45} + 1.8}{2}$$

or $R_{45} = 1.6$.

**16.58 Survey the technical literature and explain the mechanism by which negative springback can occur in V-die bending. Show that negative springback does not occur in air bending.**

By the student. The development of negative springback can be explained by observing the sequence of deformation in the sketch below (see also Fig. 16.20c on p. 444). If we remove the bent piece at stage (b), it will undergo regular (positive) springback. At stage (c) the ends of the piece are touching the male punch; note that between stages (c) and (d), the part is actually being bent in the direction opposite to that between stages (a) and (b). Note also the lack of conformity of the punch radius and the inner radius of the part in both (b) and (c); in stage (d), however, the two radii are the same. Upon unloading (retracting the punch), the part in stage (d) will springback inward because it is being unbent from stage (c), both at the tip of the punch and in the two arms of the part. The amount of this inward (negative) springback can be greater than the positive springback because of the large strains that the material has undergone in the small bend area in stage (b). The net result is negative springback.

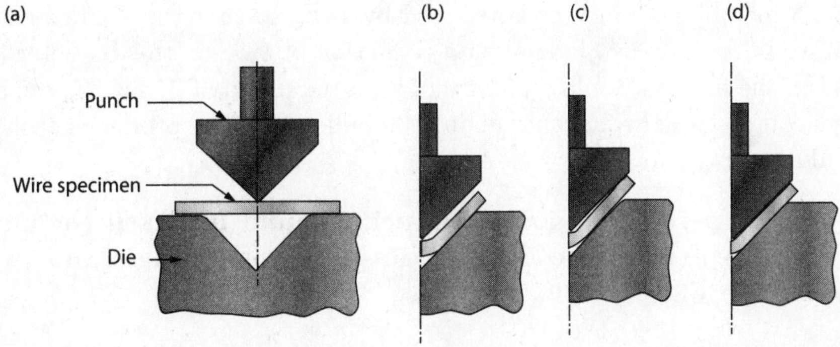

**16.59 Using the data in Table 16.3 and referring to Eq. (16.5), calculate the tensile reduction of area for the materials and the conditions listed in the table.**

By the student. The reduction of area for these materials at room temperature are calculated and are presented below (the numbers are rounded):

| Material | Soft | Hard |
|---|---|---|
| Aluminum alloys | 50 | 7 |
| Beryllium copper | 50 | 10 |
| Brass, low-leaded | 50 | 17 |
| Magnesium | 8 | 4 |
| Steels | | |
| austenitic stainless | 33 | 7 |
| low-C, low-alloy and HSLA | 33 | 10 |
| Titanium | 29 | 13 |
| Titanium alloys | 14 | 10 |

**16.60 What is the force required to punch a square hole, 100 mm on each side, in a 1-mm thick 5052-O aluminum sheet, by using flat dies? What would be your answer if beveled dies are used?**

The maximum punch force, $F$, is given by Eq. (16.1) on p. 428 as

$$F = 0.7TL(\text{UTS})$$

For this case $L = 400$ mm $= 0.4$ m, $T = 1$ mm $= 0.001$ m, and UTS is 190 MPa for 5052-O aluminum (see Table 6.3 on p. 171). Therefore,

$$F = 0.7(0.001)(0.4)(190 \times 10^6) = 53.2 \text{ kN}$$

If the dies were beveled, the force would be much lower and would approach zero using very sharp bevel angles.

**16.61 In Example 16.4 it was stated that the reason for reducing the top of cans (necking) is to save material for making the lid. How much material will be saved if the lid diameter is reduced by 10%? By 15%?**

By the student. In Example 16.4 on p. 458, the final diameter is 2.6 in., so that the projected area is 5.3 in$^2$. If the diameter is reduced by 10%, so that the diameter is now 2.34 in., the lid area would be 4.30 in$^2$, indicating a reduction of 19%. If the diameter is reduced by 15%, to 2.21 in., the lid area would be 3.84 in$^2$, for a reduction of 27.6%. These are very significant numbers considering the fact that about 100 billion cans are produced each year in the United States alone.

**16.62 Estimate the percent scrap in producing round blanks if the clearance between blanks is one-tenth of the blank radius. Consider single and two-row blanking, as sketched in Fig. P16.62.**

A repeating element for part (a) is shown to the right. The area of the unit cell is $A = (2.2R)(2.1R) = 4.62R^2$. The area of the circle is $3.14R^2$. Therefore, the percent scrap is

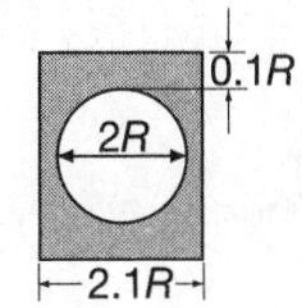


$$\%\text{scrap} = \frac{4.62R^2 - 3.14R^2}{4.62R^2} \times 100\% = 32\%$$

Using the same approach, it can be shown that the scrap is 26%.

**16.63 Assume that you are an instructor covering the topics described in this chapter, and you are giving a quiz on the numerical aspects to test the understanding of the students. Prepare two quantitative problems and supply the answers.**

By the student. This is a challenging open-ended question and requires considerable focus and understanding on the part of the students, and has been found to be a very valuable homework problem.

## SYNTHESIS, DESIGN, AND PROJECTS

**16.64 Examine some of the products in your home that are made of sheet metal and discuss the process or combination of processes by which you think they were made.**

By the student. Some examples are:

(a) Aluminum foil: Produced by rolling two sheets at once, as evidenced by the difference in the appearance of the two surface finishes: one surface is shiny (roll side) and the other is dull (facing the other sheet). The foil can be cut to desired widths and lengths in slitting lines (see Fig. 16.6 on p. 430).

(b) Housings for appliances such as refrigerators, washers, and dryers: Produced by cold-rolled steel stock, then leveled (see Fig. 13.7 on p. 356) and slit to desired dimensions.

(c) Baking pans and saucepans: Rolled stock drawn or stamped to final dimensions, edges trimmed, and turned in.

**16.65 Consider several shapes to be blanked from a large sheet (such as oval, triangular, L-shaped, and so forth) by laser-beam cutting and sketch a nesting layout to minimize scrap generation.**

By the student. There are many possible answers depending on the particular shapes analyzed. Because laser cutting allows flexibility (see Section 27.6 on p. 851), some possible nesting layouts are shown below.

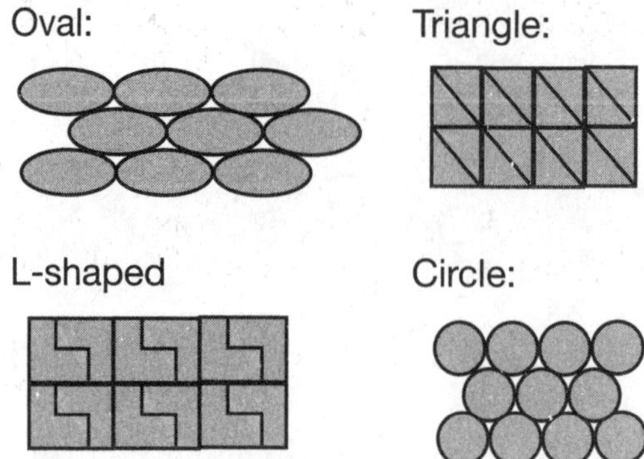


**16.66 Give several product applications for (a) hemming and (b) seaming.**

By the student. Some examples of hemming include oil pans and edges of metal tables and automobile hoods. Seaming is commonly done on cans such as for shaving cream and on beverage containers to attach the top to the can body (see, for example, Fig. 16.31 on p. 452).

**16.67 Many axisymmetric missile bodies are made by spinning. What other methods could you use if spinning processes were not available?**

By the student. Missile components which are spun usually have large cross-sections. Some of these parts could be made by explosive forming or welding of a number of smaller rolled and stamped pieces. Smaller components could possibly be forged or formed by stretch forming.

**16.68 Give several structural designs and applications in which diffusion bonding and superplastic forming can be used jointly.**

By the student. Applications of superplastic forming are mostly in the aerospace industry. Some structural frame members, which normally are placed behind aluminum sheet and thus are not visible, are made by superplastic forming techniques. Two examples shown below (from W.F. Hosford and R.M. Cadell, *Metal Forming, Mechanics and Metallurgy*, 2nd ed., Prentice Hall, 1993).

Aircraft wing panel, produced through internal pressurization.

Sheet-metal parts.

**16.69 Inspect sheet-metal parts in an automobile and describe your thoughts as to which of the processes or combinations of processes were used in making them. Comment on the reasons why more than one process may have to be used.**

By the student. As examples: (a) Body panels are obtained from sheet-metal forming and shearing. (b) Frame members (only visible when looked at from underneath) are made by roll forming. (a) Ash trays are made from stamping, combined with shearing.

**16.70 Name several parts that can be made in compound dies and several others that can be made in transfer dies.**

By the student. Examples of parts made in compound dies are watch battery casings, shotgun shells, and automobile battery terminals. Examples of parts made in transfer dies include connecting rods, wrenches, and knives.

**16.71 On the basis of experiments, it has been suggested that concrete - either plain or reinforced - can be a suitable material for dies in metal-forming operations, especially for large parts. Describe your thoughts regarding this suggestion, considering die geometry and any other factors that may be relevant.**

By the student. Concrete has, for example, been used in explosive forming for large dome-shaped parts intended as the nose cones for intercontinental ballistic missiles (ICBM). However, this is very rare because the concrete will never allow production of smooth surfaces and because the concrete can easily fracture at stress risers.

**16.72 Metal cans are either two-piece (in which the bottom and sides are integral) or three-piece (in which the sides, the bottom, and the top are each separate pieces). For a three-piece can, should the vertical seam in the can body be (a) in the rolling direction, (b) normal to the rolling direction, or (c) oblique to the rolling direction? Prove your answer.**

By the student. Among the major concerns for a beverage can is that the wall not fail under internal pressurization. Because the can be assumed to be a thin-walled, closed-end, internally pressurize container, the hoop stress, $\sigma_h$, and the axial stress, $\sigma_a$, are given by

$$\sigma_h = \frac{pr}{t} \qquad \sigma_a = \frac{1}{2}\sigma_h = \frac{pr}{2t}$$

where $p$ is the internal pressure, $r$ is the can radius, and $t$ is the sheet thickness. These are two principal stresses; the third principal stress is in the radial direction, but it is so small that it can be neglected. The body of a three-piece can is made by bending the cold-rolled sheet into a cylindrical shape (see, for example, Fig. 16.22 on p. 445). Since the sheet is strong in its rolling direction and noting that the hoop stress is the major stress, the seam should be normal to the rolling direction of sheet, as also shown in Fig. 16.17b on p. 441.

**16.73 Investigate methods for determining optimum blank shapes for deep-drawing operations. Sketch the optimally shaped blanks for rectangular cups, and optimize their layout on a large metal sheet.**

By the student. Optimal shaping of blanks requires considerable experience as well as the use of techniques such as finite element simulations and slip-line field theory. An example of an optimum blank for a typical oil pan cup is sketched below.

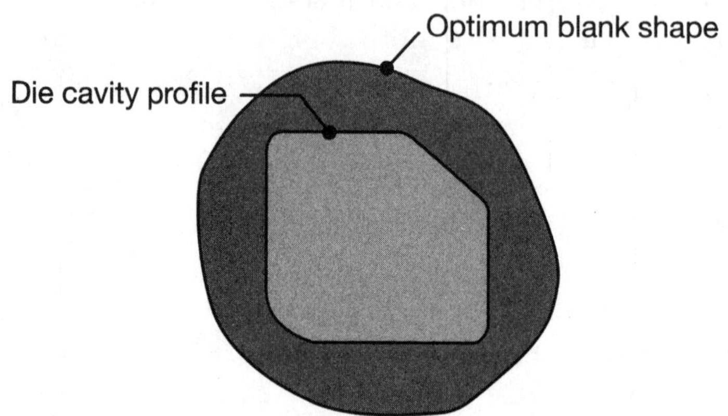


**16.74 The following design in Fig. P16.74 is proposed for a metal tray - the main body of which is made from cold-rolled sheet steel. Noting its features and that the sheet is bent in two different directions, comment on various manufacturing considerations. Include factors such as anisotropy of the rolled sheet, its surface texture, the bend directions, the nature of the sheared edges, and the way the handle is snapped in for assembly.**

By the student. Several observations can be made. Note that a relief notch design, as shown in Fig. 16.52 on p. 472, has been used. It is a valuable experiment to have the students cut the blank from paper and verify that the tray is produced by bending only because of this notch. As such, the important factors are bendability, and scoring such as shown in Fig. 16.55 on p. 474, and avoiding wrinkling such as discussed in Fig. 16.53 on p. 473.

**16.75 Using a ball-peen hammer, strike the surface of aluminum sheets of various thicknesses until they develop a curvature. Describe your observations about the shapes produced.**

By the student. This is an interesting experiment; it is the principle of forming sheet metals into various shapes using simple hammers (or even round rocks) and dates back many millennia (see Table I.2 on p. 5). It involves basically the shot peening mechanism, described in Section 34.2 on p. 1060. See also Fig. 2.13c on p. 81 and consider the effects of a round indenter in hardness testing, noting the depth of the surface layer of material that would be deformed with a ball-peen hammer with respect to the sheet thickness. For thinner sheets, this layer would complete penetrate the sheet, expanding the bottom surface laterally, and thus making it curve upward (i.e., holds water). Conversely, for thicker sheets and plates, only the top layer is expanded laterally, and thus the sheet bends downward (i.e., sheds water).

**16.76 Inspect a common paper punch and observe the shape of the punch tip. Compare it with those shown in Fig. 16.10 and comment on your observations.**

By the student. Hand punches will rarely be beveled because the forces are so low that the functioning of the punch is not compromised by the lack of beveling. However, many paper punches have a bevel (or a similar shape) to make the punching operation smoother. The students may make simple punches with various shapes and make observations regarding this topic and validate the statements made on p. 433.

**16.77 Obtain an aluminum beverage can and slit it half lengthwise with a pair of tin snips. Using a micrometer, measure the thickness of the can bottom and the wall. Estimate the thickness reductions in ironing and the diameter of the original blank.**

By the student. Note that results can vary somewhat based on the specific practices at the canmaking facility. The results of one such measurement are: sidewall thickness=0.003 in., the can bottom=0.0120 in., can diameter=2.6 in., and can height=5 in. From this data, the thickness reduction in ironing can be found to be

$$\%\text{red} = \frac{t_o - t_f}{t_o} \times 100\% = \frac{0.0120 - 0.003}{0.012} \times 100\% = 75\%$$

The initial blank diameter is obtained by volume constancy. The volume of the can after deep drawing and ironing is

$$V_f = \frac{\pi d_c^2}{4} t_o + \pi d t_w h = \frac{\pi (2.5 \text{ in.})^2}{4}(0.012 \text{ in.}) + \pi(2.5 \text{ in.})(0.003 \text{ in.})(5 \text{ in.}) = 0.1767 \text{ in}^3$$

Since the initial blank thickness, to, is the same as the can bottom thickness (that is, 0.0120 in.), the diameter of the original blank is found as

$$0.1767 \text{ in}^3 = \frac{\pi d^2}{4} t_o = \frac{\pi d^2}{4}(0.012 \text{ in.}) \quad \rightarrow \quad d = 4.33 \text{ in.}$$

# Chapter 17

# Processing of Metal Powders

## QUALITATIVE PROBLEMS

**17.15 Why is there density variation in the compacting of powders? How is it reduced?**

The main reason for density variation in compacting of powders (Section 17.3 on p. 490) is associated with mechanical locking and friction among the particles; this leads to variations in pressure depending on distance from the punch and from the container walls (see Fig. 17.11 on p. 493). The variation can be reduced by having double-acting presses, lowering the frictional resistance of the punch and die surfaces, or by adding lubricants that reduce inter-particle friction among the powders.

**17.16 What is the magnitude of the stresses and forces involved in powder compaction?**

Compaction pressures depend, among others, on the powder metal and are given in Table 17.1 on p. 493. The students should compare this values with the strength of sold metals, such as those given in Table 2.2 on p. 67 and various other tables in the text (see also Table 40.1 on p. 1240). Although the forces required in most P/M parts production are usually less than 100 tons, press capacities generally range from 200 to 300 tons, and can be higher. Comparing the pressures with the yield strengths, one can note that the pressures are roughly on the same order.

**17.17 Give the reasons why powder-injection molding is an important process.**

Powder-injection molding (p. 497) has become an important process because of its versatility and economics. Complex shapes can be obtained at high production rates using powder metals that are blended with a polymer or wax (see PIM in Fig. 17.14 on p. 495). Also, the parts can be produced with high density to net or near-net shape.

**17.18 How does the equipment used for powder compaction vary from those used in other metalworking operations?**

As described in Section 17.3.1 on p. 493, several types of presses are used for P/M compaction, depending on various factors. For ease of operation, these presses are vertical and highly automated. Metalworking operations also utilize similar equipment, including horizontal presses, as described in sections of chapters on processes such as forging and cold extrusion (see, for example, Sections 14.8 on p. 390 and 15.6 on p. 414). Abrasive resistance is a major factor in P/M die and punch material selection; consequently, the dies in all these operations are made of similar and sometimes identical materials. Processes such as isostatic pressing utilize flexible molds, which is not the case in forging and extrusion. An important difference is that in P/M, it can be advantageous to have a multi-action press so that compaction densities are more uniform (see Fig. 17.11d on p. 493). The students are encouraged to make further comments.

**17.19 Why do mechanical and physical properties depend on the density of P/M parts?**

The mechanical properties, especially strength, ductility, and elastic modulus, depend on density (see also bottom of p. 491). Not only is there less material in a given volume for less dense P/M parts, but voids are stress concentrations, and the less dense material will have more and larger voids. Physical properties, such as electrical and thermal conductivity, are also adversely affected because (since air is a poor conductor) the less dense the P/M part is, the less material is available to conduct electricity or heat, as shown in Fig. 17.10 on p. 492. (See also answer to Problem 10.22.)

**17.20 What are the effects of the different shapes and sizes of metal particles in P/M processing?**

The shape, size, size distribution, porosity, chemical purity, and bulk and surface characteristics of metal particles (see Fig. 17.3 on p. 485) are all important because, as expected, they have significant effects on permeability and flow characteristics during compaction and in subsequent sintering operations. It is beneficial to have angular shapes with approximately equally sized particles to aid in bonding.

**17.21 Describe the relative advantages and limitations of cold and hot isostatic pressing.**

Cold isostatic pressing (CIP) and hot isostatic pressing (HIP) both have the advantages of producing compacts with effectively uniform grain structure and density, thereby making shapes with uniform strength and toughness (see Section 17.3.2 on p. 494). The main advantage of HIP is its ability to produce compacts with essentially 100% density, good metallurgical bonding of powders, and very good mechanical properties; however, the process is relatively expensive and is therefore used mainly for aerospace applications.

**17.22 Are the requirements for punch and die materials in powder metallurgy different from those for forging and extrusion? Explain.**

In processes such as forging and extrusion and P/M compaction, abrasive wear resistance (see Section 33.5 on p. 1046) is a major factor in die and punch material selection. For that reason, the dies on these operations utilize similar and sometimes identical materials. Processes such as isostatic pressing utilize flexible molds, which is not used in forging and extrusion. (See also answer to Problem 17.18.)

**17.23 We have stated that P/M can be competitive with processes such as casting and forging. Explain why this is so, giving ranges of applications.**

By the student. Powder metallurgy has become economically competitive with other operations for several reasons. One is the major advantage of producing net or near-net shapes, thus eliminating costly and time-consuming finishing operations. Also, scrap is reduced or eliminated (see Table 40.6 on p. 1250). Functionally, P/M parts are advantageous because of their lubricant-entrapment characteristics, thus reducing the need for external lubricantion in some applications. The high initial cost associated with tooling applies equally to forging, so this can be considered a common drawback to both operations.

**17.24 Explain the reasons for the shapes of the curves shown in Fig. 17.10 and for their relative positions on the charts.**

The end points of the curves in Fig. 17.10a on p. 492 are not surprising because at low compaction pressures, the density of the P/M parts is low, and at high compacting pressures it approaches the theoretical density (i.e., that of the bulk material). Note that the concavity of the curves is downward, because to increase the density further, smaller and smaller voids must be filled which require much higher pressures. Thus, it is easier to shrink larger cavities in the material than smaller ones. The reasons for the beneficial aspects of density increases (Fig. 17.10b) have been discussed in the answer to Problem 17.19.

**17.25 Should green compacts be brought up to the sintering temperature slowly or rapidly? Explain your reasoning.**

Rapid heating can cause excessive thermal stresses in the part being sintered and can lead to distortion or cracking; on the other hand, it reduces cycle times. Slow heating has the advantage of allowing heating and diffusion to occur more uniformly.

**17.26 Because they undergo special processing, metal powders are more expensive than the same metals in bulk form, especially powders used in powder-injection molding. How is the additional cost justified in powder-metallurgy parts?**

By the student. The additional cost can easily be justified because of the numerous advantages inherent in P/M production (see also p. 508). For example, P/M parts can be produced at net or near-net shapes, thus reducing or eliminating finishing operations. Powder metallurgy allows the production of relatively complex shapes from exotic alloys which would otherwise be difficult to manufacture by other means. Also, the self-lubricating capability of sintered metal powders makes P/M parts attractive for bushings, gears, races, and cams; the ability to make alloys with compositions that cannot be cast is attractive for particular applications, especially in the electronics industry. Compaction of powders has certain advantages over other forming operations, such as forging, because by controlling porosity (hence their density) makes them advantageous in applications where weight is critical. (See Chapter 40 for various cost considerations.)

**17.27 In Fig. 17.11e, we note that the pressure is not uniform across the diameter of the compact at a particular distance from the punch. What is the reason for this variation?**

The nonuniformity of the pressure in the figure (on p. 493) is due to the frictional resistance at the die walls and within the powder particles throughout the compact. The pressure will drop away from the punch because these effects are cumulative, and are similar to the pressure drop in a water-pumping system.

**17.28 Why do the compacting pressure and the sintering temperature depend on the type of powder metal?**

The compacting pressure depends on the type of metal because interparticular adhesion must take place to develop (minimal) strength in the greenware stage. The compacting pressure is dependant on the powder metal because the softer the material, the larger the contact areas for a given pressure. In sintering, diffusion and vapor and liquid phase transport are dependent on the melting temperature of th material.

**17.29 Comment on the shapes and the ranges of the curves of process capabilities in Fig. 17.14.**

By the student. There are many acceptable answers, such as the recognition that few parts are very large and very complex, so that these processes serve the vast number of applications. Also, the relative popularity of P/M is explained by its noted flexibility compared to other processes.

## QUANTITATIVE PROBLEMS

**17.30 Estimate the maximum tonnage required to compact a brass slug 2.5 in. in diameter. Would the height of the slug make any difference in your answer? Explain your reasoning.**

As we can see in Table 17.2 on p. 499, the compacting pressure for brass can be as high as 700 MPa = 100 ksi. Thus the force required can be as high as

$$F = (100 \text{ ksi})(A) = (100 \text{ ksi})(\pi/4)(2.5 \text{ in.})^2 = 491 \text{ kip} = 245 \text{ tons}$$

As can be seen in Fig. 17.11e on p. 493, the higher the slug the greater is the pressure drop. This situation can be alleviated by using double punches. Also, note that we have used the highest pressure listed in the table.

**17.31 Refer to Fig. 17.10a; what should be the volume of loose, fine iron powder in order to make a solid cylindrical compact 25 mm in diameter and 15 mm high?**

The volume of the cylindrical compact is $V = \pi[(25)^2/4]15 = 7360 \text{ mm}^3$. Loose, fine iron powder has a density of 1.40 g/cm$^3$ (see Fig. 17.10a on p. 492). Density of iron is 7.86 g/cm$^3$ (see Table 3.1 on p. 103). Therefore, the weight of iron used is

$$W = \rho V = (7.86 \text{ g/cm}^3)(7360 \text{ mm}^3)(10^{-3} \text{ cm}^3/\text{mm}^3) = 57.8 \text{ g}$$

Therefore, the initial volume is

$$V = W/\rho = 57.8/1.40 = 41.3 \text{ cm}^3$$

**17.32 Determine the shape factors for (a) a cylinder with dimensional ratios of 1:1:1 and (b) a flake with ratios of 1:10:10.**

(a) The volume of this cylinder is

$$V = (\pi/4)(1)^2(1) = \pi/4$$

The equivalent diameter for a sphere of the same volume is

$$D = (6V/\pi)^{1/3} = 1.14$$

The surface area is

$$A = (\pi)(1)(1) + (2)(\pi/4)(1)^2 = 3\pi/2$$

Therefore, $A/V = (3\pi/2)/(\pi/4) = 6$. Hence the shape factor SF is $(1.14)(6) = 6.84$.

(b) The volume of the flakelike particle is $V = (10)(10)(1) = 100$. Note that this is in arbitrary units. The equivalent diameter for a sphere is

$$D = (6V/\pi)^{1/3} = 5.75$$

The surface area $A$ of the particle is

$$A = (2)(10)(10) + (4)(10)(1) = 240$$

Therefore, $A/V = 240/100 = 2.4$. Thus the shape factor SF is $(5.75)(2.4) = 13.8$.

**17.33 Estimate the number of particles in a 400-g sample of iron powder, if the particle size is 75 $\mu$m.**

The density of iron is 7.86 g/cm$^3$. The particle diameter $D$ is 75 $\mu$m = 0.0075 cm. The volume of each spherical particle is

$$V = (4/3)(\pi)(D/2)^3 = (\pi/6)(5.27 \times 10^{-8}) \text{ cm}^3$$

Thus its mass is $(5.27)(\pi/6)(10^{-8}) = 2.75 \times 10^{-8}$ g. Therefore, the number of particles $N$ in the 300-g sample is

$$N = 400/2.75 \times 10^{-8} = 1.45 \times 10^{10}$$

**17.34 Assume that the surface of a copper particle is covered by an oxide layer 0.1 mm in thickness. What is the volume (and the percentage of volume) occupied by this layer, if the copper particle itself is 60 $\mu$m in diameter?**

Because $60 \gg 0.1$, the volume of the oxide layer can be estimated as

$$V = 4\pi r^2 t = (4\pi)(30)^2(0.1) = 1130 \mu\text{m}^3$$

**17.35 Survey the technical literature to obtain data on shrinkage during the sintering of P/M parts. Comment on your observations.**

By the student. Excellent sources are powder metallurgy source books and general reference materials. Shrinkage values obtained will have a large range, depending on particle morphology and compaction approaches.

**17.36 Plot the total surface area of a 100-gram sample of aluminum, as a function of the natural log of particle size.**

The density of aluminum is 2.7 g/cm$^3$ (see Table 3.1 on p. 103). The mass of each particle is:

$$m = \rho V = \left(2.7\text{ g/cm}^3\right)\left(\frac{\pi}{6}D^3\right)$$

So the number of particles is given by

$$N = \frac{100\text{ g}}{m} = \frac{100\text{ g}}{\left(2.7\text{ g/cm}^3\right)\left(\frac{\pi}{6}D^3\right)} = \left(70.7\text{ cm}^3\right)\left(D^{-3}\right)$$

The total surface area of these particles is

$$A = N\pi D^2 = \left(70.7\text{ cm}^3\right)\left(D^{-3}\right)\pi D^2 = \left(222\text{ cm}^3\right)D^{-1}$$

where $D$ is in centimeters ($\mu$m × 10,000). The desired plot is then shown below.

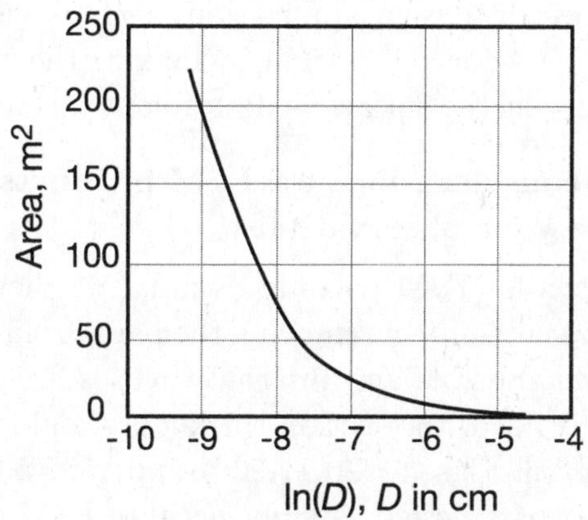


**17.37 A coarse copper powder is compacted in a mechanical press at a pressure of 20 tons/in$^2$. During sintering, the green part shrinks an additional 8%. What is the final density?**

From Figure 17.10 on p. 492, the copper density after compaction is around 7 g/cm$^3$. If the material shrinks an additional 7%, then the volume is $1/(0.93)^3$ times the original volume, so the density will be around 8.7g/cm$^3$.

**17.38 A gear is to be manufactured from iron powders. It is desired that it have a final density 90% that of cast iron, and it is known that the shrinkage in sintering will be approximately 5%. For a gear that is 2.5 in. in diameter and has a 0.75 in. hub, what is the required press force?**

From Table 3.1, the density of iron is 7.86g/cm$^3$. For the final part to have a final density of 90% of this value, the density after sintering must be 7.07g/cm$^3$. Since the part contracts 5% during sintering, the density before sintering must be 6.06g/cm$^3$. Referring to Figure 17.10 on p. 492, the required pressure for this density is around 20 tons/in$^2$. The projected area is $A = \pi/4(2.5^2 - 0.75^2) = 4.47$ in$^2$. The required force is then 89 tons, or roughly 90 tons.

**17.39 Assume that you are an instructor covering the topics described in this chapter, and you are giving a quiz on the numerical aspects to test the understanding of the students. Prepare two quantitative problems and supply the answers.**

By the student. This is an outstanding, open-ended question that requires considerable focus and understanding from the students, and has been found to be a very valuable homework problem.

## SYNTHESIS, DESIGN, AND PROJECTS

**17.40 Make sketches of P/M products in which density variations (see Fig. 17.11) would be desirable. Explain why, in terms of the functions of these parts.**

Any kind of minimum-weight design application, such as aerospace and automotive, where lightly loaded areas can be reduced in weight by making the areas more porous. With bearing surfaces, a greater density at the surface is desirable, while a substrate need not be as dense.

**17.41 Compare the design considerations for P/M products to those for (a) casting and (b) forging. Describe your observations.**

The design considerations for P/M parts are similar to those for casting and forging. The similarities are due to the necessity of removing the parts from the dies or molds. Hence, tapers should be used whenever possible and internal cavities are difficult to manufacture. Large flat surfaces should be avoided, the section thickness should be uniform. Some of the design considerations are shown in Figs. 17.20-17.22 on pp. 505-507. There are many simularities with casting and forging part design, mainly because P/M parts need to be ejected just as forgings and the pattern for casting need to be ejected. However, there are some differences. For example, engraved or embossed lettering is difficult in P/M but can be done easily in casting. P/M parts should be easily ejectable; castings are more flexible in this regards.

**17.42 Are there applications in which you, as a manufacturing engineer, would not recommend a P/M product? Explain.**

P/M products have many advantages, but they do not completely attain the strength of forgings in a given part volume. Any application where a volume is restricted but strength needs to be maximized are poor applications for P/M parts. For example, bolts, rivets, architectural channels, and biomedical implants are poor P/M applications. Also, fatigue applications are not good applications for P/M parts, because cracks can propagate easier through the (porous) structure.

**17.43 Describe in detail other methods of manufacturing the parts shown in Fig. 17.1.**

By the student. These parts could be produced through forging, casting or machining processes.

**17.44 How large is the grain size of metal powders that can be produced in atomization chambers? Conduct a literature search to determine the answer.**

By the student. Perhaps the best illustration of the size limitation are the pellets used in shotgun shells, which are roughly 0.375 in. in diameter.

**17.45 Plot the opening size versus the mesh size for screens used in powder-size sorting.**

This requires a literature search to find how mesh sizes are defined. The following data is from the ASM reference text *Powder Metallurgy*:

| Mesh No. | 80 | 100 | 120 | 140 | 170 | 200 | 230 | 270 | 325 | 400 |
|---|---|---|---|---|---|---|---|---|---|---|
| Particle size, $\mu$m | 177 | 149 | 125 | 105 | 88 | 74 | 63 | 53 | 44 | 37 |

The desired plot is then very straightforward:

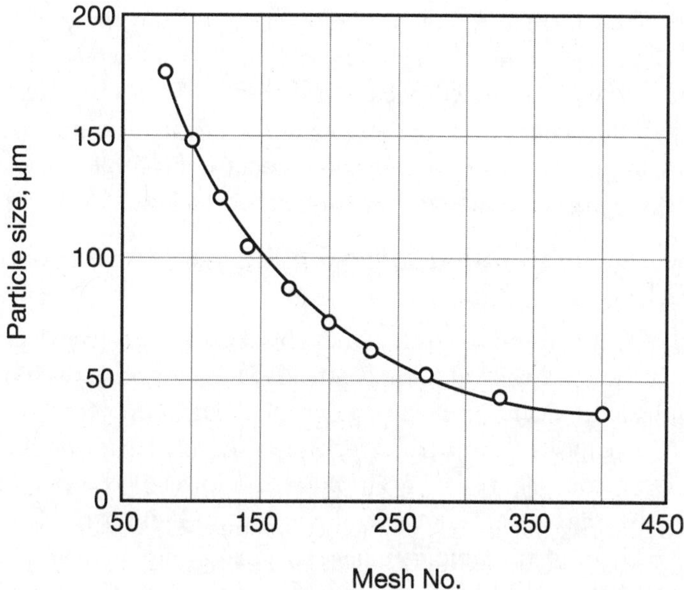


**17.46 Use the Internet to locate suppliers of metal powders, and compare the cost of the powder to the cost of ingots for five different materials.**

By the student. Ingot costs can vary depending on the size and the popularity of the material. This can be very challenging since the particular alloys may not be found in both powder and ingot forms.

**17.47 It is known that in the design of P/M gears, the hub outside diameter should be as far as possible from the root of the gear. Explain why this is the case.**

The reason for this is twofold. First of all, it is very difficult to get a good pressure in the cross section containing the root if the distance is small. Secondly, if the distance is small, it acts as a large stress concentration, which could cause part failure before sintering, especially during ejection.

**17.48 Explain why powder-metal parts are commonly used for machine elements requiring good frictional and wear characteristics and for mass produced parts.**

There are many acceptable answers to this question. Powder-metal parts are very commonly used for tribological machine elements like gears, bearings, races, and cams, because they can be impregnated with liquid lubricant. The main advantage to impregnating the P/M part with lubricant is that the component becomes self-lubricating. That is, when the temperature increases, the impregnated lubricant expands and percolates from the surface, thereby providing lubrication and wear ressistance. Mass produced parts are common because the high tooling costs of P/M and the additional processing steps of sintering makes P/M unattractive for low production runs.

**17.49 It was stated that powder injection molding competes well with investment casting and small forgings for various materials, but not with zinc and aluminum die castings. Explain why.**

MIM is commonly performed for metals with high melting temperatures. These metals are also very stiff in general, and would need very high compaction forces. MIM needs a fine enough powder that can be mixed with a polymer and injection molded, thus the material costs are high. On the other hand, the applications for magnesium and aluminum die castings are large-volume applications where cost is a concern. Examples are camera frames, fittings, toys, etc., and these applications are not well-suited for MIM as a result.

**17.50 Describe how the information given in Fig. 17.14 would be helpful to you in designing P/M parts.**

There are many possible answers to this question, and the answer depends on the experiences of the student. In general, the value is to consider a part and then judge its complexity. This allows one to quickly determine which powder metallurgy processes are suitable for that part. For example, if a part is a tube with a length of 0.5 m, then one would consider this to be simple; perhaps the complexity is 1.5 (it would be lower if the part were a cylinder instead of a tube). Clearly, one would not use compaction and sintering (P/F) because of the large size, and this would be a valuable conclusion. One would instead investigate CIP and HIP for this large part. Thus, Fig. 17.14 can quickly aid in identifying the best process for a part.

**17.51 We have stated that in the process shown in Fig. 17.18, shapes produced are limited to axisymmetric parts. Do you think it would be possible to produce other shapes as well? Describe how you would modify the design of the setup to make those shapes, and explain the difficulties that may be encountered.**

The spray deposition or Osprey process can be used to make parts that are assymetric, but it is in general not used to do so. First of all, it should be noted that sometimes a cylindrical billet is produced, and the billet is withdrawn in the same direction as the metal spray. If a die is used to define the shape, then an assymetric shape can be produced. Another option would be to perform shape rolling forms of powder rolling on the workpiece.

# Chapter 18

# Processing of Ceramics, Glass, and Superconductors

## QUALITATIVE PROBLEMS

**18.15 Inspect various products at home, work, or in stores. Noting their shape, color, and transparency, identify those that are made of (a) ceramic, (b) glass, and (c) glass ceramics.**

By the student. The following are typical examples (see also p. 513):

- Ceramic: Opaque or translucent materials, such as coffee cups, ovenware, floor tiles, and plates.
- Glass: Transparent materials, such as drinking glasses, windows, lenses, and TV and desktop computer screens.
- Glass ceramic: A typically white material, such as cookware (Corningware); other applications of ceramic glasses are rarer but include high-temperature heat exchangers.

**18.16 Describe the differences and similarities in processing metal powders versus ceramics.**

By the student. Some of the similarities are:

- Both involve an initial powder form.
- Both involve sintering or firing.
- Both can produce porous parts.
- Both can be injection molded.

Some of the differences include:

- Ceramics are commonly glazed in a second firing operation, whereas this is rare for metals except when enameling.
- Ceramic processing involves water-based slurries, while this does not occur with metals.

**18.17 What should be the property requirements for the metal balls in a ball mill?**

The balls in a ball mill (see Fig. 17.6b on p. 487) effectively crush and grind the material into a powder, hence the desirable mechanical properties obviously are high hardness and toughness, and high resistance to wear and corrosion. An important physical property is high density so that as the balls tumble, more energy is available for a given size ball mill.

**18.18 Which property of glasses allows them to be expanded to large dimensions by blowing? Can metals undergo such behavior? Explain.**

The property of glass which allows bottle production (see Fig. 18.10 on p. 524) is the fact that glass behaves in a superplastic manner (high strain-rate sensitivity; Section 2.2.7 on p. 74) and can undergo very large uniform elongations at elevated temperatures. Glass is a supercooled liquid, without a clearly defined melting point. Thus, glasses will deform readily at temperatures above their glass-transition temperature and will solidify into shapes imparted by the molds.

**18.19 Explain why ceramic parts may distort or warp during drying. What precautions should be taken to avoid this situation?**

Ceramic parts may warp during drying because of uneven shrinkage across the part, due to uneven diffusion and evaporation of moisture. The moisture loss can be made more uniform by drying the ceramic in a more humid or less hot environment; these of course also result in longer drying times.

**18.20 What properties should plastic sheets have to be used in laminated glass? Why?**

The plastic sheets should have high ductility and toughness (to dissipate energy) and be able to form a strong bond with the glass on both side of the plastic (to hold the broken glass pieces together).

**18.21 It is stated that the higher the coefficient of thermal expansion of a glass and the lower its thermal conductivity, the higher the level of the residual stresses developed. Explain why.**

The coefficient of thermal expansion is important in the development of residual stresses because a given temperature gradient will result in a greater residual strain upon complete cooling. Thermal conductivity is important because the higher the thermal conductivity, the more uniform the temperature throughout the molten glass and the more uniform the strains upon cooling. The more uniform the strains, the less the magnitude of residual stresses. (See also p. 107.)

**18.22 Are any of the processes used for making discrete glass products similar to ones described in preceding chapters? Describe them.**

By the student. For example:

- Pressing of glass is similar to closed-die forging.

- Blowing of glass is similar to bulging or hydroforming.
- Production of glass fibers is similar to extrusion and drawing.
- Flat glass sheet or plate production is similar to drawing or rolling, depending on the particular method used.

**18.23 Injection molding is a process that is used for powder metals, polymers, and ceramics. Explain why is this so.**

Powder metals and ceramics are initially in powder form, and when mixed with a thermoplastic, create a material that can flow and be formed in molds using injection molding. Ultimately, the thermoplastic is still used for the molding process, but powder metals and ceramics can use this process because they are particles suspended in the polymer. Thermoplastics have the attractive abilitity to flow readily as a fluid and solidify in a cooled mold, and injection molding of plastics is a straightforward and well-established process (see Section 19.3 on p. 544)..

**18.24 Are there any similarities between the strengthening mechanisms used on glass and those used on metallic materials? Explain.**

The basic strengthening mechanism for glass is by thermal or chemical tempering (see Section 18.4 on p. 525) and for metallic materials it is by heat treating (see Chapter 4) or surface modifications (described in Chapter 34). Strengthening mechanisms for nonmetallic materials will depend on the particular material; for polymers, for example, it is principally by strengthening with reinforcements (see Chapter 9). The student is encouraged to elaborate further.

**18.25 Explain the phenomenon of static fatigue and how it affects the service life of a ceramic or glass component.**

Static fatigue occurs under a constant load and in environments where water vapor is present. Typical examples of applications that are susceptible to static fatigue include load-bearing members (such as a glass rod under tension) and glass shelving (supporting various objects, including books).

**18.26 Describe and explain the differences in the manner in which each of the following flat surfaces would fracture when struck with a heavy piece of rock: (a) ordinary window glass, (b) tempered glass, and (c) laminated glass.**

By the student. The students are encouraged to conduct simple experiments with these types of glasses. (a) Will typically develop radial cracks as well as various secondary cracks, e.g., window glass, when a rock or baseball is thrown at it. (b) Will shatter into a large number of small pieces, e.g., fireplace glass. (c) Will shatter into numerous pieces but the pieces will be held together due to the toughness of the plastic layer in between the two glass layers, e.g., windshields.

**18.27 Is there any flash that develops in slip casting? How would you propose to remove such flash?**

There is typically a flash at the parting line of the mold halves (see Fig. 18.3 on p. 516) or parts where the mold has more than two sections. The flash can be gently removed through trimming with a knife or wire brush while the ceramic is in the green state, or they can be ground after the ceramic is fired.

**18.28 Are there similarities between slip casting and shell-mold casting? Explain.**

By the student. There are several similarities; for example, in the part shape (hollow parts), the required use of molds, in part size, similar part tolerances and complexities.

## QUANTITATIVE PROBLEMS

**18.29 For Example 18.1, calculate (a) the porosity of the dried part if the porosity of the fired part is to be 9% and (b) the initial length, $L_o$, of the part if the linear shrinkages during drying and firing are 8% and 7%, respectively.**

(a) For this case we have

$$V_a = (1 - 0.09)V_f = 0.91V_f$$

Because the linear shrinkage during firing is 7%, we write

$$V_d = V_f/(1 - 0.07)^3 = 1.24V_f$$

Therefore,

$$\frac{V_a}{V_d} = \frac{0.91}{1.24} = 0.73, \text{ or } 73\%$$

Consequently, the porosity of the dried part is (1 - 0.73) = 0.27, or 27%.

(b) We can now write

$$\frac{(L_d - L)}{L_d} = 0.07$$

or

$$L = (1 - 0.07)L_d$$

Since $L = 20$ mm, we have

$$L_d = 20/0.93 = 21.51 \text{ mm}$$

And thus

$$L_o = (1 + 0.08)L_d = (1.08)(21.51) = 23.23 \text{ mm}$$

**18.30 What would be the answers to Problem 18.29 if the quantities given were halved?**

(a) For this case we have

$$V_a = (1 - 0.045)V_f = 0.955V_f$$

Because the linear shrinkage during firing is 3.5%, we write

$$V_d = V_f/(1 - 0.035)^3 = 1.112V_f$$

Therefore,

$$V_a/V_d = 0.955/1.112 = 0.86, or 86\%$$

Consequently, the porosity of the dried part is (1 - 0.86) = 0.14, or 14%.

(b) We can now write

$$\frac{(L_d - L)}{L_d} = 0.035$$

or

$$L = (1 - 0.035)L_d$$

Since $L = 20$ mm, we have

$$L_d = \frac{20}{0.965} = 20.73 \text{ mm}$$

And thus

$$L_o = (1 + 0.04)L_d = (1.04)(20.73) = 21.56 \text{ mm}$$

**18.31 Assume that you are an instructor covering the topics described in this chapter and you are giving a quiz on the numerical aspects to test the understanding of the students. Prepare two quantitative problems and supply the answers.**

By the student. This has been found to be a very valuable homework problem.

## SYNTHESIS, DESIGN, AND PROJECTS

**18.32 Describe similarities and differences between the processes described in this chapter and those (a) in Part II on metal casting and (b) in Part III on forming.**

By the student. For example, between P/M and ceramics parts and castings, there are similarities in that parts are porous, the part complexity is similar, and P/M and casting both use metals. For P/M and forgings, we note that similar equipment and tooling materials are used, and finishing operations are similar. The student is encouraged to elaborate further.

**18.33 Consider some ceramic products with which you are familiar and outline a sequence of processes that you think were used to manufacture them.**

By the student. Some of the most common ceramic parts include coffee cups, dishes, electronic components and automotive spark plugs. The sequence of processes used will vary widely depending on the particular part to be made. A coffee cup is an interesting example: It is generally slip cast or injection molded, depending on the number needed; the handle is attached in a separate process if the cup was slip cast and the flash is removed if the cup was injection molded. The greenware is then fired, resulting in the ceramic part. In some cases, tints or stains will then be applied, and glazing (glass particles in a slurry) is applied for improved appearance; the ceramic is then re-fired to obtain the glazed surface (see p. 520) suitable for food contact.

**18.34 Make a survey of the technical literature and describe the differences (if any) between the quality of glass fibers made for use in reinforced plastics and those made for use in fiber-optic communications. Comment on your observations.**

By the student. The glass fibers in reinforced plastics has a much smaller diameter and has to be high quality for high strength (see Sections 9.2.1 on p. 241 and 18.3.4 on p. 525). The glass fibers for communications applications are formulated for optical properties and the strength is not a major concern, although some strength is needed for installation.

**18.35 How different are the design considerations for ceramics from those for other materials? Explain.**

By the student. Ceramics are brittle, very notch sensitive and hence not suitable for impact loadings. On the other hand, ceramics have exceptional properties at high temperatures, are very strong in compression, have corrosion resistance, and are resistant to wear because of their high hardness. (See also Section 18.5 on p. 528 and various sections on materials processing.)

**18.36 Locate a ceramics/pottery shop and investigate the different techniques used for coloring and decorating a ceramic part. What are the different methods of applying a metallic finish to the part?**

By the student. Decorations can be done in a number of ways. For example, while still in the green state, a dye can be applied (such as by spraying or with a brush) to the ceramic part which permeates into the part. When fired, the dye remains in the lattice to provide color, and may also change color. Another option is to use conventional paints and coatings after firing.

**18.37 Give examples of designs and applications where static fatigue should be taken into account.**

By the student. Static fatigue occurs under a constant load and in environments where water vapor is present. See also Problem 18.25.

**18.38 Perform a literature search and make a list of automotive parts made of ceramics. Explain why they are made of ceramics.**

By the student. Typical parts are: Spark plugs, decorative knobs, fuel filters, valve lifters, and heating coils. These parts utilize different aspects of ceramics; for example, the spark plugs use the high-temperature electrically insulative properties of ceramics, the knobs use the aesthetic advantages, and valve lifter use the high wear resistance that can be attained with ceramics.

**18.39 Describe your thoughts on the processes that can be used to make (a) small ceramic statues, (b) whiteware for bathrooms, (c) common brick, and (d) floor tile.**

By the student. The answers will vary because of the different manufacturing methods used for these products. Some examples are:

(a) Small ceeramic statues are usually made by slip casting, followed by firing to fuse the particles and develop strength, followed by decorating and glazing.

(b) Whiteware for bathrooms are either slip cast or pressed, then fired, and sometimes glazed and re-fired.

(c) Common brick is wet pressed or slip cast, then fired.

(d) Floor tile is hot pressed or dry pressed, fired, and sometimes glazed and re-fired.

**18.40 As we have seen, one method of producing superconducting wire and strip is by compacting powders of these materials, placing them into a tube, and drawing them through dies or rolling them. Describe your thoughts concerning the steps and possible difficulties involved in each step of this production.**

By the student. Concerns include fracture of the green part before or during drawing, and its implications; inhomogeneous deformation that can occur during drawing and rolling and its possible effects as a fracture-causing process; the inability of the particles to develop sufficient strength during this operation; and possible distortion of the part from its drawn or rolled shape during sintering.

**18.41 We have explained briefly the characteristics of bulletproof glass. Describe your own thoughts on possible new designs for this type of glass. Explain your reasoning.**

By the student. Ultimately, the applications should seek to exploit the ability of this material to dissipate impact energy safely. Examples include guards for machinery, protective barriers for hockey rinks, and windows of all types.

# Chapter 19

# Forming and Shaping Plastics and Composite Materials

## QUALITATIVE PROBLEMS

**19.22 Describe the features of a screw extruder and its functions.**

By the student. A typical extruder is shown in Fig. 19.2 on p. 537. The three principal features of the screw shown are:

- Feed section: In this region, the screw is intended to entrain powder or pellets from the hopper; as a result, the flight spacing and depth is larger than elsewhere on the screw.
- Melt section: In the melt section, the flight depth is very low and the plastic is melted against the hot barrel; also, gases that are entrained in the feed section are vented.
- Metering section: This region produced the pressure and flow rate needed for the extrusion operation.

Note that screws are designed for particular polymers, so the feed, melt, and metering sections are polymer-specific. Also, some extruders use two screws to increase the internal shearing and mixing of the polymer.

**19.23 Explain why injection molding is capable of producing parts with complex shapes and fine detail.**

The reason is mainly due to the attractive features of thermoplastics. When melted, they are a viscous liquid that can flow into intricate cavities under pressure, and then cool and solidify in the desired shape (see also Section 19.3 on p. 544).

**19.24 Describe the advantages of applying traditional metal-forming techniques described in Chapters 13 through 16 to forming (a) thermoplastics and (b) thermosets.**

By the student. Applying traditional metalworking techniques to shaping of plastics is advantageous for a number of reasons. Since the desired stock shapes are similar (e.g., sheet), efficient and reliable processes can be used. Being able to utilize similar machines allows the application of many years of research, development, and experience associated with machine design and process optimization to materials which have only existed for the last few decades.

**19.25 Explain the reasons why some plastic-forming processes are more suitable for certain polymers than for others.**

By the student. For example, it is difficult to extrude thermosets because curing is impossible during the extrusion process. Plastics which are produced through reaction molding are difficult to produce through other means, and other processes are not readily adaptable to allowing sufficient mixing of the two ingredients. Injection molding of composites is difficult because fluidity of the material is essential to ensure proper filling of the die, but characteristics and presence of the fibers interferes with this process.

**19.26 Describe the problems involved in recycling products made from reinforced plastics.**

By the student. The main problems are that recycling usually requires the use of a single type of material, and that some plastics (mainly hard and brittle polymers) are more difficult to chop into small pieces for further processing than others. With reinforced plastics, this requires that the reinforcement be separated from the matrix, a very difficult task and uneconomical task. Note that matrices are often thermosets, so it is not practical to melt the matrix and separate the fibers from a molten phase.

**19.27 Can thermosetting plastics be used in injection molding? Explain.**

Thermosetting plastics are suitable for injection molding. The basic modification which must be made to the process is that the molds must be heated to allow polymerization and cross-linking to occur in the mold cavity (see p. 544). The major drawback associated with this change is that, because of the longer cycle times, the process will not have as high a production rate as injection molding of thermoplastics.

**19.28 By inspecting plastic containers, such as ones for talcum powder, you can see that the integral lettering on them is raised rather than depressed. Can you offer an explanation as to why they are molded in that way?**

By the student. The containers are produced through blow molding. The parison is pressed against the container walls by the internal pressure and then cooled upon contact with the die. The reason why the lettering is usually raised is due to the fact that it is much easier to produce the lettering on the mold walls by machining or shaping into it, using processes such as end milling (see Fig. 24.2d on p. 725). Raised letters on mold walls would be very difficult and expensive to produce, and in fact unnecessary. (See also Problem 14.22.)

**19.29 Outline the precautions that you would take in shaping (a) reinforced plastics and (b) other composites.**

By the student. (a) In addition to the fact that there must be good bonding between the plastic and the reinforcement, reinforced plastics will be stiffer, generally less ductile than the bulk plastic, and have anisotropic properties. Furthermore, reinforcements such as glass fibers are very abrasive and thus the flow of the material within mold cavities is important. (b) Others such as metal-matrix and ceramic-matrix composites have similar considerations, especially as they are more in bulk form and as not large sheets. The manner of flow of the material in the die cavities is important, as otherwise brittle fibers will fracture and their distribution may be nonuniform, or voids may even form within the composite. (See also Sections 19.14 and 19.15 on pp. 570 and 572, respectively.)

**19.30 Describe the factors that contribute to the cost of each forming and shaping process described in this chapter.**

By the student. Section 19.16 and Table 19.2 on p. 574 will be helpful in the answer to this equestion. Note that equipment and tooling costs vary significantly among various processes. For example, in extrusion and related processes that involve a screw (injection molding, injection blow molding), the major costs are attributed to the capital investment in the machinery and tooling. Other considerations include the level of automation, the the labor involved, and the type of plastics used.

**19.31 An injection-molded nylon gear is found to contain small pores. It is recommended that the material be dried before molding it. Explain why drying will solve this problem.**

The probable reason is that the porosity is due to entrapped moisture in the material. Note also that nylon absorbs water (hygroscopic; see p. 205) thus drying will alleviate this situation.

**19.32 Explain why operations such as blow molding and film-bag making are performed vertically. Why is the movement of the material upward?**

By the student. Film-bag making is done vertically (see Fig. 19.5 on p. 541) to keep the symmetry of the part and prevent sagging (due to gravitational force) of one side, which would the case if done horizontally. Blow molding can be done either vertically or horizontally.

**19.33 Comment on the principle of operation of the tape-laying machine shown in Fig. 19.25b. How is the cost for such a machine justified?**

By the student. As the caption to Fig. 19.25 states, these machines are numerically controlled, as discussed in Chapter 38. These are, in effect, very large gantry robots that are programmed to dispense tape in programmed patterns. The cost for such a machine is justified, as is usually the case, by analyzing the desired production quantities and costs associated with alternate production methods. The example in Fig. 19.25 shows a rather large part; hand lay-up of tape would be labor intensive, which cannot be justified for larger production runs.

**19.34 Typical production volumes are given in Table 19.2. Comment on your observations and explain why there is such a wide range.**

By the student. Consider the characteristics and cycle times involved in each of these processes listed in Table 19.2 on p. 574, as described in various sections of the chapter. Note that production quantities depend on factors such as the type of process, the type of plastics used and the time required for cooling in mold cavities, type of machinery and its level of automation. For comparison, casting topics are covered in Chapters 10 through 12 and forging in Chapter 14. The wide variety of machining processes and machinery are covered in Part IV.

**19.35 What determines the cycle time for (a) for injection molding, (b) thermoforming, and (c) compression molding?**

The cycle time for injection molding is determined by several factors, including:

- Material: Thermoplastics need much less time than thermosets, and certain thermoplastics will need less time to cool and solidify than others (different thermal properties).
- Part shape: If the part has a low volume and large surface area, it will cool rapidly.
- Initial temperature: If a plastic is injected at a temperature much above its solidification temperature, it will require more time to cool.

The considerations for thermoforming and compression molding are similar. The students are encouraged to analyze and elaborate further.

**19.36 Does the pull-in defect (sink marks) shown in Fig. 19.31c also occur in metal forming and casting processes? Explain.**

The type of defect shown in Fig. 19.31c on p. 573 also occurs in metal forming (because of the flow of the material into the die cavity) and casting processes (because of excessive, localized surface shrinkage during solidification and cooling in the mold). This is described in different handbooks, but it should be noted that 'sink marks' is a terminology restricted to polymer parts. For example, in Bralla, J.G., *Design for Manufacturability Handbook*, 2nd. ed., pp. 5.51, the sink marks are referred to as 'dishing' for investment casting, and on p. 5.64 the same features are referred to as 'shrink marks'.

**19.37 Comment on the differences between the barrel section of an extruder and that of an injection-molding machine.**

By the student. Some of the basic differences between an extruder and an injection-molding machine barrel are:

- The extruder involve more heating from the heating elements and less from friction, so there will be more (or larger capacity) heating elements and temperature sensors in an extruder barrel.
- Extruders do not utilize torpedoes or reciprocating screws.
- Extruders may use multiple screws to improve mixing in the barrel.

**19.38 What determines the time intervals at which the indexing head in Fig. 19.16c rotates from station to station?**

By the student. The question is basically asking what factors determine the cycle time in blow molding. The answer depends on several factors, including: The particular polymer used (which affects melting and processing temperature, thermal conductivity, and specific heat), tooling material and tooling temperature, bottle and parison shape, injection pressure, and the use (if any) of release agents.

**19.39 Identify processes that are suitable for making small production runs on plastic parts, of say, 100 parts.**

By the student. Refer to the last column (economical production quantity) in Table 19.2 on p. 574 and note that low quantities involve processes in which tooling costs must be kept low. Thus, the most suitable processes would be casting and machining (because of the readily available and versatile machine tools). Rapid prototyping operations, described in Chapter 20, may also be suitable if the quantities are sufficiently small and part characteristics are acceptable.

**19.40 Identify processes that are capable of producing parts with the following fiber orientations in each: (a) uniaxial, (b) cross-ply, (c) in-plane random, and (d) three-dimensional random.**

By the student. Some suggestions are:

(a) Uniaxial fiber orientations can be produced though pultrusion, tape lay-up, and filament winding.

(b) Cross-ply can be produced by tape lay-up and filament winding.

(c) Random orientations can be produced with prepregs and vacuum forming, open-mold processing, and injection molding.

## QUANTITATIVE PROBLEMS

**19.41 Estimate the die-clamping force required for injection molding five identical 6-in. diameter disks in one die. Include the runners of appropriate length and diameter.**

Assuming a pressure of 10,000 psi, which is rather low pressure, and that the die is set up as follows, with 1-in. diameter risers and 2-in. thick disks:

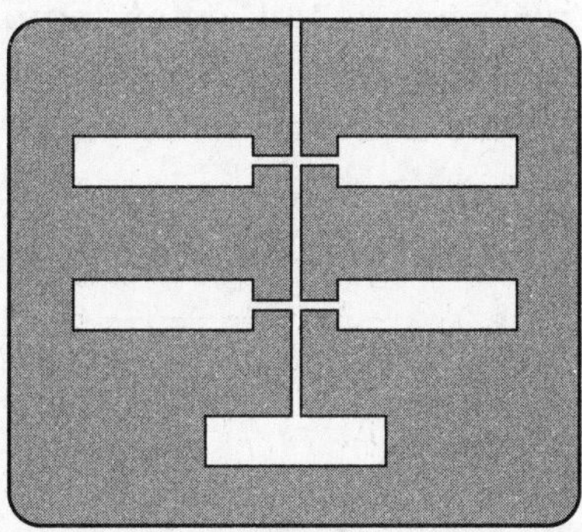

The surface area is approximately $A = (5\pi/4)(6 \text{ in.})(2 \text{ in.}) + (1 \text{ in.})(20 \text{ in.}) = 67 \text{ in}^2$. The clamping force required to balance the injection pressure is then

$$F = pA = (10,000 \text{ psi})(67 \text{ in}^2) = 670,000 \text{ lb} = 335 \text{ tons}$$

**19.42 A two-liter plastic beverage bottle is made from a parison with a diameter that is the same as that of the threaded neck of the bottle and is 5 in. long. Assuming uniform deformation during blow molding, estimate the wall thickness of the tubular portion of the parison.**

A typical two-liter plastic beverage bottle is approximately $L = 9$ in. long and $D = 4.25$ in. in diameter; its wall thickness $t$ is 0.015 in. Thus, the volume of material is

$$V = \pi DLt = \pi(4.25)(9)(0.015) = 1.8 \text{ in}^3$$

The parison is 5 in. long and its diameter is about 1 1/8 in. Thus, its thickness, $t_p$, should be

$$t_p = (1.8)/(\pi)(1.125)(5) = 0.10 \text{ in.}$$

**19.43 Make a survey of a variety of sports equipment and identify the components made of composite materials. Explain the reasons for and advantages of using composites for these specific applications.**

By the student. Various answers are possible for this question, and it depends to some degree on the flexibility in the design of composite materials. For example, a golf ball is a type of composite material, with a liquid core encapsulated in a rubber membrane, surrounded by a wound rubber layer, and molded cover. Fiber-reinforced sporting goods include tennis rackets, baseball bats, hockey sticks, cross bows and arrows, skis, and javelins.

**19.44 Consider a styrofoam drinking cup. Measure the volume of the cup and its weight. From this information, estimate the percent increase in volume that the polystyrene beads have undergone.**

By the student. The answer will vary somewhat, depending the cup manufacturer and method and accuracy of measurement. It is not unusual to find that the polystyrene has expanded by 80% or more during its processing.

**19.45 During the sterilization process for producing intravenous (IV) bags for medical applications, the polymer bags are subjected to an internal pressure of 30 psi. If the bag diameter is 4 in. and its shape can be approximated as a thin-walled, closed-end, cylindrical pressure vessel, what should be the wall thickness to ensure that the bag does not burst during sterilization? Assume that the allowable tensile stress of the polymer is 10 ksi.**

From a solid mechanics text, it can be found that the longitudinal stress is $\sigma = pr/2t$ and the hoop stress is $\sigma = pr/t$. Using the distortion-energy (von Mises) yield criterion, we have:

$$\begin{aligned} 2Y^2 &= \sqrt{(\sigma_1 - \sigma_2)^2 + (\sigma_2 - \sigma_3)^2 + (\sigma_3 - \sigma_1)^2} \\ &= \sqrt{\left(\frac{pr}{t} - \frac{pr}{2t}\right)^2 + \left(\frac{pr}{2t}\right)^2 + \left(\frac{pr}{t}\right)^2} \\ &= \frac{pr}{t}\sqrt{\frac{1}{4} + \frac{1}{4} + 1} = 1.22\frac{pr}{t} \end{aligned}$$

Substituting for $p$, $r$, and $Y$ gives $t = 0.3\ \mu\text{m} = 0.012\ \mu\text{in}$. Note that most IV bags are thicker than this, so that failure during sterilization is rare.

## SYNTHESIS, DESIGN, AND PROJECTS

**19.46 Give examples of several parts suitable for insert molding. How would you manufacture these parts if insert molding were not available?**

By the student. Most examples are from the electronics industry, but there are others (see, for example, the parts shown in Fig. 19.9 on p. 545). Propeller shafts for toy boats can be insert molded with plastic propellers on shafts that are knurled (see Fig. 23.11 on p. 675) to keep the propeller from slipping. If insert molding were not available, suitable operations would be press fitting the inserts into molded holes or cavities, and mechanical assembly using various fasteners.

**19.47 Give other examples of design modifications in addition to those shown in Fig. 19.31.**

By the student. Other examples would include referring to die swell, as shown in Fig. 19.3 in p. 538, and noting that the die opening must be smaller than the desired shape (see also Problem 19.65). In addition, strengthening ribs also can be used to eliminate or control part distortion. There are a large number of design modifications that can be found in the technical literature. For example, Bralla, J.G., *Design for Manufacturability Handbook*, 2nd. ed., contains many recommendations in Chapter 6, pp. 6.1-6.207.

**19.48 With specific examples, discuss the design issues involved in making products out of plastics, when compared to reinforced plastics.**

By the student. Design considerations are covered in Section 19.15 on p. 572. Reinforced plastics are superior to conventional plastics in terms of strength and strength-to-weight ratios (see, for example, Table 7.1 on p. 192), but not in cost. As an example, consider the design of pressure vessels for delivering oxygen for emergency passenger use on aircraft. Certainly a container can be produced from plastic, but the weight of an optimized pressure vessel will be lower for a reinforced filament-wound container, even though the cost is higher.

**19.49 Inspect various plastic components in your car and identify the processes that could have been used in making them.**

By the student. As examples: (a) Small components such as coffee-cup holders and the like are injection molded. (b) Dashboards are thermoformed or vacuum-bag formed from fiber-reinforced prepregs. (c) Radio knobs can be insert molded or injection molded. (d) Body panels can be thermoformed.

**19.50 Explain the design considerations involved in replacing a metal beverage can with one made completely of plastic.**

By the student. As in all substitutions, the major concern is economic (i.e., the can should not cost more than the metal alternative. As we know, metal cans are very reliable, so a polymer bottle must also be as reliable and have good strength and other characteristics desirable for beverage containers. There are marketing issues; can the plastic container be made as appealing as a metal container and is a distribution network available (such as vending machines that are designed for metal cans). Environmental issues can have an impact as well, since a recycling infrastructure is less developed for polymers than for aluminum.

**19.51 Inspect several similar products that are made either from metals or from plastics, such as a metal bucket and a plastic bucket of similar shape and size. Comment on their respective shapes and thicknesses and explain the reasons for their differences, if any.**

By the student. The basic difference between metals and plastics have been discussed on various occasions; see also Section 7.1 on p. 191. Some examples:

(a) Metal buckets are thinner than plastic ones, and are more rigid; plastic buckets have to be thicker because of their much lower elastic modulus.

(b) Metal pens (mechanical pencils) and plastic pens; the polymer pens are much thicker, because they must feel rigid for its intended use.

(c) Plastic vs. metal forks and spoons; although no major difference in overall size, the plastic ones are more flexible but they are made more rigid by increasing the section modulus (as can be observed by inspecting the handle designs).

**19.52 Write a brief paper on how plastic coatings are applied to (a) electrical wiring, (b) sheet-metal panels, (c) wire baskets, racks, and similar structures, and (d) handles for electrician's tools, such as wire cutters and pliers requiring electrical insulation.**

By the student. The paper should elaborate on the differences between various processes, such as coextrusion, hot dipping, and insert molding.

**19.53 Inspect several electrical components (such as light switches, outlets, and circuit breakers) and describe the processes used in making them.**

By the student. The plastic components are usually injection molded and then assembled, but some very ingenious designs using insert molding can be found in these products. Also, integrated circuits and many other electrical components are potted.

**19.54 Based on experiments, it has been suggested that polymers (either plain or reinforced) can be a suitable material for dies in sheet-metal forming operations described in Chapter 16. Describe your thoughts regarding this suggestion, considering die geometry and any other factors that may be relevant.**

By the student. This is already done in operations such as hydroforming and to some extent in rubber forming. However, the polymers that can be used to replace conventional metal dies must have sufficient rigidity, strength, and wear resistance. Considering these desirable characteristics, the use of plastic dies are likely to be appropriate and economical for relatively short production runs. The main reason polymer tooling has become of greater interest is the proliferation of rapid prototyping technologies that yield good plastic inserts or tools with low cost and lead times.

**19.55 Think of plastic parts that are made using two or more of the processes described in this chapter.**

By the student. This can be interpreted in two ways: it could be interpreted as parts that can be made by alternative processes, some examples of which are:

- Plastic bottles can be made by blow molding, injection molding or, for high-pressure applications, by filament winding.
- Plastic plate can be made by calendaring or extrusion.
- Candy trays can be made by inection molding or thermoforming.

Another interpretation of this problem is listing products that require a combination of two or more processes in order to make them. Examples of these parts include:

- Candy trays are produced from a film that is extruded, then blown and then is thermoformed. Indeed, most thermoformed parts will be produced from blown films.
- As discussed in the chapter, plastic bottles can be produced from extruded or injection molded parisons.
- Golf balls use a combination of processes. One example is an injection molded core (sometimes with a liquid encapsulated within), filament wound with elastomer, then insert injection molded to produce a cover.

**19.56 As we know, plastic forks, spoons, and knives are not particularly strong or rigid. What suggestions would you have to make them better? Describe processes that could be used for producing them and comment on the production costs involved.**

By the student. See also Problem 19.51. Plastic spoons, forks, and knives are not particularly strong or rigid, but they are inexpensive because they are mass produced typically by injection molding. Stiffening ribs can, for example, be designed into them to increase their stiffness, or they can be made larger and thicker. If strength is a key issue, then stronger plastics can be used (see Table 7.1 on p. 192).

**19.57 For ease of sorting for recycling, a rapidly increasing number of plastic products are now identified with a triangular symbol with a single-digit number at its center and two or more letters under it. Explain what these numbers indicate and why they are used.**

By the student. This information can be found on p. 213 as:

| | |
|---|---|
| 1 | Polyethylene |
| 2 | High-density polyethylene |
| 3 | Vinyl |
| 4 | Low density polyethylene |
| 5 | Polypropylene |
| 6 | Polystyrene |
| 7 | Other |

The reason for these numbers is that they easily identify the plastics according to their class, and thus recycling is greatly simplified. Also, the recycled polymer quality is greatly improved because the same kind of polymer is recycled together.

**19.58 Explain the similarities and differences between the product design principles for the processes described in this chapter and those for the chapters in Part III. Describe your observations.**

By the student. There are several similarities. For example, sharp corners are to be avoided (as in casting and forging, as well as in extrusion dies), letters should be raised instead of depressed (as in casting and forging), warpage is a concern (as in casting and sheet-metal forming). The differences include factors such as the magnitude of temperatures involved and the forces required to perform the operations.

**19.59 Make a survey of the technical literature and describe how different types of (a) pneumatic tires, (b) automotive hoses, and (c) garden hoses are manufactured.**

By the student. Tires are produced by molding, followed by vulcanization to develop the highly cross-linked polymer structure. Some reinforced automotive hoses are coextruded with a metal reinforcement. Garden hoses are similary manufactured using reinforcing polymeric webs during extrusion.

**19.60 Obtain a boxed kit for assembling a model car or airplane. Examine the injection-molded parts provided and describe your thoughts on the layout of the molds to produce these parts.**

By the student. This is an interesting project and allows a simple study of a complex mold layout. The layout of the mold shows part balance - note that the material is fairly evenly distributed across the mold cross section. The gate is well made allowing parts to be broken off with ease. The molds are well crafted, with great details.

**19.61 Using the Internet, obtain the following information:**

**(a) Cost of raw polystyrene beads and raw polyethylene pellets.**

**(b) Melt properties (such as glass-transition temperatures and melting temperatures) of plastics.**

**(c) Availability of polymer additives, such as coloring agents and flow property additives; and**

**(d) Sizes, features, and costs of injection-molding machines.**

By the student. The results will vary depending on the source, and can be an interesting sub-problem to encourage students to optimize the problem. For example, the student can be encouraged to find the lowest cost source for various polymers.

**19.62 In injection-molding operations, it is common practice to remove the part from its runner, place the runner in a shredder, and recycle them to produce pellets. List the concerns you may have in using such recycled pellets for products, as against "virgin" pellets.**

By the student. Some concerns are:

- The polymer may become chemically contaminated by tramp oils or parting agents used in the die.

- Wear particles from the shredder may contaminate the polymer.
- The polymer may be chemically degraded from the heating and cooling cycle encountered in injection molding.
- The molecular weight of the shredded polymer may be much smaller than the original polymer so that the mechanical properties of the recycled stock may be inferior.

**19.63 An increasing environmental concern is the very long period required for degradation of polymers in landfills. Noting the information given in Section 7.8 on biodegradable plastics, perform a literature search on the trends and developments in the production of these plastics.**

By the student. A recent trend is to use polymers that, if they do not degrade in sufficiently short time, can be incinerated without producing volatile organic compounds as combustion products. Also, the problem has been mitigated somewhat in recent years through introduction of new materials. For example, perhaps the problem receiving the most meadia attention in the 1980s was the degredation time associated with diapers for babies and small children. Modern diapers use hydrogel powders that degrade rapidly when exposed to rain or groundwater, and they also use innovative paper liners to eliminate the environmentally suspect polymers. In summary, most polymers in use today are (a) able to be recycled; (b) able to be safely incinerated or (c) quickly degradable.

**19.64 Inspect some plastic slats for venetian blinds and describe your thoughts on how to produce them. Compare them with sheet-metal slats and comment on their relative cross-sections, curvature, and performance characteristics.**

By the student. The answer will vary depending on the particular venetian blinds considered. Some are extruded and cut to length while others are thermoformed.

**19.65 Die swell in extrusion is radially uniform for circular cross-sections but is not uniform for other cross-sections, as shown in Figs. 19.3b through d. Recognizing this, make a qualitative sketch of a die profile that will produce (a) triangular and (b) gear-shaped cross-sections of extruded plastics.**

The sketches are shown below. Note that, as expected, there has to be greater recovery at corners where the strain in the extruded polymer is highest.

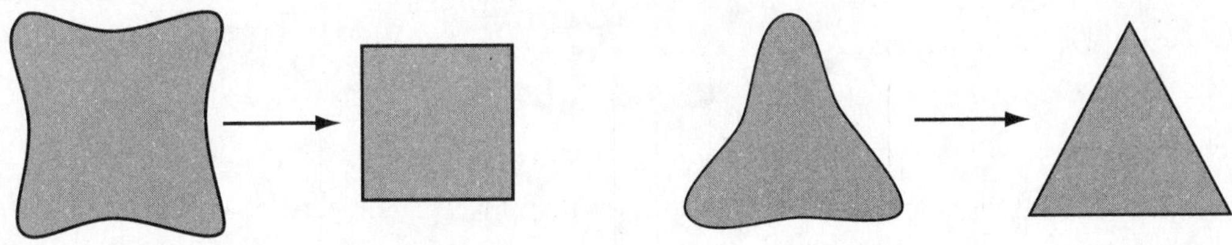

**19.66 Examine some common plastic poker chips and give an opinion on how they were manufactured.**

By the student. Inexpensive poker chips are injection molded, as can be seen by careful examination of the chip surfaces, where a parting line and gate are still visible. Higher-end poker chips, such as those in casinos, are insert molded with a metal core to add weight, and are then coated and decorated.

**19.67 Inspect various plastic products around your home and observe sink marks (see Fig. 19.31c) that typically exist on the surface opposite to the thicker sections. Make suggestions as to how they can be prevented during (a) product design and (b) manufacturing.**

By the student. See also Problem 19.36. The list will vary depending on the particular products considered. The reason for the sink marks are that the thick sections solidify last, and the polymer contracts during solidification and cooling to room temperature, just as in casting of metals. In the product design stage, there are a number of alternatives to prevent sink marks, including designing parts with uniform cross-sections, using insert molding and/or polymers that are less sensitive to contraction and changing process parameters such as injection temperature. At the manufacturing stage, one can add a contour to the die so that the final shape has relaxed to the desired shape, one can attempt to cool portions of the die more than others, or one can mold the part with a machining allowance.

**19.68 Obtain different kinds of tootpaste tubes, carefully cut them across, and comment on your observations on the type of materials used and how the tube could be produced.**

By the student. It will be noted that some collapsible tubes are blow molded, others are injection molded at one end and the other end is joined by hot-tool welding (see p. 1027). Another design is injection-molded rigid tubing where the toothpaste is pumped out. Also, some collapsible tubes have walls that are mutlilayers of different materials and welded on the closed end.

# Chapter 20

# Rapid-Prototyping Operations

## QUALITATIVE PROBLEMS

**20.10 Examine a coffee cup and determine in which orientation you would choose to produce the part if using (a) fused-deposition manufacturing or (b) laminated-object manufacturing processes.**

By the student. In fused-deposition modeling the coffee cup would be prototyped in the same orientation as when it holds coffee; this orientation is selected to minimize the volume of support material and structures needed (see Fig. 20.4 on p. 585). In laminated-object manufacturing the coffee cup would be placed on its side to minimize the numbers of layers since a "support" material is always produced. Note, however, that parts are often fit into a workspace containing many parts, so these options may not always be followed.

**20.11 How would you quickly manufacture tooling for injection molding? Explain any difficulties that may be encountered.**

By the student. There are a number of options. Depending on the polymer to be injection molded, the tooling could be made by

(a) producing a polymer tool in a rapid-prototyping operation, suitable for injection molding. (Note that injection molding can take place in polymer molds, but the cool time is longer and the mold life is lower than if aluminum or copper alloys are used for the mold.)

(b) A pattern is produced from a soft polymer or wax. The pattern is placed on a tree and investment casting from a castable alloy (such as high-silicon aluminum or cast brasses).

(c) A polymer model of a pattern plate is produced, from which one can make a sand mold for sand casting

(d) machining a block of copper or aluminum in a CNC milling machine (see, for example, Fig. 24.17 on p. 740).

**20.12 Summarize the rapid-prototyping processes and the materials which can be used for them.**

By the student. The answer is given in Table 20.1 on p. 513.

**20.13 Which processes described in this chapter are best suited for the production of ceramic parts? Why?**

For direct production of ceramic parts, three-dimensional printing is likely the best option. With the proper binder, this can also be accomplished by fused-deposition modeling, and is also possible by selective laser sintering. However, the ceramic particles will abrade the tooling in FDM and require much heat to fuse in SLS. The 3D printing approach, where a binder is sprayed onto the ceramic particles, is the best approach for making green parts, which are then fired in a furnace to fuse the powder.

**20.14 Why are so few parts in commercial products directly manufactured through rapid-prototyping operations?**

The two main reasons why so few parts are produced by rapid-prototyping operations are production cost and production time. Note that the materials used in rapid prototyping are very expensive; also, although they can be produced quickly as compared to conventional forming operations (and machining unless very expensive CNC equipment is used) mass production is not realistic. There is a quip that the production of a first forging takes six months and a million dollars, but the second forging is then almost free and takes only seconds for manufacture. With rapid prototyping, the first part takes a few hours. The second part takes a few hours, and so on, with no economies of scale. These processes are ideally suited for making single examples of products, but are not intended for mass production.

**20.15 Outline methods of producing metal parts that use the processes described in this chapter.**

This is an open-ended problem in an area of much current research interest with new methods being constantly developed. Referring to Table 20.1 on p. 582 we note that the methods that can be used to produce metal parts are:

- Selective laser sintering can be used to produce metal parts, as described on pp. 588-589. The powder metal part may then be infiltrated by a lower-melting-point metal to enhance its properties (see Section 17.5 on p. 503).
- Three-dimensional printing (p. 589) can be another method, using metal powders, followed by furnace sintering and infiltration if desired.
- Fused-deposition modeling and stereolithography also can be used to produce polymer blanks or patterns for casting operations such as sand or investment casting. In this case, the parts are not produced directly from the rapid prototyping operation, but the patterns or blanks are, which allows much smaller lead times than conventional investment or sand casting.
- Similarly, three-dimensional printing can be performed with sand particles to produce a sand mold for sand or investment casting.

- All of the polymer-based processes in this chapter can be used to also produce polymer molds for metal injection molding (see Section 17.3.3 on p. 496) to make complex powder-metal parts.

**20.16 What are the cleaning and finishing operations in rapid-prototyping processes? Why are they necessary?**

Most rapid-prototyping processes do not produce good surface finish and quality, hence additional finishing is sometimes desired. Also, in stereolithography, for example, polymer liquid residue is left on the parts, and in FDM whiskers and burrs may be developed on surfaces. Furthermore, it may be desirable to paint or decorate the parts.

**20.17** Careful analysis of a rapid-prototyped part indicates that it is made up of layers with a clear filament outline visible on a layer. Is the material a thermoset or a thermoplastic? Explain.

The filament outline suggests that the material was produced in fused-deposition modeling. This process requires adjacent layers to fuse after being extruded. Extrusion and bonding is obviously possible with thermoplastics but very difficult for a thermoset.

**20.18 What is the main difference between additive manufacturing and rapid prototyping?**

Additive manufacturing is a subset of rapid prototyping and refers to parts that are produced through the addition of material, as opposed to subtraction of material. It includes such processes as stereolithography, fused-deposition modeling, solid ground curing and three-dimensional printing (see Section 20.3 on p. 583). There are rapid-prototyping operations that do not involve additive manufacturing, such as CNC machining and virtual prototyping.

**20.19 Make a list of the advantages and limitations of each of the rapid prototyping operations described in this chapter.**

By the student. As examples, the students could investigate cost (FDM, STL have advantages over solid-ground curing, for example), material properties (see Table 20.2 on p. 582) where selective laser sintering with bronze-infiltrated steel powder would be superior, or dimensional tolerances or surface finish.

**20.20 If you are making a prototype of a toy automobile, list the post-rapid- prototyping finishing operations you would perform and why.**

By the student. The answer, as expected, depends on the particular rapid-prototyping process used to create the toy. Consider, for example, fused-deposition modeling: It may be desirable to sand or finish the surface because of the surface texture that exists from the extruded filament. A base coat and paint then can be applied, followed by detailed decorative paint, if desired. Stereolithography may require (and generally it does so) post-curing, followed by roughening (such as by sanding) to allow paint to bond well, followed by painting, as above.

## QUANTITATIVE PROBLEMS

**20.21 Using an approximate cost of \$500 per gallon for the liquid polymer, estimate the material cost of a rapid-prototyped rendering of a typical computer mouse.**

Recognizing that a mouse is mostly hollow, with a wall thickness of approximately 1/8 in., and from the overall dimensions of the mouse, the volume of plastic in it can be calculated as around 1.25 in$^3$. (The dimensions will of course vary by mouse manufacturer). Since one gallon is equal to 230 in$^3$, the cost of the plastic in the mouse would be \$2.71 (which is a very small fraction of the cost of the mouse).

**20.22 The extruder head in a fused-deposition modeling setup has a diameter of 1.25 mm (0.05 in.) and produces layers 0.25 mm (0.01-in.) thick. If the extruder head and polymer extrudate velocities are both 50 mm/s, estimate the production time for the generation of a 50-mm (2-in.) solid cube. Assume that there is a 15 second delay between layers as the extruder head is moved over a wire brush for cleaning.**

Note that although the calculations are shown below, in practice the rapid-prototyping software can easily make this calculation. First, if the thickness of the cube is 50 mm, and the layers are 0.25 mm thick, there are 200 layers, for a total 'inactive' time of (200)(15 s)=3000 s. Note also that the cross-section of the extruded filament in this case is highly elliptical, and thus its shape is not easily determined from the information given in the problem. However, we know that the polymer extrudate speed is 50 mm/s and the orifice diameter is 1.25 mm, hence the volume flow rate is

$$Q = vA = (50 \text{ mm/s}) \left[\frac{\pi}{4}(1.25 \text{ mm})^2\right] = 61.36 \text{ mm}^3/\text{sec}$$

The cube has a volume of (50)(50)(50)=125,000 mm$^3$ and the time required to extrude this volume is 125,000/61.36=2037 s. Hence the total production time is 2037 s + 3000 s = 5037 s = 1.4 hrs.

**20.23 Using the data for Problem 20.22 and assuming that the porosity for the support material is 50%, calculate the production rate for making a 100-mm (4-in.) high cup with an outside diameter of 88 mm (3.5 in.) and wall thickness of 6 mm (0.25 in.). Consider both the case with the (a) closed-end up and (b) down.**

(a) Closed-end down. For this case, there is no support material needed. There are 400 layers, so the 'inactive' time is 6000s. The cup wall volume is

$$V = \frac{\pi}{4}d^2t + \pi dht = \frac{\pi}{4}(87.5 \text{ mm})^2(6.25 \text{ mm}) + \pi(87.5 \text{ mm})(100 \text{ mm})(6.26 \text{ mm})$$

or $V = 209,000$ mm$^3$. This takes $209.000/61.36 = 3400$ s to extrude; the total time is $6000 + 3400 = 9400$ s $= 2.6$ hours.

(b) Closed-end up. Now, in addition to the wall, the interior must be filled with support for the closed-end on top. The volume of the cup is

$$V = \frac{\pi}{4}d^2h = \frac{\pi}{4}(87.5 \text{ mm})^2(100 \text{ mm}) = 601,000 \text{ mm}^3$$

Since the support material has a porosity of 50%, the time required to extrude the support material is $t = 300,000/61.36 = 4900$ s $= 1.36$ hrs. Therefore, the total time for producing the part and the support is $2.6 + 1.36 = 3.96$, or about four hours.

## SYNTHESIS, DESIGN, AND PROJECTS

**20.24 A current topic of research is to produce parts by rapid-prototyping operations and then to use them in experimental stress analysis in order to infer the strength of the final parts produced by conventional manufacturing operations. List your concerns with this approach and outline means of addressing these concerns.**

A large number of concerns can be raised, and this answer is only representative of possible responses. Depending on the particular process, the parts made from rapid prototyping may be anisotropic, and therefore very different from other materials. Also, the thermoplastics from FDM may behave differently from brittle castings, while the thermosets may not represent ductile forgings very well.

**20.25 Because of relief of residual stresses during curing, long unsupported overhangs in parts from stereolithography will tend to curl. Suggest methods of controlling or eliminating this problem.**

The techniques are similar to those for casting where the same problem was encountered. They include making certain that long sections are not used when possible, using stiffening ribs in the part and using tapered sections.

**20.26 Because rapid-prototyping machines represent a large capital investment, few companies can justify the purchase of their own system. Consequently, service companies which produce parts based on their customers' drawings have become common. Conduct an informal survey of such service companies and determine the classes of rapid-prototyping machines that are used, and determine their percentages.**

By the student. There are numerous such services that can be quickly found on Internet search engines. However, as the cost of rapid-prototyping machines continues to decrease and their use becomes more widespread, more and more companies are acquiring in-house rapid-prototyping capabilities. An interesting modification to this problem is to investigate the annual volume of rapid-prototyping projects outsourced by companies.

**20.27 One of the major advantages of stereolithography is that it can use semi-transparent polymers so that internal details of parts can be readily discerned. List and describe a few parts in which this feature is valuable.**

By the student. The transparent feature is especially useful for (a) flow visualization, such as with a new heat-exchanger design; (b) investigating mating parts to make sure the interface is as intended; and (c) implantable medical devices, where the body part is made from stereolithography for visualization of how the devices function.

**20.28 A manufacturing technique is being proposed which uses a variation of fused-deposition modeling where there are two polymer filaments that are melted and mixed before being extruded in order to produce the workpiece. What advantages does this method have?**

By the student. There are several advantages to this approach, including:

- If the polymers have different colors (for example, black and white or blue and white) blending the polymers can produce a part with a built-in color scheme.
- If the polymers have different mechanical properties, then functionally graded materials can be produced, that is, materials with a designed blend of mechanical properties.
- Higher production rates and workpiece properties may be achieved.
- If the second polymer can be leached, it can be developed into a technique for producing porous polymers or ship-in-the-bottle type parts.

**20.29 Identify the RP processes described in this chapter that you can, on a modest scale, perform with the materials available in your home or you can purchase easily at low cost. Explain how you would go about it. Consider materials such as thin plywood, thick paper, glue, and butter, and the use of various tools and energy sources.**

Numerous answers can be given to this problem and the students are encouraged to apply their creativity in formulating a solution. Some suggestions are:

- Paper, plywood, or cardboard can be cut and glued together to form three-dimensional objects, similar to those made by laminated-object manufacturing.
- Glue, butter, or chocolate can be drizzled or placed onto wax paper, and chilled. The chilled layer can then be attached to other layers, thus simulating fused-deposition modeling or three-dimensional printing.
- Sand can be placed on sheets of paper, and drizzled on top with glue to make layers, similar to three-dimensional printing.

**20.30 Design a machine that uses rapid-prototyping technologies to produce ice sculptures. Describe its basic features, commenting on the effect of size and shape complexity on your design.**

By the student. A number of machines can be designed, including:

- A machine can use the principles of ballistic particle manufacturing to spray small droplets of water onto a frozen base and produce the sculpture layer-by-layer.
- Sheets of ice can be produced and then cut with a laser. To do so, it is likely that small particles suspended in the ice will be needed to cause localized heating, or else water-jet cutting (see Section 27.8 on p. 855) can produce the layers .
- Layers of shaved ice can be sprayed using a water jet, similar to three-dimensional printing.

# Chapter 21

# Fundamentals of Machining

## QUALITATIVE PROBLEMS

**21.14 Are the locations of maximum temperature and crater wear related? If so, explain why.**

Although various factors can affect crater wear, the most significant factors in crater wear are diffusion (a mechanism whereby material is removed from the rake face of the tool) and the degree of chemical affinity between the tool and the chip. Thus, the higher the temperature, the higher the wear. Referring collectively to all the figures on pp. 625 and 633, we note that temperature and crater wear indeed are related.

**21.15 Is material ductility important for machinability? Explain.**

Let's first note that the general definition of machinability (Section 21.7 on p. 638) involves workpiece surface finish and integrity, tool life, force and power required, and chip control. Ductility directly affects the type of chip produced which, in turn, affects surface finish, the nature of forces involved (less ductile materials may lead to tool chatter), and more ductile materials produce continues chips which may not be easy to control.

**21.16 Explain why studying the types of chips produced is important in understanding cutting operations.**

It is important to study the types of chips produced (see Section 21.2.1 on p. 613) because they significantly influence the surface finish produced, cutting forces, as well as the overall cutting operation. Note, for example, that continuous chips are generally associated with good surface finish and steady cutting forces. Built-up edge chips usually result in poor surface finish; serrated chips can have similar effects. Discontinuous chips usually result in poor surface finish and dimensional accuracy, and involve cutting forces that fluctuate. Thus, the type of chip is a good indicator of the overall quality of the cutting operation.

**21.17 Why do you think the maximum temperature in orthogonal cutting is located at about the middle of the tool-chip interface? (Hint: Note that the two sources of heat are (a) shearing in the primary shear plane and (b) friction at the tool-chip interface.)**

It is reasonable that the maximum temperature in orthogonal cutting is located at about the middle of the tool-chip interface (see, for example, Fig. 21.12 on p. 625). The chip reaches high temperatures in the primary shear plane, and the temperature would decrease from then on. If no frictional heat was involved, we would expect the highest temperature to occur at the shear plane. After the chip is formed, it slides up the rake face of the tool. The friction at the tool-chip interface is a heat source and thus increases the temperature, and hence the temperature due only to frictional heating would be highest at the end of the tool-chip contact length. These two opposing effects are additive and, as a result, we find that the temperature is highest somewhere in between the tool tip and the end of the tool-chip contact zone.

**21.18 Tool life can be almost infinite at low cutting speeds. Would you then recommend that all machining be done at low speeds? Explain.**

Tool life can be almost infinite at very low cutting speeds (see Fig. 21.16 on p. 629) but this reason alone would not necessarily justify using low cutting speeds. Most obviously, low cutting speeds remove less material in a given time which, unless otherwise justified, would be economically undesirable. Lower cutting speeds also often also lead to the formation of a built-up edge and discontinuous chips, thus affecting surface finish. (See also Example 21.4 on p. 631.)

**21.19 Explain the consequences of allowing temperatures to rise to high levels in cutting.**

By the student. There are several consequences of allowing temperatures to rise to high levels in cutting (see also pp. 623-624), such as: (a) Tool wear will be accelerated due to high temperatures. (b) High temperatures will cause dimensional changes in the workpiece, thus reducing dimensional accuracy. (c) Excessively high temperatures in the cutting zone can induce thermal damage and metallurgical changes to the machined surface.

**21.20 The cutting force increases with depth-of-cut and decreasing rake angle. Explain why.**

It is logical that the cutting force increases as the depth of cut increases and rake angle decreases. Deeper cuts remove more material, thus requiring a higher cutting force. As the rake angle, $\alpha$, decreases, the shear angle, $\phi$ , decreases (see Eqs. (21.3) and (21.4) on p. 612), and hence shear energy dissipation and cutting forces increase.

**21.21 Why is it not always advisable to increase cutting speed in order to increase production rate?**

The main consideration here is that as the cutting speed increases, tool life decreases. See also Example 21.4 on p. 631 and note that there has to be an optimum cutting speed, as also discussed in Section 25.8 on p. 783.

**21.22 What are the consequences if a cutting tool chips?**

By the student. Tool chipping has various effects, such as poor surface finish and dimensional control of the part being machined; possible temperature rise; and cutting force fluctuations and increases. Chipping is indicative of a harmful condition for the cutting tool material, and often is followed by more extreme failure.

**21.23 What are the effects of performing a cutting operation with a dull tool? A very sharp tool?**

By the student. There are many effects of performing a cutting operation with a dull tool. Note that a dull tool has an increased tip radius (see Fig. 21.22 on p. 636); as the tip radius increases (the tool dulls), the cutting force increases due to the fact that the effective rake angle is decreased. In addition, we can see that shallow depths of cut may not be possible because the tool may simply ride over the surface without producing chips. Another effect is inducing surface residual stresses, tearing, and cracking of the machined surface due to the heat generated by the dull tool tip rubbing against this surface. Dull tools also increase the tendency for BUE formation, which leads to poor surface finish.

**21.24 To what factors do you attribute the difference in the specific energies when machining the materials shown in Table 21.2? Why is there a range of energies for each group of material?**

The differences in specific energies observed in Table 21.2 on p. 622, whether among different materials or within types of materials, can be attributed to differences in the mechanical and physical properties of these materials, which affect the cutting operation. For example, as the material strength increases, so does the total specific energy. Differences in frictional characteristics of the tool and workpiece materials would also play a role. Physical properties such as thermal conductivity and specific heat, both of which increase cutting temperatures as they decrease (see Eq. (21.19a) on p. 624), also could be responsible for such differences in practice. These points are confirmed when one closely examines Table 21.2 and observes that the ranges for materials such as steels, refractory alloys, and high-temperature alloys are large, in agreement with our knowledge of the large variety of materials which fall under these categories.

**21.25 Explain why it is possible to remove more material between tool resharpenings by lowering the cutting speed.**

The main consideration here is that as the cutting speed increases, tool life decreases. See Example 21.4 on p. 631. As the example states, there is, of course, an optimum cutting speed, as also discussed in Section 25.8 on p. 783.

**21.26 Noting that the dimension d in Fig. 21.4a is very small, explain why the shear strain rate in metal cutting is so high.**

The shear strain rate in metal cutting is high even though the dimension $d$ is very small. Referring to Fig. 21.4 on p. 611, we note that shear-strain rate is defined as the ratio of shear velocity, $V_s$, to the dimension $d$ in the shear plane. Since $V_s$ is on the same order of magnitude as the cutting speed, $V$, and the dimension $d$ is very small (on the order of $10^{-2}$ to $10^{-3}$ in.), the shear strain rate is very high.

**21.27 Explain the significance of Eq. (21.7).**

The significance of Eq. (21.7) on p. 619 is that it determines an effective rake angle for oblique cutting (a process of more practical significance in most machining operations), which we can relate back to the simpler orthogonal cutting models for purposes of analysis. Oblique cutting is extremely complicated otherwise, and certainly cannot be treated effectively in an undergraduate textbook without Eq. (21.7).

**21.28 Comment on your observations regarding Figs. 21.12 and 21.13.**

By the student. General observations are as follows:

(a) The maximum temperature, both on flank and rake faces, are at a location approximately halfway along the tool-workpiece contact surfaces.

(b) Temperatures and their gradients can be very high.

(c) Cutting speed has a major effect on temperature.

(d) Chip temperatures are much higher than workpiece temperatures.

**21.29 Describe the consequences of exceeding the allowable wear land (Table 21.4) for various cutting-tool materials.**

The major consequences would be:

(a) As the wear land increases, the wear flat will rub against the machined surface and thus temperature will increase due to friction.

(b) Dimensional control will become difficult and surface damage may result.

(c) Some burnishing may also take place on the machined surface, leading to residual stresses and temperature rise.

(d) Cutting forces will increase because of the increased land, requiring greater power for the same machining operation.

**21.30 Comment on your observations regarding the hardness variations shown in Fig. 21.6a.**

By the student. What is obvious in Fig. 21.6a on p. 21.6a on p. 615 is that the chip undergoes a very high degree of strain hardening, as evidenced by the hardness distribution in the chip. Also, there is clearly and not surprisingly an even higher level of cold work in the built-up edge, to as much as three times the workpiece hardness.

**21.31 Why does the temperature in cutting depend on the cutting speed, feed, and depth-of-cut? Explain in terms of the relevant process variables.**

Refer to Eq. (21.19a) on p. 624. As cutting speed increases, there is less time for the heat generated to be dissipated, hence temperature increases. As feed increases (such as in turning; see Fig. 21.2 on p. 608) or as the depth of cut increases (such as in orthogonal cutting), the chip is thicker. With larger thickness-to-surface area of the chip, there is less opportunity for the heat to be dissipated, hence temperature increases.

**21.32 You will note that the values of a and b in Eq. (21.19b) are higher for high-speed steels than for carbides. Why is this so?**

As stated on p. 624, the magnitudes of $a$ and $b$ depend on the type of cutting tool as well as the workpiece materials. Factors to be considered include thermal conductivity and friction at the tool-chip and tool-workpiece interfaces. Carbides have higher thermal conductivity than high-speed steels (see Table 21.1 on p. 649) and also have lower friction. Consequently, these constants are lower for carbides; in other words, the temperature is less sensitive to speed and feed.

**21.33 As shown in Fig. 21.14, the percentage of the total cutting energy carried away by the chip increases with cutting speed. Why?**

The reason is due to the fact that as cutting speed increases, the heat generated (particularly that portion due to the shear plane deformation) is carried away at a higher rate. Conversely, if the speed is low, the heat generated will have more time to dissipate into the workpiece.

**21.34 Describe in detail the effects that a dull tool can have on cutting operations.**

By the student. There are many effects of performing a cutting operation with a dull tool. Note that a dull tool has an increased tip radius (see Fig. 21.22 on p. 636); as the tip radius increases (the tool dulls), the cutting force increases due to the fact that the effective rake angle is decreased. In addition, we can see that shallow depths of cut may not be possible because the tool may simply ride over the surface without producing chips. Another effect is inducing surface residual stresses, tearing, and cracking of the machined surface due to the heat generated by the dull tool tip rubbing against this surface. Dull tools also increase the tendency for BUE formation, which leads to poor surface finish.

**21.35 Explain whether it is desirable to have a high or low (a) n value and (b) $C$ value in the Taylor tool-life equation.**

As we can see in Fig. 21.17 on p. 629, high $n$ values are desirable because, for the same tool life, we can cut at higher speeds, thus increasing productivity. Conversely, we can also see that for the same cutting speed, high n values give longer tool life. Note that as $n$ approaches zero, tool life becomes extremely sensitive to cutting speed. These trends can also be seen by inspecting Eq. (21.20a) on p. 628. As for the value of $C$, note that its magnitude is the same as the cutting speed at $T = 1$. Consequently, it is desirable to have high $C$ values because we can cut at higher speeds, as can also be seen in Fig. 21.17.

**21.36 The tool-life curve for ceramic tools in Fig. 21.17 is to the right of those for other tool materials. Why?**

Ceramic tools are harder and have higher resistance to temperature; consequently, they resist wear better than other tool materials shown in the figure. Ceramics are also chemically inert even at the elevated temperatures of machining. The high hardness leads to abrasive wear resistance, and the chemical inertness leads to adhesive wear resistance.

**21.37 Why are tool temperatures low at low cutting speeds and high at high cutting speeds?**

At very low cutting speeds, as energy is dissipated in the shear plane and at chip-tool interface, it is conducted through the workpiece and/or tool and eventually to the environment. At higher speeds, conduction cannot take place quickly enough to prevent temperatures from rising significantly. At even higher speeds, however, the heat will be taken away by the chip, hence the workpiece will stay cool. This is one of the major advantages of high speed machining (see Section 25.5 on p. 760).

**21.38 Can high-speed machining be performed without the use of a cutting fluid?**

Yes, this is precisely the emphasis of Case Study 25.1 on p. 779. The main purposes of a cutting fluid (see Section 21.12 on p. 665) is to lubricate and to remove heat, usually accomplished by flooding the tool and workpiece by the fluid. In high speed machining, most of the heat is conveyed from the cutting zone through the chip, so the need for a cutting fluid is less (see also Fig. 21.14 on p. 626).

**21.39 Given your understanding of the basic metal-cutting process, what are the important physical and chemical properties of a cutting tool?**

Physically, the important properties are hardness (especially hot hardness), toughness, thermal conductivity and thermal expansion coefficient. Chemically, it must be inert to the workpiece material at the cutting temperatures.

## QUANTITATIVE PROBLEMS

**21.40 Let $n = 0.5$ and $C = 300$ in the Taylor equation for tool wear. What is the percent increase in tool life if the cutting speed is reduced by (a) 30% and (b) 50%?**

The Taylor equation for tool wear is given by Eq. (21.20a) on p. 628, which can be rewritten as

$$C = VT^n$$

Thus, for the case of $C = 300$ and $n = 0.5$, we have $300 = V\sqrt{T}$.

(a) To determine the percent increase in tool life if the cutting speed is reduced by 30%, let $V_2 = 0.7V_1$. We may then write

$$0.7V_1\sqrt{T_2} = V_1\sqrt{T_1}$$

Rearranging this equation, we find that $T_2/T_1 = 2.04$, hence tool life increases by 104%.

(b) To determine the percent increase in tool life if the cutting speed is reduced by 50%, we follow the same procedure and find that $T_2/T_1 = 4$. This means that tool life increases by (4 - 1)/1 = 3, or 300%.

**21.41 Assume that, in orthogonal cutting, the rake angle is 15° and the coefficient of friction is 0.2. Using Eq. (21.3), determine the percentage increase in chip thickness when the friction is doubled.**

We begin with Eq. (21.1b) on p. 611 which shows the relationship between the chip thickness and depth of cut. Assuming that the depth of cut and the rake angle are constant, we can rewrite this equation as

$$\frac{t_o}{t_c} = \frac{\cos(\phi_2 - \alpha)\sin\phi_2}{\cos(\phi_1 - \alpha)\sin\phi_2}$$

Now, using Eq. (21.3) on p. 612 we can determine the two shear angles. For Case 1, we have from Eq. (21.4) that $\mu = 0.2 = \tan\beta$, or $\beta = 11.3°$, and hence

$$\phi_2 = 45° + \frac{15°}{2} - \frac{11.3°}{2} = 46.85°$$

and for Case 2, where $\mu = 0.4$, we have $\beta = \tan^{-1} 0.4 = 21.8°$ and hence $\phi_2 = 41.6°$. Substituting these values in the above equation for chip thickness ratio, we obtain

$$\frac{t_o}{t_c} = \frac{\cos(\phi_2 - \alpha)\sin\phi_1}{\cos(\phi_1 - \alpha)\sin\phi_2} = \frac{\cos(41.6° - 15°)\sin 46.85°}{\cos(46.85° - 15°)\sin 41.6°} = 1.16$$

Therefore, the chip thickness increased by 16%.

**21.42 Derive Eq. (21.11).**

From the force diagram shown in Fig. 21.11 on p. 620, we express the following:

$$F = (F_t + F_c \tan\alpha)\cos\alpha$$

and

$$N = (F_c - F_t \tan\alpha)\cos\alpha$$

Therefore, by definition,

$$\mu = \frac{F}{N} = \frac{(F_t + F_c \tan\alpha)\cos\alpha}{(F_c - F_t \tan\alpha)\cos\alpha}$$

**21.43 Taking carbide as an example and using Eq. (21.19b), determine how much the feed should be reduced in order to keep the mean temperature constant when the cutting speed is tripled.**

We begin with Eq. (21.19b) on p. 624 which, for our case, can be rewritten as

$$V_1^a f_1^b = (3V_1)^a f_2^b$$

Rearranging and simplifying this equation, we obtain

$$\frac{f_2}{f_1} = 3^{-a/b}$$

For carbide tools, approximate values are given on p. 624 as $a = 0.2$ and $b = 0.125$. Substituting these, we obtain

$$\frac{f_2}{f_1} = 3^{-(0.2/0.125)} = 0.17$$

Therefore, the feed should be reduced by (1-0.17) = 0.83, or 83%.

**21.44 Using trigonometric relationships, derive an expression for the ratio of shear energy to frictional energy in orthogonal cutting, in terms of angles $\alpha$, $\beta$, and $\phi$ only.**

We begin with the following expressions for $u_s$ and $u_f$, respectively (see p. 622):

$$u_s = \frac{F_s V_s}{w t_o V} \quad \text{and} \quad u_f = \frac{F V_c}{w t_o V}$$

Thus their ratio becomes

$$\frac{u_s}{u_f} = \frac{F_s V_s}{F V_c}$$

The terms involved above can be defined as

$$F = R \sin \beta$$

and from Fig. 21.11 on p. 620,

$$F_s = R \cos(\phi + \beta - \alpha)$$

However, we can simplify this expression further by noting in the table for Problem 20.48 below that the magnitudes of $\phi$ and $\alpha$ are close to each other. Hence we can approximate this expression as

$$F_s = R \cos \beta$$

Also,

$$V_s = \frac{V \cos \alpha}{\cos(\phi - \alpha)}$$

$$V_c = \frac{V \sin \alpha}{\cos(\phi - \alpha)}$$

Combining these expressions and simplifying, we obtain

$$\frac{u_s}{u_f} = \cot \beta \cot \alpha$$

**21.45 An orthogonal cutting operation is being carried out under the following conditions: $t_o = 0.1$ mm, $t_c = 0.2$ mm, width of cut = 5 mm, $V = 2$ m/s, rake angle = 10°, $F_c = 500$ N, and $F_t = 200$ N. Calculate the percentage of the total energy that is dissipated in the shear plane.**

The total power dissipated is obtained from Eq. (21.13) on p. 621 and the power for shearing from Eq. (21.14). Thus, the total power is

$$\text{Power} = (500)(2) = 1000\text{N-m/s}$$

To determine power for shearing we need to determine $F_s$ and $V_s$. We know that

$$F_s = R \cos(\phi + \beta - \alpha)$$

where

$$R = \sqrt{(500)^2 + (200)^2} = 538 \text{ N}$$

also, $\phi$ is obtained from Eq. (20.1) where $r = 0.1/0.2 = 0.5$. Hence

$$\phi = \tan^{-1}\left[\frac{(0.5)(\cos 10^\circ)}{1-(0.5)(\sin 10^\circ)}\right] = 28.4^\circ$$

We can then determine $\beta$ from the expression

$$F_c = R\cos(\beta - \alpha)$$

or,

$$500 = 538\cos(\beta - 10^\circ)$$

Hence

$$\beta = 31.7^\circ$$

Therefore,

$$F_s = 538\cos(28.4^\circ + 31.7^\circ - 10^\circ) = 345 \text{ N}$$

which allows us to calculate $V_s$ using Eq. (21.6a) on p. 613. Hence,

$$V_s = 2\cos 10^\circ / \cos(28.4^\circ - 10^\circ) = 2.08 \text{ m/s}$$

and the power for shearing is (345)(2.08) = 718 N-m/s. Thus, the percentage is 718/1000 = 0.718, or about 72%.

**21.46 Explain how you would go about estimating the $C$ and $n$ values for the four tool materials shown in Fig. 21.17.**

From Eq. (21.20) on p. 628 we note that the value of $C$ corresponds to the cutting speed for a tool life of 1 min. From Fig. 21.16 on p. 629 and by extrapolating the tool-life curves to a tool life of 1 min. we estimate the $C$ values approximately as (ranging from ceramic to HSS) 11000, 3000, 400, and 200, respectively. Likewise, the $n$ values are obtained from the negative inverse slopes, and are estimated as: 0.73 (36°), 0.47 (25°), 0.14 (8°), and 0.11 (6°), respectively. Note that these $n$ values compare well with those given in Table 21.3 on p. 628.

**21.47 Derive Eq. (21.1).**

Refer to the shear-plane length as $l$. Figure 21.3 on p. 609 suggests that the depth of cut, $t_o$, is given by

$$t_o = l\sin\phi$$

Similarly, from Fig. 21.4 on p. 611, the chip thickness is seen to be

$$t_c = l\cos(\phi - \alpha)$$

Substituting these relationships into the definition of cutting ratio gives

$$r = \frac{t_o}{t_c} = \frac{l\sin\phi}{l\cos(\phi-\alpha)} = \frac{\sin\phi}{\cos(\phi-\alpha)}$$

**21.48 Assume that, in orthogonal cutting, the rake angle, $\alpha$, is 25° and the friction angle, $\beta$, is 30° at the chiptool interface. Determine the percentage change in chip thickness when the friction angle is 50°. (Note: Do not use Eq. (21.3) or (21.4).**

This problem is similar to Problem 20.41 above. However, since it states that we cannot use Eq. (21.3) on p. 612, we have to find a means to determine the shear angle, $\phi$, first. This requires further reading by the student to find other shear-angle relationships similar to Eq. (21.3) or Eq. (21.4), with the guidance of the instructor and referring to the Bibliography at the end of this chapter. Note that many researchers have measured shear plane angles and developed shear plane angle relationships; this solution is only one example of an acceptable answer, and students should be encouraged to find a solution based on their own literature review. Indeed, such a literature review is an invaluable exercise.

This solution will use experimental measurements of the shear plane angle obtained by S. Kobayashi and printed in Kalpakjian, S., *Manufacturing Processes for Engineering Materials*, 3rd ed., 1997:

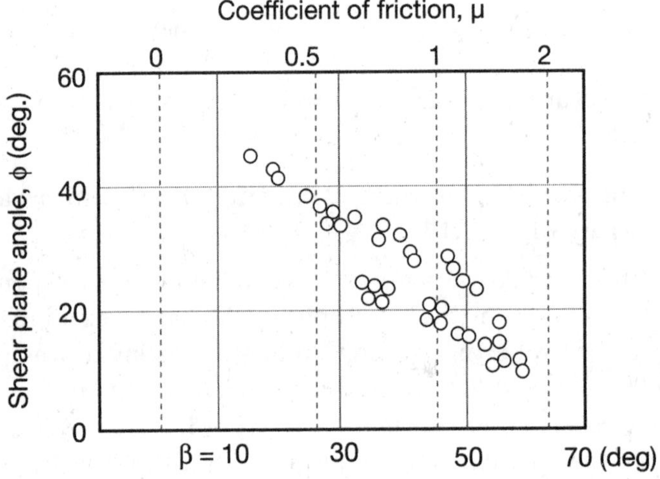


From this chart, we can estimate that for $\beta = 30°$, $\phi$ is approximately 25° and if $\beta = 50^circ$, $\phi = 15°$. We now follow the same approach as in Problem 20.41. We begin with Eq. (21.1) on p. 600 which shows the relationship between the chip thickness and depth of cut. Assume that the depth of cut and the rake angle are constant, we can rewrite this equation as

$$\frac{t_o}{t_c} = \frac{\cos(\phi_2 - \alpha)\sin\phi_1}{\cos(\phi_1 - \alpha)\sin\phi_2} = \frac{\cos(15° - 25°)\sin 25°}{\cos(25° - 25°)\sin 15°} = 1.60$$

Therefore, the chip thickness increased by 60 percent.

**21.49 Show that, for the same shear angle, there are two rake angles that give the same cutting ratio.**

By studying Eq. (21.1b) on p. 611, we note that the denominator can give the same value for the angle $(\phi - \alpha)$ that is either positive or negative. Therefore, the statement is correct.

**21.50 With appropriate diagrams, show how the use of a cutting fluid can change the magnitude of the thrust force, $F_t$ , in Fig. 21.11.**

Note in Fig. 21.11 on p. 620 that the use of a cutting fluid will reduce the friction force, $F$, at the tool-chip interface. This, in turn, will change the force diagram, hence the magnitude of the thrust force, $F_t$. Consider the sketch given below. The left sketch shows cutting without an effective cutting fluid, so that the friction force, $F$ is large compared to the normal force, $N$. The sketch on the right shows the effect if the friction force is a smaller fraction of the normal force because of this cutting fluid. As can be seen, the cutting force is reduced with the effective fluid. The largest effect is on the thrust force, but there is a noticeable effect on cutting force. This effect becomes larger as the rake angle increases.

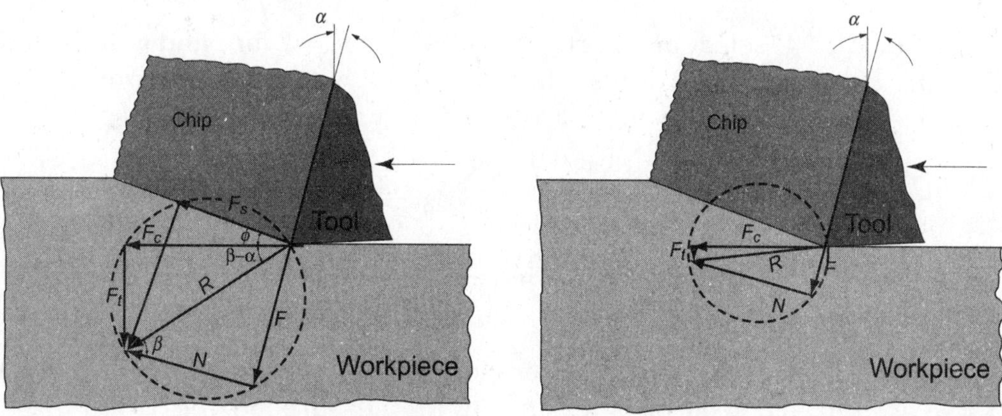


**21.51 For a turning operation using a ceramic cutting tool, if the speed is increased by 50%, by what factor must the feed rate be modified to obtain a constant tool life? Use $n = 0.5$ and $y = 0.6$.**

Equation (21.22) on p. 628 will be used for this problem. Since the tool life is constant, we can write the following:

$$C^{1/n}V_1^{-1/n}d_1^{-x/n}f_1^{-y/n} = C^{1/n}V_2^{-1/n}d_2^{-x/n}f_2^{-y/n}$$

Note that the depth of cut is constant, hence $d_1 = d_2$, and also it is given that $V_2 = 1.5V_1$. Substituting the known values into this equation yields:

$$V_1^{-2}f_1^{-0.6/0.5} = (1.5V_1)^{-2}f_2^{-0.6/0.5}$$

or

$$1.5^2 = \left(\frac{f_2}{f_1}\right)^{-1.2}$$

so that

$$\frac{f_2}{f_1} = \left(1.5^2\right)^{1/1.2} = 50.8$$

**21.52 In Example 21.3, if the cutting speed, $V$, is doubled, will the answer be different? Explain.**

Refer to Example 21.3 on p. 630. The values of $n = 0.5$ and $C = 400$ are preserved, and the values of $V_2 = 2V_1$ will be used. The Taylor tool life equation can be written as

$$2V_1\sqrt{T_2} = V_1\sqrt{T_1}$$

Simplifying this expression,

$$\frac{\sqrt{T_2}}{\sqrt{T_1}} = \frac{V_1}{2V_1} = \frac{1}{2} \quad \rightarrow \quad \frac{T_2}{T_1} = 0.25$$

Therefore, the life has been reduced by 75%.

**21.53 Using Eq. (21.24) select an appropriate feed for $R = 1$ mm and a desired roughness of 1 $\mu$m. How would you adjust this feed to allow for nose wear of the tool during extended cuts? Explain your reasoning.**

If $R_a = 1\ \mu\text{m}$, and $R = 1$ mm, then

$$f^2 = (1\ \mu\text{m})(8)(1\ \text{mm}) = 8 \times 10^{-9}\ \text{m}^2 \quad \rightarrow \quad f = 0.089\ \text{mm/rev}$$

If nose wear occurs, then the radius will increase. The feed will similarly have to increase, per the equation above.

**21.54 Using a carbide cutting tool, the temperature in a cutting operation with a speed of 300 ft/min and feed of 0.002 in./rev is measured to be 1200°F. What is the approximate temperature if the speed is doubled? What speed is required to lower the maximum cutting temperature to 900°F?**

Equation (21.19a) on p. 624 is needed to solve this problem, which is rewritten as:

$$T_{\text{mean}} = \frac{1.2Y_f}{\rho c}\sqrt[3]{\frac{Vt_o}{K}} \quad \rightarrow \quad \frac{T_{\text{mean}}}{\sqrt[3]{V}} = \frac{1.2Y_f}{\rho c}\sqrt[3]{\frac{t_o}{K}}$$

Note that the text warns that appropriate units need to be used. It is reasonable in this case to use °F instead of °R, because, clearly, a cutting speed near zero does not lead to temperatures below room temperature. Therefore, using $T_{\text{mean}} = 1200°\text{F}$ and $V = 300$ ft/min yields

$$\frac{T_{\text{mean}}}{\sqrt[3]{V}} = \frac{1.2Y_f}{\rho c}\sqrt[3]{\frac{t_o}{K}} = \frac{1200°\text{F}}{\sqrt[3]{300\ \text{ft/min}}}$$

For the first part of the problem, we take $V = 600$ ft/min, yielding

$$\frac{T_{\text{mean}}}{\sqrt[3]{600}} = \frac{1200°\text{F}}{\sqrt[3]{300\ \text{ft/min}}}$$

or $T_{\text{mean}} = 1511°\text{F}$. If the maximum temperature is lowered to 900°F, then we have

$$\frac{900°\text{F}}{\sqrt[3]{V}} = \frac{1200°\text{F}}{\sqrt[3]{300\ \text{ft/min}}}$$

which is solved as $V = 126$ ft/min.

**21.55 Assume that you are an instructor covering the topics described in this chapter, and you are giving a quiz on the numerical aspects to test the understanding of the students. Prepare two quantitative problems and supply the answers.**

By the student. This open-ended question requires considerable focus and understanding on the part of students, and has been found to be a very valuable homework problem.

## SYNTHESIS, DESIGN, AND PROJECTS

**21.56 As we have seen, chips carry away the majority of the heat generated during machining. If chips did not have this capacity, what suggestions would you make in order to be able to carry out machining processes without excessive heat? Explain.**

By the student. If chips couldn't carry away the heat, then some other means would be needed to cool the workpiece and the cutting tool. The obvious solution is a generous flood of cutting fluid or more advanced methods such as high-pressure systems or through the cutting tool system, as described on p. 668.

**21.57 Tool life is increased greatly when an effective means of cooling and lubrication is implemented. Design methods of delivering this fluid to cutting zone and discuss the advantages and limitations of your design.**

By the student. See pp. 667-668.

**21.58 Design an experimental setup whereby orthogonal cutting can be simulated in a turning operation on a lathe.**

By the student. This can be done simply by placing a thin-walled tube in the headstock of a lathe (see Fig. 21.2 on p. 608, where the solid bar is now replaced with a tube) and machining the end of the tube with a simple, straight tool. The feed on the lathe will become the depth of cut, $t_o$, in orthogonal cutting, and the chip width will be the same as the wall thickness of the tube.

**21.59 Describe your thought on whether chips produced during machining can be used to make useful products. Give some examples of possible products and comment on their characteristics and differences if the same products were made by other manufacturing processes. Which types of chips would be desirable for this purpose?**

By the student. This can be a challenging problem and many students may conclude (incorrectly) that there are no useful products that can be made from chips. However, the following are some examples:

- Short or discontinuous chips, as well as thin and long chips, can be used as metal reinforcing fibers for nonmetallic materials such as polymers or cement.

- Shaved sheet can be produced from metal, as described in Problem 21.62.
- Metal filters can be produced by compacting the chips into solid shapes, as can be done using powder-metallurgy techniques.
- Novel jewelry can be produced from chips.

**21.60 We have stated that cutting tools can be designed so that the tool-chip contact length is reduced by recessing the rake face of the tool some distance away from its tip. Explain the possible advantages of such a tool.**

By the student. The principal reason is that by reducing the tool-chip contact, the friction force, $F$, is reduced, thus cutting forces are reduced. Chip morphology may also change. The student is encouraged to search the technical literature regarding this question.

**21.61 We have stated the chip formation mechanism can also be observed by scraping the surface of a stick of butter with a sharp knife. Using butter at different temperatures, including frozen, conduct such an experiment. Keep the depth of cut constant and hold the knife at different angles (to simulate the tool rake angle), including oblique scraping. Describe your observations regarding the type of chips produced. Also comment on the force that your hand feels while scraping and whether you observe any chatter when the butter is very cold.**

By the student. This is a simple experiment to perform. By changing the temperature of the stick of butter and the knife angle, one can demonstrate various chip formations and observe the changes that occur when the temperature is changed. Chattering of the knife and how it is related to chip morphology can also be explored.

**21.62 Experiments have shown that it is possible to produce thin, wide chips, such as 0.08 mm (0.003 in.) thick and 10 mm (4 in.) wide, which would be similar to rolled sheet. Materials have been aluminum, magnesium, and stainless steel. A typical setup would be similar to orthogonal cutting, by machining the periphery of a solid round bar with a straight tool moving radially inward. Describe your thoughts on producing thin metal sheet by this method, its surface characteristics, and its properties.**

By the student. There are some advantages to this material. The material has undergone an intense shear during cutting, and therefore the material develops a fine grained, highly oriented structure. One side (that against the tool) will have a shiny surface finish, while the other side is rough (see chip surfaces in Fig. 21.3a on p. 609 and Fig. 21.5 on p. 614).

**21.63 Describe your thoughts on recycling of chips produced during machining in a plant. Include considerations regarding chips produced by dry cutting versus those produced by machining with a cutting fluid.**

By the student. Chips are now recycled more commonly, although cutting-fluid reclamation (removal) is often attempted before melting the chips. Cutting fluids often can cause volatile organic compounds (to be exhausted upon combustion) so this can be an environmental issue. Also, an effort must to be made to keep classes of materials separate; for example, aluminum and steel chips have to be separated for recycling.

# Chapter 22

# Cutting-Tool Materials and Cutting Fluids

## QUALITATIVE PROBLEMS

**22.16 Explain why so many different types of cutting-tool materials have been developed over the years. Why are they still being developed further?**

The reasons for the availability of a large variety of cutting-tool materials is best appreciated by reviewing the top eight parameters in the first column in Table 22.2 on p. 638. Among various factors, the type of workpiece material machined, the type of operation, and the surface finish and dimensional accuracy required all affect the choice of a cutting-tool material. For example, for interrupted cutting operations such as milling, we need toughness and impact strength. For operations where much heat is generated due, for example, to high cutting speeds, hot hardness is important. If very fine surface finish is desired, then materials such as ceramics and diamond would be highly desirable. These materials continue to be investigated further because, as in all other materials, there is much progress to be made for reasons such as to improve properties, extend their applications, develop new tool geometries, and reduce costs. The students are encouraged to comment further.

**22.17 Which tool-material properties are suitable for interrupted cutting operations? Why?**

In interrupted cutting operations, it is desirable to have tools with a high impact strength and toughness. From Tables 22.1 and 22.2 on pp. 649-650, the tool materials which have the best impact strength are high speed steels, and to a lesser extent, cast alloys and carbides. Therefore, one would prefer to use high-speed steels and carbides in interrupted cutting operations. In addition, in these operations, the tool is constantly being heated and reheated. It is therefore desirable to utilize materials with low coefficients of thermal expansion and high thermal conductivity to minimize thermal stresses in the tool which could lead to tool failure.

**22.18 Describe the reasons for coating cutting tools with multiple layers of different materials.**

There are several reasons for applying multiple coatings to a cutting tool, as also described in Section 22.5 on p. 656. One of the most obvious is that a given coating material may not bond well directly to the tool surface. A sandwiched layer of coating to which both the metal and the desired coating can bond successfully will increase the life of the tool. Also, one can combine the benefits from different materials. For example, the outermost layer can be a coating which is best from a hardness or low frictional characteristic to minimize tool wear. The next layer can have the benefit of being thermally insulating, and a third layer may be of a material which bonds well to the tool. Using these multiple layers allows a synergistic result in that the weaknesses of one coating can be compensated for with another layer.

**22.19 Make a list of the alloying elements used in high-speed steels. Explain why they are so effective in cutting tools.**

Typical alloying elements for high-speed steel are chromium, vanadium, tungsten, and cobalt. These elements impart higher strength and higher hardness at elevated temperatures. See Section 5.5.1 on p. 157 for further details on the effects of various alloying elements in steels.

**22.20 As we have stated in Section 22.1, tool materials can have conflicting properties in machining operations. Describe your observations regarding this matter.**

The brief discussion below should be viewed as illustrative of the type of answers that can be generated by the students. One well-known example of conflicting properties is the competition between hardness and ductility. Hardness is desirable for good wear resistance (see Section 33.5 on p. 1046), and for this reason it is advisable to perform hardening processes such as proper heat treating to high-speed steels. One of the consequences of hardening operations is that the ductility of the tool material may be compromised. If the machining operation is one of interrupted cutting (as in milling), or if chatter occurs, it is better to have good ductility and toughness to prevent premature tool fracture. The students are encouraged to comment further.

**22.21 Comment on the purposes of chamfers on inserts and their design features.**

As the shown in Fig. 22.5 on p. 655, chamfers serve to increase the edge strength of inserts because, in a sense, they effectively increase the included angle of the insert. Thus, resistance to chipping and fracture also increases. Furthermore, as discussed in Section 17.6 on p. 505, a chamfer is good design practice if the insert is produced by powder metallurgy techniques.

**22.22 Explain the economic impact of the trend shown in Fig. 22.6.**

The obvious economic impact can be deduced when also considering the axiom "time is money." As the cutting time decreases, the production cost decreases. Notice that the ordinate in Fig. 22.6 on p. 658 is a log scale, which indicates that the reduction in time will be an ever decreasing difference with given time increments. However, the trend is still that parts manufactured by machining are less costly as the years progress.

**22.23 Why does temperature have such an important effect on tool life?**

Temperature has a large effect on the life of a cutting tool for several reasons. First, all materials become weaker and less hard as they become hotter; therefore, higher temperatures will weaken and soften an otherwise ideal material. Second, chemical reactivity typically increases with increasing temperature, as does diffusion between the workpiece and the cutting tool. Third, the effectiveness of cutting fluids is compromised at excessive temperatures, meaning there is higher friction to overcome, and therefore more tool wear is expected. Finally, in interrupted cutting, there can be excessive thermal shock if the temperatures are high.

**22.24 Ceramic and cermet cutting tools have certain advantages over carbide tools. Why, then, are they not completely replacing carbide tools?**

Ceramics are preferable to carbides in that they have a lower tendency to adhere to metals being cut, and have a very high abrasion resistance and hot hardness. However, ceramics are generally brittle, and it is not unusual for them to fail prematurely. Carbides are much tougher than ceramics, and are therefore much more likely to perform as expected even when conditions such as chatter occurs. Also, it should be noted that ceramic tools have limits to their geometry; sharp noses are likely to be chipped and high rake angle tools will have suspect strength if made from ceramics. Carbide tools are preferable for these geometries when needed.

**22.25 Can cutting fluids have any adverse effects? If so, what are they?**

Cutting fluids can have adverse effects on the freshly machined surfaces, as well as various components of the machine tool and the lubricants used on the machines themselves, such as altering their viscosity and lubricating capabilities. If a cutting fluid is very effective as a coolant, it could lead to thermal shock in interrupted cutting operations. Cutting fluids have to be replaced periodically because they degrade, adversely affecting their performance. This degradation can be due to intense shear in the cutting zone, contamination by other materials, or from bacteria attacking the oil (or, more commonly, the emulsifier). If the cutting is no longer effective because of this degradation, workpiece quality will be compromised, but then there is the additional environmental concern associated with fluid disposal. (See also bottom of p. 665.)

**22.26 Describe the trends you observe in Table 22.2.**

By the student. Table 22.2 on p. 650 lists the cutting-tool materials in the approximate order of their development (from left to right). In terms of mechanical properties of the tool materials, the trend is towards development of harder materials with improved wear resistance. The tradeoff, however, can be a reduction in toughness, impact strength, and chipping resistance. The benefits of the trend is that cutting can take place faster, with greater depths of cut (except for diamond tools) and with better surface finish. Other limitations are the decreasing thermal shock resistance and increasing costs of the tool materials towards the right of the table.

**22.27 Why are chemical stability and inertness important in cutting tools?**

Chemical stability and inertness are important for cutting tools in order to maintain low friction and wear. One of the causes of friction is the shear stress required to break the microwelds in the interfaces between tool and workpiece materials (see Fig. 33.5 on p. 1043). If the tool material is inert, the microwelds are less likely to occur, and friction and wear will thus be reduced. It is also important that the workpiece and the cutting tool not bond chemically; this can lead to diffusion and adhesive wear.

**22.28 How would you go about measuring the effectiveness of cutting fluids? Explain any difficulties that you might encounter.**

By the student. The effectiveness of cutting fluids can be measured in a number of ways. The most effective and obvious is to test different cutting fluids under actual cutting operations. Other methods are to heat the fluids to the temperatures typically encountered in machining, and measure the fluid's viscosity and other properties such as lubricity, specific heat, density, etc. The chemical reactivity of the cutting fluid can also be tested against workpiece materials (see Chapter 33 for details). The students are encouraged to develop their own ideas for such tests.

**22.29 Titaniumnitride coatings on tools reduce the coefficient of friction at the toolchip interface. What is the significance of this?**

The tool-chip interface is the major source of friction in cutting, hence a major source of energy dissipation. Also, reducing friction will increase the shear angle and produce thinner chips and requiring less shear energy (see p. 612). These reductions will, in turn, reduce the cutting forces and hence the total energy required to perform the cutting operation. Reducing friction also reduces the amount of heat generated, which results in lower temperatures, with beneficial effects such as extending tool life and maintaining dimensional accuracy. (See also Problem 21.19.)

**22.30 Describe the necessary conditions for optimal utilization of the capabilities of diamond and cubic boron nitride cutting tools.**

Because diamond and cBN are brittle, impact due to factors such as cutting-force fluctuations and poor quality of the machine tools used must be minimized. Thus, interrupted cutting (such as milling or turning splines) should be avoided. Machine tools should have sufficient stiffness to avoid chatter and vibrations (see Chapter 25). Tool geometry and setting is also important to minimize stresses and possible chipping. The workpiece material must be suitable for diamond or cBN; for example, carbon is soluble in iron and steels at elevated temperatures as seen in cutting, and diamond would not be suitable for these materials.

**22.31 List and comment on the advantages of coating high-speed steel tools.**

As stated in Section 22.5.1 on p. 657, tool coatings have several important functions. Although high-speed steels have toughness and shock resistance, their hot hardness decreases with temperature (see Fig. 22.1 on p. 648). Many coatings have been developed with very high hardness. Also, coating materials can be produced from materials with more chemical inertness than high-speed steels. Thus coatings enhance these properties with resistance to temperature and wear.

**22.32 Explain the limits of application when comparing tungsten-carbide and titanium-carbide cutting tools.**

Refer to Section 22.4 on p. 653. Tungsten carbide is generally used for cutting nonferrous metals and alloys because of the chemical similarity of tungsten and iron on the periodic table. Thus, although tough, its wear resistance is not as high with ferrous alloys. Titanium carbide has higher wear resistance in machining steels and cast iron at high speeds.

**22.33 Negative rake angles are generally preferred for ceramic, diamond, and cubic boron nitride tools. Why?**

Although hard and strong in compression, these materials are brittle and relatively weak in tension. Consequently, negative rake angles (which indicate larger included angle of the tool tip; see, for example, Fig. 21.3 on p. 609) are preferred mainly because of the lower tendency to cause tensile stresses and chipping of the tools.

**22.34 Do you think that there is a relationship between the cost of a cutting tool and its hot hardness? Explain.**

Generally, as hot hardness increases, the cost of the tool material increases. For example, ceramics have high hot hardness and are generally made of inexpensive raw materials. However, their production into effective and reliable tool materials involves major steps (see Section 18.2 on p. 514) and, hence, expenses (also known as value added; see bottom of p. 2). Likewise, carbides utilize expensive raw materials as well as involving a number of processing steps (see Example 17.4 on p. 504). Diamond and cubic boron nitride are expensive as well.

**22.35 Survey the technical literature and give some typical values of cutting speeds for high-speed-steel tools and for a variety of workpiece materials.**

By the student. Good sources for such a literature search are periodicals, trade magazines, and cutting-tool vendors whose product specifications will include recommended cutting speeds and various other useful data. See also Table 23.4 starting on pp. 682-684.

**22.36 In Table 22.1, the last two properties listed can be important to the life of the cutting tool. Why?**

The last two properties in Table 22.1 on p. 649 are thermal conductivity and coefficient of thermal expansion. These properties are important in thermal cracking or shock of the tool material due to internal thermal stresses developed when subjected to thermal cycling, as in interrupted cutting operations. (See Section 3.6 on p. 107 for details.)

**22.37 It has been stated that titanium-nitride coatings allow cutting speeds and feeds to be higher than those for uncoated tools. Survey the technical literature and prepare a table showing the percentage increase of speeds and feeds that would be made possible by coating the tools.**

By the student. Good sources for such a literature search are periodicals, trade magazines, and cutting-tool vendors whose product specifications will include data on speeds and feeds. See also Table 23.4 on pp. 682-684.

**22.38 You will note in Fig. 22.1 that all tool materials have a wide range of hardnesses for a particular temperature, especially carbides. Describe all the factors that are responsible for this wide range.**

By the student. There are many reasons for the range of hardnesses, including:

- All of the materials can have variations in their microstructure, and this can significantly affect the hardness. For example, compare the following two micrographs of tungsten carbide, showing a fine-grained (left) and coarse-grained (right) tungsten carbide. (*Source:* Trent, E.M., and Wright, P.K., *Metal Cutting* 4th ed., Butterworth Heinemann, 2000, pp. 178-185).

- There can be a wide range in the concentration of the carbide compared to the cobalt binder in carbide tools.
- For materials such as carbon tool steels, the carbon content can be different, as can the level of case hardening of the tool.
- 'High speed steels' and 'ceramics' are generic terms with a large range of chemistries.
- Cutting tool materials are available in a wide variety of sizes and geometries, and the hardness will vary accordingly. For example, a large rake angle tool is more susceptible to chipping (see Fig. 22.4 on p. 655), so such tools may be hardened to a lower extent in order to preserve some toughness in the material.

**22.39 List and explain the considerations involved in the decision to recondition, recycle, or discard a cutting tool.**

By the student. The main considerations are structural, economic, and environmental. For example, a tool can only be reconditioned so many times before it is structurally unsound and could fracture prematurely. If the cost of reconditioning exceeds the cost of a new tool, then clearly reconditioning is wasteful. If the cutting tool is an expensive material or where discarding it introduces environmental hazards, it should be recycled instead of discarded.

**22.40 Referring to Table 22.1, state which tool materials would be suitable for interrupted cutting operations. Explain.**

By the student. Interrupted cutting operations basically require cutting-tool materials that have high impact strength (toughness) as well as thermal-shock resistance. Note in Table 22.1 on p. 649 that high-speed steels are by far the toughest; however, their resistance to high temperatures is rather low and have limited tool life in such operations. Consequently, although not as tough, carbides, cermets, and polycrystalline cubic boron nitride and diamond are used widely in interrupted cutting various workpiece materials, as shown in Table 24.2 on p. 736. These tool materials are continuously being developed for increasing toughness and resistance to edge chipping.

**22.41 Which of the properties listed in Table 22.1 is, in your opinion, the least important in cutting tools? Explain.**

By the student. It would appear that modulus of elasticity and density are not particularly important in cutting. However, as a very low order effect, elastic modulus may have some influence in very high precision machining operations because of the deflections involved. As for density, although the cutting tool itself has a rather small mass compared to other components, in high-speed operations where tool reversals may be involved, inertia effects can be important.

**22.42 If a drill bit is intended for woodworking applications, what material is it most likely to be made from? (Hint: Temperatures rarely rise to 400 °C in woodworking.) Are there any reasons why such a drill bit cannot be used to drill a few holes in a metal? Explain.**

Because of economic considerations, woodworking tools are typically made of carbon steels, with some degree of hardening by heat treatment. Note from Fig. 22.1 on p. 648 that carbon steels maintain a reasonably high hardness for temperatures less than 400F. For drilling metals, however, the temperatures are high enough to soften the carbon steel (unless drilling at very low rotational speeds), thus quickly dulling the drill bit.

**22.43 What are the consequences of a coating having a different coefficient of thermal expansion than the substrate?**

Consider the situation where a cutting tool and the coating are stress-free at room temperature when the tool is inserted. Then consider the situation when the tool is used in cutting and the temperatures are very high. A mismatch in thermal expansion coefficients will cause high thermal strains at the temperatures developed during machining. This can result in a separation (delamination) of the coating from the substrate.

**22.44 Discuss the relative advantages and limitations of near-dry machining. Consider all relevant technical and economic aspects.**

Refer to Section 22.12.1 on p. 669. The advantages are mostly environmental as there is no cutting fluid which would add to the manufacturing cost, or to dispose of or treat before disposal. This has other implications in that the workpiece doesn't have to be cleaned, so no additional cleaning fluids, such as solvents, have to be used. Also, lubricants are expensive and difficult to control. However, cutting-fluid residue provides a protective oil film on the machined part from the environment, especially with freshly machined metals that begin to rapidly oxidize.

## QUANTITATIVE PROBLEMS

**22.45 Review the contents of Table 22.1. Plot several curves to show range relationships, if any, among parameters such as hardness, transverse rupture strength, and impact strength. Comment on your observations.**

By the student. There are many variables that can be selected for study; some will give no apparent relationship but others will give some correlation. For example, below is a plot of hardness compared to compressive strength and elastic modulus. Note that the hardness of cubic boron nitride and diamond have been extrapolated from Fig. 2.14 on p. 84 and are only estimates for illustrative purposes. It should be noted that the plot is restricted to the materials in Table 22.1. In general, there is no trend between hardness and elastic modulus, but Table 22.1 has a small selection of materials suitable for cutting tools.

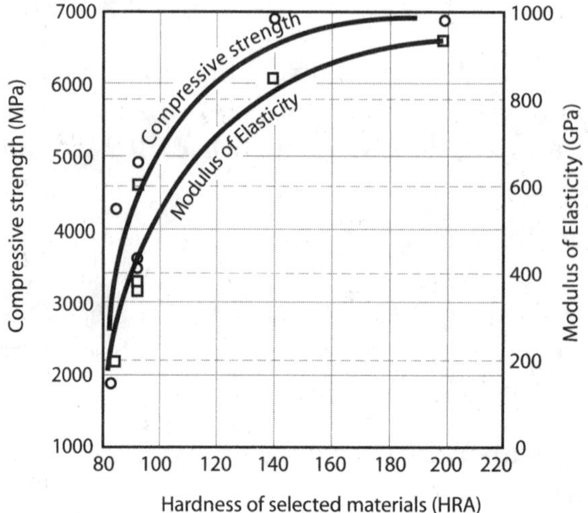


**22.46 Obtain data on the thermal properties of various cutting fluids. Identify those that are basically effective coolants (such a water-based fluids) and those that are basically good lubricants (such as oils).**

By the student. Most cutting fluids are emulsions (water-based fluids), but they may be provided as a base oil, and the supplier will report data for the base oil only. The actual emulsion produced from this base oil will have higher specific heat and superior thermal properties. Properties such as thermal conductivity and specific heat can be linearly interpolated from the water concentration according to rules of mixtures. This is a challenging problem because thermal properties are usually not readily available. The most common practice for applying the lubricant is flooding (see p. 667), so that most heat is removed by convection. Predicting convection coefficients using well-characterized fluids is extremely difficult.

**22.47 The first column in Table 22.2 shows seven properties that are important to cutting tools. For each of the tool materials listed in the table, add numerical data for each of these properties. Describe your observations, including any data that overlaps.**

There are many acceptable answers since all of the tool materials in the table have a wide range of values. Also, some of the measures are qualitative, such as chipping resistance and thermal-shock resistance. Cutting speeds depend on the workpiece material and its condition, as well as the quality of surface desired. However, examples of acceptable answers are:

| **Property** | **Material** | | | |
|---|---|---|---|---|
| | **HSS** | **Cast-cobalt alloys** | **Cubic boron nitride** | **Diamond** |
| Hot hardness | 60 HRA | 75 HRA | 4000 HK | 7000 HK |
| Impact strength, J | 4 | 1 | < 0.5 | < 0.2 |
| Cutting speed, m/min | 90 | 300 | 400 | 760 |
| Thermal conductivity, W/m-K (shock resistance) | 40 | - | 13 | 500 |

## SYNTHESIS, DESIGN, AND PROJECTS

**22.48 Describe in detail your thoughts regarding the technical and economic factors involved in tool material selection.**

By the student. The technical and economic factors are constantly in competition. Among the technical factors are (see pp. 647-648):

- A tool material with sufficiently high hot hardness for strength and wear resistance.
- Chemical stability and inertness for adhesive wear resistance.
- Toughness for fracture prevention.
- High thermal conductivity to minimize severe temperature gradients.

Among the economic factors are:

- Tool cost should be minimized.
- The material should be readily available.

**22.49 One of the principal concerns with coolants is degradation due to biological attack by bacteria. To prolong life, chemical biocides are often added, but these biocides greatly complicate the disposal of coolants. Conduct a literature search regarding the latest developments in the use of environmentally benign biocides in cutting fluids.**

By the student. There are a few approaches, such as: (a) Increase the pH to an extent to where no microorganisms can survive. (b) Develop chemical agents which directly kill microorganisms (biocides). (c) Use a chemical which the microorganism ingests and which, in turn, poisons the microbe.

**22.50 Contact several different suppliers of cutting tools or search their web sites. Make a list of the costs of typical cutting tools of various sizes, shapes, and features.**

By the student. Very useful websites are those for major suppliers such as Kennametal, Iscar, Sandvik, Carboloy, and Valenite; general product catalogues are also helpful. In comparing costs from older and newer cost data, it will be noted that, as in many other products, costs vary (up or down) by time. (See also Section 40.9 on p. 1261.)

**22.51 As you can see, there are several types of cutting-tool materials available today for machining operations. Yet, there is much research and development that is being carried out on these materials. Make a list of the reasons why you think such studies are being conducted. Comment on each with a specific application or example.**

By the student. This is a challenging and rich topic for literature studies. For example, students could examine this question based on requirements for cutting-tool materials for machining of new materials such as nanophase materials and composites. The students can also consider this question as an issue of the continued trend in increasing cutting speeds and tool life.

**22.52 Assume that you are in charge of a laboratory for developing new or improved cutting fluids. On the basis of the topics presented in this and in Chapter 21, suggest a list of topics for your staff to investigate. Explain why you have chosen those topics.**

By the student. For example, one approach would be to direct the students to current conference programs, so that they can examine the technical papers currently being presented. Appropriate sources would be the Society of Tribologists and Lubrication Engineers (www.stle.org) and the American Society of Mechanical Engineers (www.asme.org). Among the major research topics of current interest are:

- The use of environmentally benign cutting fluids, such as vegetable oil-based fluids.
- The use of ionic fluids.
- Elimination of cutting fluids (dry or near-dry machining; see p. 669).
- Formulation of additives, such as detergents, lubricity additives, and alkalinity modifiers.

**22.53 Survey the technical literature and describe the trends in new cutting-tool materials and coatings. Which of these are becoming available to industry?**

By the student. As discussed throughout this chapter, there is much ongoing research on cutting-tool materials. Currently, major research interests are focused on nanophase materials (see Section 6.16 on p. 186) and coatings, as well as the development of improved tool coatings.

# Chapter 23

# Machining Processes Used to Produce Round Shapes: Turning and Hole Making

## QUALITATIVE PROBLEMS

**23.15 Explain the reasoning behind the various design guidelines for turning.**

By the student. The design guidelines, given in Section 23.3.6 on p. 697, are mostly self-explanatory, such as the need to design parts so that they can be easily fixtured. However, some examples of some reasoning are as follows:

- Sharp corners, tapers, steps, and major dimensional variations in the part should be avoided. It's easiest for a lathe to be set up to perform straight turning, thus unnecessary dimensional variations make the lathe operation much more difficult. The difficulty with sharp corners, especially internal corners, is that the minimum corner radius is that of the nose radius of the cutting tool (see Figs. 21.15 on p. 627, 21.23 on p. 637, and 23.4c on p. 677). Also, small nose radii lead to increased likelihood of tool chipping or breakage.
- Blanks to be machined should be as close to the final dimensions as possible; this is, of course, a valuable general concept. It is important in turning because tool life is limited and the number of roughing cuts before a finishing cut is taken should be minimized.

**23.16 You will note that we have used both the terms "tool strength" and "tool-material strength." Do you think there is a difference between them? Explain.**

By the student. There is a difference between tool-material strength and tool strength. Tool material strength is a property of the material (see Table 22.1 on p. 649); thus, for example, the compressive strength of carbides is higher than that for high-speed steels. The tool strength, on the other hand, refers to the ability of a particular cutting tool to resist fracture or failure. This depends not only on the tool material itself but also on the tool geometry, as shown in Figs. 22.4 and 22.5 on p. 655.

**23.17 Explain why the sequence of drilling, boring, and reaming produces a hole that is more accurate than just drilling and reaming it.**

The difficulty is largely due to the fact that drilling, because of its inherent flexibility, does not necessarily produce a hole that is accurate in its coordinate, whereas boring is an operation that is better controlled.

**23.18 Explain why machining operations may be necessary even on net-shape or near-net-shape parts made by precision casting, forming, or powder-metallurgy products.**

By the student. Many applications require better dimensional tolerances or surface finish than those produced by casting, forging, or powder metallurgy. Machining operations can remove unevenness from parts, such as those caused by defects or through uneven deformation and warping upon cooling. Many processes, by their nature, will not impart a sufficiently smooth surface finish to the workpiece, and it is often necessary to machine (or grind, polish, etc.) them for improved dimensional accuracy. Other parts require surface features that cannot be obtained through other manufacturing methods.

**23.19 What are the consequences of drilling with a drill bit that has not been properly sharpened?**

By the student. The consequences are similar to those shown in Fig. 21.22 on p. 636. Note that drilling is similar to the cutting operation shown, except that a circular chip is removed. Thus, a drill bit that is not properly sharpened has a large nose radius, and this has the consequences of causing the effective rake angle to increase (so that the force and energy required are increased, as is temperature), as well as increase the likelihood of surface smearing and burnishing, instead of removing material.

**23.20 A badly oxidized and uneven round bar is being turned on a lathe. Would you recommend a small or a large depth-of-cut? Explain your reasons.**

Because oxides are generally hard and abrasive (see p. 1037), consequently, light cuts will cause the tool to wear rapidly. Thus it is highly desirable to cut right through the oxide layer on the first pass. Note that an uneven round bar will cause significant variations in the depth of cut being taken; thus, depending on the degree of eccentricity, it may not always be possible to do so since this can be self-excited vibration and lead to chatter.

**23.21 Describe the problems, if any, that may be encountered in clamping a workpiece made of a soft metal in a three-jaw chuck.**

A common problem in clamping any workpiece into a chuck is that the jaws will bite into the workpiece (see, for example, Fig. 23.3 on p. 677), possibly leaving an impression that may be unsightly or functionally unacceptable. Shim stock, made of a softer material, can be used between the jaws and the workpiece to minimize damage to the workpiece surface. Parts may also be designed for convenient clamping into chucks, or provided with flanges or extensions which can be gripped by the chuck, which can later be removed.

**23.22 Does the force or torque in drilling change as the hole depth increases? Explain.**

The force and torque may increase as the hole depth increases, but not by a significant amount. The factors which would increase the force and torque are contact area between the tool and cylindrical surface of the hole and difficulties in removing chips from the bottom of deep holes and possible clogging. Unless the hole depth is very deep, these are usually considered unimportant and the force and torque can be taken as constant.

**23.23 Explain the similarities and differences in the design guidelines for turning and for boring.**

By the student. Turning and boring are quite similar operations in terms of dimensional tolerances and surface finish. In both cases, secure clamping is necessary, which is the reason the clamped lengths are similar. Interrupted surfaces in both cases can lead to vibration and chatter. The differences in the two operations are that, in boring, the workpiece size is not critical. Workpieces that are suitable for boring can naturally be held in various fixtures, and vertical boring machines can accommodate very large parts (see, for example, Fig. 23.18 on p. 704). On the other hand, in typical turning operations very large parts can be difficult to mount.

**23.24 What are the advantages and applications of having a hollow spindle in the headstock of a lathe?**

The main advantage is the ability to feed stock through the headstock of the lathe (Fig. 23.2). This is particularly important in automatic bar machines (see p. 691).

**23.25 Explain how you would go about producing a taper on a round workpiece on a lathe.**

Tapers can be produced by mounting the round workpiece out of line with the tailstock. In addition, tapers can be machined using a template on a tracer lathe. In modern practice, however, tapers and various other shapes are machined automatically and economically using numerical-control (CNC) lathes. Note in Figs. 23.11 and 23.12 on pp. 694 and 695, for example, the complex shapes that can be machined on such lathes.

**23.26 Assume that you are asked to perform a boring operation on a large-diameter hollow workpiece. Would you use a horizontal or a vertical boring mill? Explain.**

By the student. It is apparent that, because of size and weight limitations, a horizontal setup is desirable. See, for example, Fig. 23.18 mon p. 704.

**23.27 Explain the reasons for the major trend in producing threads by thread rolling versus thread cutting. What would be the differences (if any) in the types of threads produced and their performance characteristics?**

By the student. Thread rolling is described on pp. 362-364. The main advantages of thread rolling over thread cutting are the speeds involved (thread rolling is a very high production rate process) and the fact that the threads will undergo extensive cold working (plastic deformation; see Fig. 13.17c), leading to stronger work-hardened threads. Cutting is still used for making threads(see Section 23.3.8 on p. 700) because it is a very versatile operation and much more economical for low production runs (since expensive dies are not required). Note that internal threads also can be rolled, but this is not nearly as common as machining the threads and can be a difficult operation.

**23.28 In some materials the hole drilled can be smaller than the diameter of the drill. Explain this phenomenon and identify the relevant material properties that could influence it.**

It's not difficult to visualize why this situation can occur. Examining the geometry of drills in Fig. 23.19 on p. 705, one can see that as the drill progressively moves into a hole it is producing, it is loading the workpiece material radially. When the drill is removed, elastic recovery can lead to a smaller hole. Also note that residual stresses are relieved by removing material in drilling, and when the drill is removed, elastic recovery can lead to a smaller hole than the drill diameter.

**23.29 Describe your observations concerning the contents of Tables 23.2 and 23.4 and explain why those particular recommendations are made.**

By the student. Some observations are listed below:

- Referring to Table 23.2 on p. 678, note that the side rake angle is high for aluminum but low for titanium. This can be explained by the benefits of maintaining higher compression on the shear plane for titanium (to obtain higher ductility), a situation not needed for aluminum.
- Note from Table 23.4 on p. 682 that the cutting speeds for steels are much lower than those for copper alloys. This can be explained by power requirements associated with machining steels.
- Note that the tools used in Table 23.4 vary by workpiece material. For example, no diamond is listed for steel, explainable by the solubility of carbon in steel at elevated temperatures.

**23.30 We have seen that cutting speed, feed, and depth-of-cut are the main parameters in a turning operation. In relative terms, at what values should these parameters be set for a (a) roughing operation and (b) finishing operation?**

(a) For a finishing operation, with good surface finish, they should be set at high speed, low feed, and low depth of cut. (b) For a roughing operation, where surface finish is not as important, they should be set at low speed and high feed and depth of cut. This can be seen from Eq. (21.24) and Fig. 21.23 on p. 637: where surface finish is critical, feed and depth of cut should be low. Speed does not appear in this equation; the main effect of speed is to generate chatter at higher speeds. This, when surface finish is not critical, speed can be set high. When surface finish is critical, it is important to avoid chatter. This is discussed in greater detail in Section 25.4 on p. 775.

**23.31 Explain the economic justification for purchasing a turret lathe instead of a conventional lathe.**

As we have seen, turret lathes (see p. 692) have multiple tools and can perform a variety of operations such as turning, threading, drilling, facing, and cut off. Thus, the amount of time required for setting up the tools is greatly reduced as compared to common lathe operations.

Because manufacturing time is an important element in the overall cost of production (see Section 40.9), turret lathes can be justified economically.

**23.32 The footnote to Table 23.11 states that (in drilling) as the hole diameter increases, speeds and feeds should be reduced. Explain why.**

As hole depth increases, elastic recovery in the workpiece causes normal stresses on the surface of the drill, thus the stresses experienced by the drill are higher than they are in shallow holes. These stresses, in turn, cause the torque on the drill to increase and may even lead to its failure. Reduction in feeds and speeds can compensate for these increases.

**23.33 In modern manufacturing with computer-controlled machine tools, which types of metal chips would be undesirable and why?**

Referring to Fig. 21.5 on p. 614, we note the following: Continuous chips are not desirable because (a) the machines mostly untended and operate at high speeds, thus chip generation is at a high rate (see also chip collection systems, p. 700) and (b) continuous chips would entangle on spindles and machine components, and thus severely interfere with the cutting operation. Conversely and for that reason, discontinuous chips or segmented chips would be desirable, and indeed are typically produced using chipbreaker features on tools, Note, however, that such chips can lead to vibration and chatter, depending also on the characteristics of the machine tool (see Section 25.4 on p. 775).

**23.34 List and explain the factors that contribute to poor surface finish in the processes described in this chapter.**

By the student. One factor is explained by Eq. (21.24) on p. 637, which gives the roughness in a process such as turning. Clearly, as the feed increases or as the tool nose radius decreases, the roughness will increase. Other factors that affect surface finish are built-up edge (see, for example, Figs. 21.5 and 21.6 on pp. 614-615), dull tools or tool-edge chipping (see Fig. 21.18 on p. 632), or chatter (Section 25.4 on p. 775).

**23.35 The operational severity for reaming is much less than that for tapping, even though they are both internal material-removal processes which can be difficult. Why?**

Tapping (p. 716) produces a significant amount of chips and their removal through the hole being tapped can be difficult as they can get clogged (and can cause tap fracture), thus contributing to the severity of the tapping operation. Control of processing parameters and use of effective cutting fluids are thus important. Chipless tapping, on the other hand, does not present such difficulties.

**23.36 Review Fig. 23.6 and comment on the factors involved in determining the height of the zones (cutting speed) for various tool materials.**

The main reasons for a range of acceptable cutting speeds shown in Fig. 23.6 on p. 681 are based on tool life and surface finish of the workpiece. One can appreciate that tool life depends not only on the cutting-tool material, but also on the workpiece material and its condition, as well as the particular tool geometry. It is therefore to be expected that there will be a wide range of feeds and speeds for each cutting-tool material.

**23.37 We have stated that some chucks are power actuated. Make a survey of the technical literature and describe the basic design of such chucks.**

By the student. This is a good project for students to conduct an Internet search and collect product literature, as well as referring to various product catalogues. Power chucks are available with a variety of designs, and can be pneumatic, hydraulic, or electrically actuated.

**23.38 What operations can typically be performed on a drill press but not on a lathe?**

Lathes can perform many of the operations that can be done on a drill press. The workpieces (typically round) are mounted in a chuck on the headstock and the drill bit is placed in the tailstock. Note, however, that only holes on the axis of rotation of the lathe can be produced. Drill presses are much more suitable for locating several holes in a workpiece, especially with CNC machines, as shown, for example, in Figs. 37.10 and 37.12a on pp. 1158-1159.

**23.39 Explain how gun drills remain centered during drilling. Why is there a hollow, longitudinal channel in a gun drill?**

Gun drills remain centered because of the tip design because, as stated on p. 708, of the presence of bearing pads. The hole in the center of the drill is for pumping the cutting fluid, which cools the workpiece and the tool, lubricates the interfaces, and washes chips from the drilling zone.

**23.40 Comment on the magnitude of the wedge angle on the tool shown in Fig. 23.4.**

The wedge angle is very important. As shown in Figs. 22.4 and 22.5 on p. 655, the wedge angle has a large effect on the strength of the cutting tool, and therefore its resistance to chipping and fracture. (See also Problems 22.21 and 22.33.)

**23.41 If inserts are used in a drill bit, is the shank material important? If so, what properties are important? Explain.**

Recognizing that inserts on a drill bit are rather small (see Fig. 23.21 on p. 707) and the temperature of the inserts will be very high, it is important that the shank material be able to effectively extract heat from the inserts. Also, if the inserts are brazed in place (which is a decreasing practice because they are not indexable and are time-consuming to make), the thermal expansion coefficients of the insert and the shank should be matched to avoid thermal stresses. The shank must provide rigidity and damping to avoid chatter, and must have reasonable cost.

**23.42 Refer to Fig. 23.10b and (in addition to the tools shown) describe other types of cutting tools that can be placed in toolholders to perform other machining operations.**

By the student. Referring to Fig. 23.1 on p. 675, not that a tool for each of these operations could be included. In addition, reamers, taps, and drills of all types also could be used (see Fig. 23.20 on p. 707).

## QUANTITATIVE PROBLEMS

**23.43 Calculate the same quantities as in Example 23.1 for high-strength titanium alloy and at $N = 800$ rpm.**

The maximum cutting speed is

$$V = (800)(\pi)(0.5) = 1257 \text{ in./min} = 105 \text{ ft/min}$$

and the cutting speed at the machined diameter is

$$V = (800)(\pi)(0.480) = 100 \text{ ft/min}$$

The depth of cut is unchanged at 0.010 in. and the feed is given by

$$f = 8/800 = 0.01 \text{ in./rev}$$

Taking an average diameter of 0.490 in., the metal removal rate is

$$\text{MRR} = \pi(0.490)(0.010)(0.01)(800) = 0.123 \text{ in}^3\text{/min}$$

The actual time to cut is

$$t = \frac{6}{(0.01)(800)} = 0.75 \text{ min}$$

From Table 21.2 on p. 622 let's take the unit power for titanium alloys as 5 W-s/mm$^3$, or 2 hp-min/in$^3$. Note that we used the upper limits of the power because the problem states that the titanium is of high strength. Thus, the power dissipated is

$$\text{Power} = (2)(0.1) = 0.2 \text{ hp} = 79,200\text{in.-lb/min}$$

The torque is given by

$$\text{Torque} = \frac{79,200}{(800)(2)(\pi)} = 15.7 \text{ in.-lb}$$

Therefore the cutting force is

$$F_c = \frac{15.7}{(0.490/2)} = 64 \text{ lb}$$

**23.44 Estimate the machining time required to rough turn a 0.4-m long, annealed copper-alloy round bar from 60-mm diameter to 55-mm diameter using a high-speed-steel tool. (See Table 23.4.) Estimate the time required for a carbide tool.**

Referring to Table 23.4 on p. 684, annealed copper alloys can be machined at a maximum cutting speed of 535 m/min=8.9 m/s using uncoated carbides. The footnote to the table states that the speeds for high-speed steels are about one-half the value for uncoated carbides, so the speed will be taken as 268 m/min = 4.46 m/s for HSS. For rough turning, the depth of cut varies, but a mean value is taken from the table as 4.5 mm, or 0.0045 m. The maximum cutting speed is at the outer diameter and is given by (see Table 23.3 on p. 680)

$$V = \pi D_o N \quad \rightarrow \quad 535 \text{ m/min} = (N)(\pi)(0.06 \text{ m})$$

and hence $N = 2840$ rpm for HSS and 1420 rpm for carbide. Because it is rough turning, the feeds can be taken as the higher values in Table 23.4 on p. 684. Using the value of 0.75 mm/rev, or 0.00075 m/rev, for materials with low hardness such as aluminum, the time to cut is obtained from Eq. (23.2) on p. 679 as

$$t = \frac{l}{fN} = \frac{0.4 \text{ m}}{(0.00075 \text{ m/rev})(2840 \text{ rpm})} = 0.188 \text{ min} = 11.3 \text{ s}$$

The time for carbide is likewise found to be about 6 s.

**23.45 A high-strength cast-iron bar 5 in. in diameter is being turned on a lathe at a depth-of-cut d = 0.050 in. The lathe is equipped with a 15-hp electric motor and has a mechanical efficiency of 80%. The spindle speed is 500 rpm. Estimate the maximum feed that can be used before the lathe begins to stall?**

Note that $D_{|rmave} = 4.975$ in. Since the lathe has a 15-hp motor and a mechanical efficiency of 80%, we have (15)(0.8)=12 hp available for the cutting operation. For cast irons the specific power required is obtained from Table 21.2 on p. 622 as between 0.4 and 2 hp-min/in$^3$. We will use the average value to obtain a typical number so that the specific power will be taken as 1.2 hp-min/in$^3$. Therefore, the maximum metal removal rate is

$$\text{MRR} = \frac{12 \text{ hp}}{1.2 \text{ hp-min/in}^3} = 10 \text{ in}^3/\text{min}$$

The metal removal rate is also given by Eq. (23.1a) on p. 679 as

$$\text{MRR} = \pi D_{\text{ave}} d f N$$

Therefore, the maximum feed, $f$, is

$$f = \frac{\text{MRR}}{\pi D_{\text{ave}} d N} = \frac{10}{\pi(4.975)(0.05)(500)} = 0.026 \text{ in./rev}$$

**23.46 A 0.4-in. diameter drill is used on a drill press operating at 300 rpm. If the feed is 0.005 in./rev, what is the MRR? What is the MRR if the drill diameter is doubled?**

The metal removal rate in drilling is given by Eq. (23.3) on p. 709. Thus, for a 0.4-in. drill diameter, with the spindle rotating at 300 rpm and a feed of 0.005 in./rev, the MRR is

$$\text{MRR} = \left(\frac{\pi D^2}{4}\right)(f)(N) = \left[\frac{(\pi)(0.4)^2}{4}\right](0.005)(300) = 0.19 \text{ in}^3/\text{min}$$

If the drill diameter is tripled, the metal removal rate will be increased eightfold because MRR depends on the diameter squared. The MRR would then be (0.19)(8)=1.5 in$^3$/min.

**23.47 In Example 23.4, assume that the workpiece material is high-strength aluminum alloy and the spindle is running at $N = 600$ rpm. Estimate the torque required for this operation.**

If the spindle is running at 600 rpm, the metal removal rate is

$$\text{MRR} = (210)\left(\frac{600}{800}\right) = 158 \text{ mm}^3/\text{s}$$

From Table 21.2 on p. 622, the unit power for high-strength aluminum alloys is estimated as 1 W-s/mm$^3$. The power dissipated is then

$$\text{Power} = (158)(1) = 158 \text{ W}$$

Since power is the product of the torque on the drill and its rotational speed, the rotational speed is $(600)(2\pi)/60 = 63$ rad/s. Hence the torque is

$$\text{Torque} = \frac{158}{63} = 2.5 \text{ N-m}$$

**23.48 In a drilling operation, a 0.5-in. drill bit is being used in a low-carbon steel workpiece. The hole is a blind hole, which will be tapped to a depth of 1 in. The drilling operation takes place with a feed of 0.010 in./rev and a spindle speed of 700 rpm. Estimate the time required to drill the hole prior to tapping.**

The velocity of the drill into the workpiece is $v = fN = (0.010 \text{ in./rev})(700 \text{ rpm}) = 7$ in./min. Since the hole is to be tapped to a depth of 1 in. it should be drilled deeper than this distance. Note from the text on p. 706 that the point angle for steels ranges from 118° to 135°, so that (using 118° to get a larger number and conservative answer) the drill actually has to penetrate at least a distance of

$$l = 1 + \frac{d}{2}\sin(90^\circ - 118^\circ/2) = 1 + \left(\frac{0.5 \text{ in.}}{2}\right)(\sin 31^\circ) = 1.13 \text{ in.}$$

In order to make sure that the tap doesn't strike the bottom of the hole, let's specify that the drill should penetrate 1.25 in., which is the nearest 1/4 in. over the minimum hole depth. Therefore, the time required for this drilling operation is 1.25 in./(7 in./min) = 0.18 min = 11 s.

**23.49 A 3-in. diameter low-strength, stainless-steel cylindrical part is to be turned on a lathe at 600 rpm, with a depth-of-cut of 0.2 in. and a feed of 0.025 in./rev. What should be the minimum horsepower of the lathe?**

Note that $D_{\text{ave}} = 2.9$ in. The metal removal rate is given by Eq. (23.1a) on p. 679 as

$$\text{MRR} = \pi D_{\text{ave}} d f N = \pi(2.9 \text{ in.})(0.2 \text{ in.})(0.025 \text{ in./rev})(600 \text{ rpm}) = 27.3 \text{ in}^3/\text{min}$$

The energy requirement for stainless steel is at most 1.9 hp-min/in$^3$ (see Table 21.2 on p. 622). Therefore, the horsepower needed in the lathe motor is

$$\text{Power} = (1.9 \text{ hp-min/in}^3)(27.3 \text{ in}^3/\text{min}) = 52 \text{ hp}$$

**23.50 A 6-in. diameter aluminum cylinder 10 in. in length is to have its diameter reduced to 4.5 in. Using the typical machining conditions given in Table 23.4, estimate the machining time if a TiN-coated carbide tool is used.**

As we'll show below, this is a subtly complicated and open-ended problem, and a particular solution can significantly deviate from this one. From Table 23.4 on p. 604, the range of parameters for machining aluminum with a TiN-coated carbide tool is:

$$d = 0.01 - 0.35 \text{ in.}$$

$$f = 0.003 - 0.025 \text{ in.}$$

$$V = 200 - 3000 \text{ ft/min}$$

Since the total depth of cut is to be 0.75 in., it would be logical to perform three equal roughing cuts, each at $d = 0.24$ in. and a finishing cut at $d = 0.03$ in. For the roughing cuts, the maximum allowable feed and speed can be used, that is, $f = 0.025$ in./rev and $V = 3000$ ft/min. For the finishing cuts, the feed is determined by surface finish requirements, but is assigned the minimum value of 0.003 in./rev, and the speed is similarly set at a low value of $V = 200$ ft/min. The average diameter for the first roughing cut is 5.76 in., 5.28 in. for the second, and 4.80 in. for the third. The rotational speeds for 1st, 2nd, and 3rd roughing cuts are (from $V = \pi D_{\text{ave}} N$) 1980 rpm, 2160 rpm, and 2400 rpm, respectively. The mean diameter for the finishing cut is 4.53 in., and with $V = 200$ ft/min, the rotational speed is 168 rpm. The total machining time is then

$$t = \sum \frac{l}{fN} = \frac{10 \text{ in.}}{(0.025 \text{ in./rev})(1980 \text{ rpm})} + \frac{10 \text{ in.}}{(0.025 \text{ in./rev})(2160 \text{ rpm})} + \frac{10 \text{ in.}}{(0.025 \text{ in./rev})(2400 \text{ rpm})} + \frac{10 \text{ in.}}{(0.003 \text{ in./rev})(168 \text{ rpm})}$$

or $t = 20.2$ minutes.

**23.51 For the data in Problem 23.48, calculate the power required.**

This solution depends on the solution given in Problem 23.50. It should be recognized that a number of answers are possible in Problem 23.50, depending on the number of roughing cuts taken and the particular speeds and feeds selected. The power requirement will be determined by the first roughing cut since all other cuts will require less power. The metal removal rate, from Eq. (23.1a) on p. 679, is

$$\text{MRR} = \pi D_{\text{avg}} d f N = \pi (5.76 \text{ in.})(0.24)(0.025)(1980) = 215 \text{ in.}^3/\text{min}$$

Using the data from Table 20.1 on p. 622 for aluminum, the power required is

$$P = (215 \text{ in}^3/\text{min})(0.4\text{hp-min/in}^3) = 86 \text{ hp}$$

**23.52 Assume that you are an instructor covering the topics described in this chapter, and you are giving a quiz on the numerical aspects to test the understanding of the students. Prepare three quantitative problems and supply the answers.**

By the student. This is a good, open-ended question that requires considerable focus and understanding from the students, and has been found to be a very valuable homework problem.

## SYNTHESIS, DESIGN, AND PROJECTS

**23.53 Would you consider the machining processes described in this chapter as net-shape processing (requiring no further processing)? Near-net-shape processing? Explain, with appropriate examples.**

By the student. This is a challenging question for in-depth discussion and is valuable in clarifying the meaning of the concept of net-shape processing. Briefly, the processes described in this chapter can be classified as either net-shape or near-net shape. Restricting the answer to surfaces that are machined, the workpiece may, as an example, be net-shaped after turning or drilling. However, if the dimensional tolerances or surface finish from turning are not acceptable, the workpiece may need to be ground (Chapter 26). The former is an example where the processes in this chapter are net-shape operations, and the latter is an example of near-net-shape processing.

**23.54 If a bolt breaks in a hole so that the head is no longer present, it is removed by first drilling a hole in the bolt shank and then using a special tool to remove the bolt. Inspect such a tool and explain how it works. Can you think of any other means of removing the broken bolt from the hole? Explain.**

By the student. This is a good problem for students to develop an intuitive feel for the use of bolt extractors, commonly called "easy outs." This can be an inexpensive demonstration as well: A low-strength bolt can be easily sheared in a hole using a wrench and extender (to develop high torque), then asking the students to remove the bolt. Bolt extractors have left-handed threads and wedged sides. Thus, when place into a properly-sized cylinder or pre-drilled hole, the bolt extractor will wedge itself further into the hole as the extracting torque increases. Since it is a left-handed thread, it tightens as the bolt is being withdrawn.

**23.55 Describe the machine tool and the fixtures needed to machine baseball bats from wooden cylindrical stock.**

This is an outstanding problem for a literature and/or Internet search. For example, a very good description of baseball-bat manufacture is contained at www.sluggermuseum.org. Hand turning is shown below, although most wooden bats are now made on tracer lathes (p. 691) and CNC lathes.

**23.56 An important trend in machining operations is the increased use of flexible fixturing. Conduct a search on the Internet regarding flexible fixturing and comment on their design and operation.**

By the student. This is an interesting problem for a literature search. Flexible fixturing (see also Section 37.8 on p. 1176) is economically viable for intermediate production quantities; for large quantities, dedicated fixtures are more suitable. Manufacturers such as Carr-Lane have systems of components that can be combined to form flexible fixtures.

**23.57 Review Fig. 23.7d and explain if it would be possible to machine eccentric shafts (like that shown in Fig. 23.12c) on such a setup. What if the part is long compared to its cross-section?**

By the student. This is a good problem for students to develop alternatives and setup for machining. Clearly, a simple solution is that a computer-controlled lathe (see Fig. 23.10a) can be used that is programmed to accommodate the eccentric shaft. Otherwise, the workpiece can be held in a fixture where the workpiece is mounted eccentrically and the fixture is held in the chuck (CLEAR?).

**23.58 We have seen that boring bars can be designed with internal damping capabilities in order to reduce or eliminate vibration and chatter during boring machining. Referring to the technical and manufacturers' literature, describe details of designs for such boring bars.**

By the student. This is a good problem for an Internet search. As with other machine tools, the approaches used are to have boring bars that have inherent damping (see Fig. 23.17b), such as fiber-reinforced plastics (see Section 9.3 on p. 244) or using bolted joints (as shown in Fig. 25.15 on p. 777).

**23.59 Would it be difficult to use the machining processes described in this chapter on various soft nonmetallic or rubber-like materials? Explain your thoughts, commenting on the role of the physical and mechanical properties of such materials**

**on the machining operation and any difficulties in producing the desired shapes and dimensional accuracies.**

By the student. This is a very interesting question and an excellent candidate for a technical literature review. Rubberlike materials are difficult to machine mainly because of their low elastic modulus and very large elastic strains that they can undergo under external forces. Care must be taken in properly supporting the workpiece and minimizing the cutting forces. Note also that these materials become stiffer with lower temperatures, which suggests an effective cutting strategy.

**23.60 With appropriate sketches, describe the principles of various fixturing methods and workholding devices that can be used for the processes described in this chapter. Include three-point locating and three-dimensional workholding for drilling and similar operations.**

By the student. This is a good problem and instructive for students to prepare sketches of various clamps and vices in a typical machine shop, if available. Workholding is an art in itself and many ingenious devices have been developed over the years. A sampling of workholding devices can be obtained easily by surveying manufacturers web sites on the Internet.

**23.61 Make a comprehensive table of the process capabilities of the machining processes described in this chapter. Using several columns, describe the machine tools involved, type of cutting tools and tool materials used, shapes of parts produced, typical maximum and minimum sizes, surface finish, dimensional tolerances, and production rates.**

By the student. This is a challenging and comprehensive problem with many possible solutions. Some examples of acceptable answers are:

| Process | Machine tools | Cutting-tool materials | Shapes | Typical sizes |
|---|---|---|---|---|
| Turning | Lathe | Assorted; see Table 23.4 | Axisymmetric | 1-12 in. diameter, 4-48 in. length |
| Drilling | Lathe, mill drill press | Assorted, usually HSS | Circular holes | 1-100 mm (50 $\mu$m possible) |
| Knurling | Lathe, mill | Assorted, usually HSS | Rough surfaces on axisymmetric parts | Same as in turning |

**23.62 Inspect various utensils in a typical kitchen, and identify the ones that have some similarity to the processes described in this chapter. Comment on their principle of operation.**

By the student. There are a large number of possible answers, depending on the exposure of the students to different gadgets and their creativity in finding similarities among them. Some examples are:

- Apple and potato peelers that operate in similar fashion as a turning and skiving operation.

- Shaving of butter or chocolate is a process similar to orthogonal or oblique cutting.
- Restaurants will have graters and slicers that are similar to the processes in this chapter, specifically turning operations.

**23.63 In Fig. 23.14, we have shown tolerances that can be obtained by the process listed in the figure. Give specific examples of parts and applications where such ultra-high dimensional accuracy are essential.**

By the student. Various answers can be given, depending on the students' experience and level of research performed. Some examples are:

- Drilling and rough turning: Products where the surface finish and tolerances of these processes are acceptable include metal or wooden furniture, automotive engine blocks, and mounting brackets.
- Reaming and broaching: Performed where better quality holes are required such as mounting brackets for helicopter spindles.
- Honing and lapping: Used when drilling and reaming cannot produce a hole with acceptable quality. Example: Automotive cylinders for race cars, where extreme conditions are routinely encountered.

# Chapter 24

# Machining Processes Used to Produce Various Shapes: Milling, Broaching, Sawing, and Filing; Gear Manufacturing

## QUALITATIVE PROBLEMS

**24.14 Explain why broaching crankshaft bearings is an attractive alternative to other machining processes.**

Broaching (p. 742) has certain advantages such as capability to remove material at high volume rates in one setup and with good surface finish of the product. Turn broaching is the term used for broaching the bearing surfaces of crankshafts and similar parts (see top of p. 744) and is an efficient process because multiple broaches can be used and thus production rate is high. (See Fig. 23.25 on p. 667 of the 4th edition of this text.)

**24.15 Several guidelines are presented in this chapter for various cutting operations. Discuss the reasoning behind these guidelines.**

By the student. Typical design guidelines have been discussed in this chapter for a number of machines. For example, it is suggested that standard milling cutters be used and costly special cutters be avoided; this is reasonable because many CNC milling machines have automatic tool changers (see also Chapter 25) and can rapidly exchange tools. The guidelines that workpieces be rigid to resist deflection from clamping forces and cutting forces are intended to maximize the accuracy of the milling operation. For planing, it is suggested that the operation be designed so that all sides of the workpiece can be machined without having to reposition and reclamp the workpiece. This is important to minimize downtime while parts are being repositioned. Other guidelines have similar practical explanations.

**24.16 Explain why hacksaws are not as productive as band saws.**

Hacksaws and band saws both have teeth oriented to remove chips when the saw moves across a workpiece; however, a band saw has continuous motion, whereas a hacksaw reciprocates. About half of the time, the hacksaw is not producing any chips, and thus it is not as productive.

**24.17 In milling operations with horizontal- and vertical-spindle machines, which one is likely to hold dimensional accuracy better? Why?**

The answer depends on various factors such as part shape and the type of milling operations performed, tool and cutter shape and dimensions, and tool overhang. Note, however, that in a horizontal machine the arbor can be supported at the end (see Fig. 24.15 on p. 738) and, consequently, it is stiffer.

**24.18 What similarities and differences are there in slitting with a milling cutter and with a saw?**

The milling machine utilizes a rotating cutter with multiple teeth to perform the slitting operation, cutting the material across a small width. Because the cutters are rigid and the process is well controlled, good dimensional accuracy is obtained. The blades in sawing are thinner, hence thin cuts are possible. However, the blade has more flexibility (not only because it is thin but it is also long) and hence control of dimensions can be difficult. It should be noted that are several types of saws and that circular saws have been developed which produce good dimensional accuracy and thickness control (see p. 747).

**24.19 Why do machined gears have to be subjected to finishing operations? Which of the finishing processes are not suitable for hardened gear teeth? Why?**

Machined gears may be subjected to finishing operations (see Section 24.7.4 on p. 753) for a number of reasons. Since gears are expected to have long lives and, therefore, operate in the high-cycle fatigue range, surface finish is very important. Better surface finish can be obtained by various finishing operations, including inducing surface compressive residual stresses to improve fatigue life. Also, errors in gear-tooth form are corrected, resulting in smaller clearances and tighter fits, and therefore less "play" and noise in a gear train.

**24.20 How would you reduce the surface roughness shown in Fig. 24.6?**

By the student. It can readily be seen in Fig. 24.6 on p. 730 that the surface roughness can be improved by means such as (a) reducing the feed per tooth, (b) increasing the corner radius of the insert, and (c) correctly positioning the wiper blade, as shown in Fig. 24.6c.

**24.21 Why are machines such as the one shown in Fig. 24.17 so useful?**

They are useful because of their versatility; they can perform a number of operations without having to re-clamp or reposition the workpiece (which is a very important consideration for improving productivity). The headstock can be tilted on most models. These machines are also relatively simple to program and the program information for a certain part can be stored on magnetic tape or disc and recalled at a later date. The machine itself can reduce the number of tools needed to perform a given number of operations by utilizing the computer to program the tool paths. (See also Sections 38.3 and 38.4.)

**24.22 Comment on your observations concerning the designs shown in Fig. 24.20b and on the usefulness of broaching operations.**

By the student. The usefulness of broaching lies not only in the complexity of parts which can be economically produced, but also in the high surface quality. These parts would be relatively difficult to produce economically and at high rates by other machining processes.

**24.23 Explain how contour cutting could be started in a band saw, as shown in Fig. 24.25d.**

Contour cutting, as shown in Fig. 24.25d on p. 746, would best be initiated by first drilling a hole in the workpiece and then inserting the blade into the hole. Note the circle in the part, indicating the position of the drilled hole. (A similar situation exists in wire EDM, described in Section 27.5.1 on p. 849.) Depending on the part, it is also possible to simply start the cut at one of the edges of the blank.

**24.24 In Fig. 24.27a, high-speed steel cutting teeth are welded to a steel blade. Would you then recommend that the whole blade be made of high-speed steel? Explain your reasons.**

By the student. It is desirable to have a hard, abrasion-resistant material such as high-speed steel for the cutting edge and a flexible, thermally conductive material for the bulk of the blade. This is an economical method of producing saws, and to make the whole blade from HSS would be unnecessary and expensive.

**24.25 Describe the parts and conditions under which broaching would be the preferred method of machining.**

By the student. Broaching is very attractive for producing various external and internal geometric features; it is a high-rate production process and can be highly automated. Although the broach width is generally limited (see Fig. 24.22 on p. 743), typically a number of passes are taken to remove material, such as on the top surface of engine blocks. Producing notches, slots, or keyways are common applications where broaching is very useful.

**24.26 With appropriate sketches, explain the differences between and similarities among shaving, broaching, and turn broaching operations.**

By the student. Note, for example, that the similarities are generally in the mechanics of cutting, involving a finite width chip and usually orthogonal cutting. The differences include particulars of tooling design, the machinery used, and workpiece shapes.

**24.27 Would you consider the machining processes described in this chapter to be near-net or net-shape processing? Explain with appropriate examples.**

By the student. This is a good question for in-depth discussion in the classroom and is valuable for clarifying the meaning of the concept of net-shape processing. Briefly, the processes described in this chapter can be classified as either net-shape or near-net shape. Restricting the answer to surfaces that are machined, the workpiece can be net-shaped after milling. However, if the dimensional tolerances or surface finish from milling are not acceptable, the workpiece may have to be subjected to finishing operations such as grinding. The former is an example where the processes in this chapter are net-shape operations; the latter is an example of near-net-shape processing.

**24.28 Why is end milling such a versatile process? Explain with examples.**

By the student. Note the capability of the relatively high length-to-diameter ratio of end mills that are capable of removing material from small and deep recesses in the workpiece (see Figs. 21.1d on p. 21.1 and 24.2 on p. 725). For details, see Section 24.2.3 on p. 732.

**24.29 List and explain factors that contribute to poor surface finish in the processes described in this chapter.**

By the student. Note, for example, Eq. (21.24) on p. 637, which gives the roughness in a process such as turning and milling, clearly indicating that as the feed per tooth increases or as the tool radius decreases, the roughness increases. Other factors that contribute to poor surface finish are built-up edge, tool chipping or fracture, and chatter. Each of these factors can adversely affect any of the processes described in the chapter. (See also Problem 24.20.)

**24.30 Explain the possible reasons why a knife cuts well when it is moved back and forth. Consider factors such as the material cut, friction, and the dimensions of the cut.**

By the student. Students are encouraged to experiment with knives, cutting various different materials. Two main reasons why a knife cuts better when moved back and forth are: (a) the longitudinal movement reduces the vertical frictional component, hence the downward force in cutting is reduced and there is less distortion of the material being cut, and (b) no knife edge is perfectly smooth. A close look under a high-power microscope (such as a scanning electron microscope) would reveal the significant roughness. Such a rough edge would obviously act like a series of small cutting teeth, similar to a very fine saw.

**24.31 Are there size limitations to parts to be sawed? Explain.**

By the student. Obviously, there is an upper size limit to size: If the part is too large there will be an obvious interference with the machine. If the thickness of the part is no larger than two teeth, the saw will bind in the part and will bend or damage the part. Note, for example, how difficult it can be to saw sheet metal.

**24.32 Why is it difficult to use friction sawing on nonferrous metals?**

As stated on p. 748, nonferrous metals have a tendency to stick to the blade. This is undoubtedly caused by adhesion at the high temperatures and is easily attributable to the softness of these materials. Note also that these materials have a characteristically high thermal conductivity, so if any metal is melted (which is possible given the low melting temperatures of nonferrous metals), it will be quickly solidified if the severity of the operation is reduced; this can lead to welding to the blade.

**24.33 Would you recommend broaching a keyway on a gear blank before or after machining the teeth? Why?**

By the student. The keyway can be machined before the teeth is machined. The reason is that in hobbing or related processes (see Section 24.7 on p. 749), the gear blank is indexed. The key-way serves as a natural guide for indexing the blank.

## QUANTITATIVE PROBLEMS

**24.34 In milling operations, the total cutting time can be significantly influenced by (a) the magnitude of the noncutting distance, $l_c$, shown in Figs. 24.3 and 24.4 and (b) the ratio of width of cut, $w$, to the cutter diameter, $D$. Sketch several combinations of these parameters, give dimensions, select feeds and cutting speeds, etc., and determine the total cutting time. Comment on your observations.**

By the student. Students should be encouraged to consider, at a minimum, the following three cases:

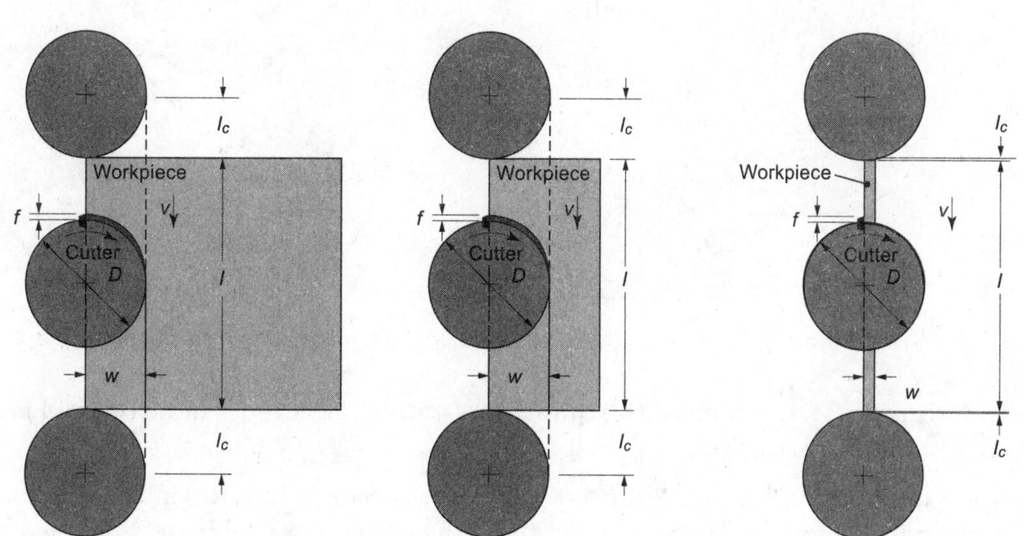


Note that $l_c$ needs to be estimated for each case. $l_c$ is shown to be equal to $\sqrt{Dw}$ in Prob. 24.36 for $D \gg w$. For $D \sim w$, it is reasonable to take $l_c = D/2$. For $w \ll D$, it is reasonable to take $l_c = 0$.

**24.35 You are performing a slab-milling operation at a specified cutting speed (surface speed of the cutter) and feed-per-tooth. Explain the procedure for determining the table speed required.**

Combining Eqs. (24.1) and (24.3) on pp. 726-727, we obtain the expression for the table speed, $v$, as

$$v = \frac{fVn}{pD}$$

Since all quantities are known, we can calculate the table speed.

**24.36 Show that the distance $l_c$ in slab milling is approximately equal to $\sqrt{Dd}$ for situations where $D \gg d$. See Fig. 24.3c.**

Referring to the figure below, the hypotenuse of the right triangle on the figure to the right is assigned the value of $x$, and is approximately equal to $D\theta$. Also, from the right triangle, $\theta = d/x$. Substituting for $\theta$, we get $x^2 = Dd$. From the Pythagorean theorem

$$l_c^2 + d^2 = x^2$$

Since $d$ is assumed to be first order small, the squared term can be assumed to be negligible. Thus,

$$l_c = x = \sqrt{Dd}$$

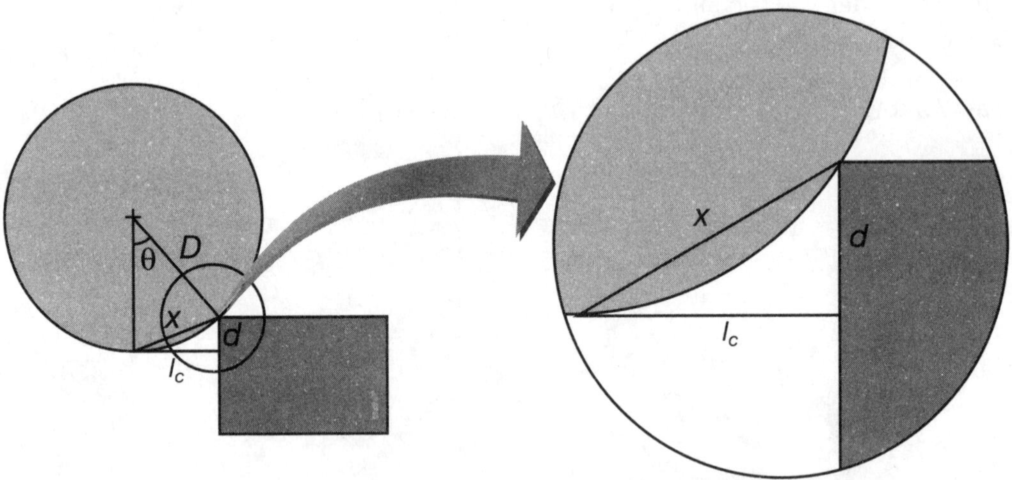


**24.37 In Example 24.1, which of the quantities will be affected when the feed is increased to $f$ = 0.02 in./tooth?**

If the feed is doubled to 0.02 in./tooth, the workpiece speed will double to 40 in./min. The metal removal rate will become 20 $\text{in}^3$/min, the power will double to 22 hp, and the cutting time will be halved to 19 s.

**24.38 Calculate the chip depth of cut, $t_c$, and the torque for Example 24.1.**

The chip depth of cut is given by Eq. (24.2) on p. 726:

$$t_c = 2f\sqrt{\frac{d}{D}} = 2(0.01)\sqrt{\frac{1/8}{2}} = 0.005 \text{ in.}$$

Since power is the product of torque and rotational speed, we find the torque to be

$$\text{Torque} = \frac{(11 \text{ hp})(550 \text{ ft-lb/s-hp})}{(2\pi)(100 \text{ rpm})(1/60 \text{ s/min})} = 578 \text{ lb-ft}$$

**24.39 Estimate the time required to face mill a 10-in.-long, 2-in.-wide brass block with a 6-in. diameter cutter with 10 high-speed-steel inserts.**

From Table 24.2 on p. 736, let's take a cutting speed for copper alloys (noting that brass has good machinability; see bottom of p. 640) of 750 ft/min, or 150 in./s. From the same table, let's take a feed per tooth of 0.2 mm, or 0.008 in. The rotational speed of the cutter is then calculated from

$$V = \pi D N$$

Hence,

$$N = \frac{V}{\pi D} = \frac{150}{\pi(6)} = 7.96 \text{ rps} = 477 \text{ rpm}$$

The workpiece speed can be obtained from Eq. (24.3) on p. 727:

$$v = fNn = (0.008 \text{ in./rev})(7.96 \text{ rev/s})(10) = 0.64 \text{ in./s}$$

The cutting time is given by

$$t = \frac{l + 2l_c}{v} = \frac{10 + (2)(3)}{0.64} = 25 \text{ s}$$

**24.40 A 10-in.-long, 1-in.-thick plate is being cut on a band saw at 150 ft/min. The saw has 12 teeth per in. If the feed per tooth is 0.003 in., how long will it take to saw the plate along its length?**

The workpiece speed, $v$, is the product of the number of teeth (12 per in.), the feed per tooth (0.003 in.), and band saw linear speed (100 ft/min). Thus the workpiece speed is

$$v = (12)(0.003)(100) = 3.6 \text{ ft/min} = 0.72 \text{ in./s}$$

Hence, for a 10-in. long plate, the cutting time is 10/0.72 = 14 s.

**24.41 A single-thread hob is used to cut 40 teeth on a spur gear. The cutting speed is 120 ft/min and the hob is 3 in. in diameter. Calculate the rotational speed of the spur gear.**

If a single-thread hob is used to cut 40 teeth, the hob and the blank must be geared so that the hob makes 40 revolutions while the blank makes one. The surface cutting speed of the hob is

$$V = \pi D N$$

hence

$$N = \frac{V}{\pi D}$$

Since the cutting speed is 100 ft/min = 1200 in./min, we have

$$N = \frac{1200}{\pi(3)} = 127 \text{ rpm}$$

Therefore, the rotational speed of the spur gear is 127/40 = 3.17 rpm.

**24.42 Assume that in the face-milling operation shown in Fig. 24.4 the workpiece dimensions are 5 in. by 10 in. The cutter is 6 in. in diameter, has 8 teeth, and rotates at 300 rpm. The depth of cut is 0.125 in. and the feed is 0.005 in./tooth. Assume that the specific energy requirement for this material is 2 hp-min/in$^3$**

**and that only 75% of the cutter diameter is engaged during cutting. Calculate (a) the power required and (b) the material removal rate.**

From the information given, we note that the material removal rate is

$$\text{MRR} = (0.005 \text{ in./tooth})(8 \text{ teeth/rev})(300 \text{ rev/min})(0.125 \text{ in.})(0.75)(6 \text{ in.})$$

or MRR $= 6.75$ in$^3$/min. Since the specific energy of material removal is given as 2 hp-min/in$^3$, we have

$$\text{Power} = (6.75)(2) = 13.5 \text{ hp}$$

**24.43 A slab-milling operation will take place on a part 250 mm long and 50 mm wide. A helical cutter 75 mm in diameter with ten teeth will be used. If the feed per tooth is 0.2 mm/tooth and the cutting speed is 0.75 m/s, find the machining time and metal removal rate for removing 6 mm from the surface of the part.**

From Eq. (24.1) on p. 726, the rotational speed, $N$, of the cutter can be calculated as:

$$V = \pi DN \quad \rightarrow \quad N = \frac{V}{\pi D} = \frac{0.75 \text{ m/s}}{\pi(0.075 \text{ m})} = 3.18 \text{ rev/s} = 190 \text{ rpm}$$

The linear speed of the cutter is given by Eq. (24.3) on p. 727 as:

$$f = \frac{v}{Nn} \quad \rightarrow \quad v = fNn = (0.2 \text{ mm})(190 \text{ rpm})(10) = 0.38 \text{ m/min}$$

If $l_c \ll l$, then $t = l/v = 0.25/0.38 = 0.657$ min $= 39.5$ s. The metal removal rate is given by Eq. (24.5) as

$$\begin{aligned} \text{MRR} &= wdv = (0.050 \text{ m})(0.006 \text{ m})(0.38 \text{ m/min}) = 1.14 \times 10^{-4} \text{ m}^3\text{/min} \\ &= 114{,}000 \text{ mm}^3\text{/min} \end{aligned}$$

**24.44 Calculate the ranges of typical machining times for face milling a 10-in.-long, 2-in.-wide cutter with a depth of cut of 0.1 in. for the following workpiece materials: (a) low-carbon steel, (b) titanium alloys, (c) aluminum alloys, and (d) thermoplastics.**

The cutting time, $t$, in face milling is by Eq. (24.4) on p. 727 as

$$t = \frac{l + l_c}{v}$$

We know that $l = 10$ in., hence as calculated in Example 24.1 (and proven in Problem 24.36), $l_c$ is obtained as

$$l_c = \sqrt{Dd} = \sqrt{(2 \text{ in.})(0.1 \text{ in.})} = 0.45 \text{ in.}$$

The remaining main variable is the feed, a range of which can be seen in Table 24.2 on p. 736 for the materials listed in the problem. For example, with low-carbon steel, the feed per tooth is 0.003-0.015 in/tooth. The cutting time, which will depend on the number of teeth, as obtained for 10 teeth in the cutter is listed below:

| Material | Maximum time (s) | Minimum time (s) |
|---|---|---|
| Low-carbon steel | 348 | 70 |
| Titanium alloys | 348 | 70 |
| Aluminum alloys | 348 | 58 |
| Thermoplastics | 348 | 58 |

**24.45 Explain whether the feed marks left on the workpiece by a face-milling cutter (as shown in Fig. 24.13a) are segments of true circles. Describe the parameters you consider in answering this question.**

They are not true circles, although they may appear to be circular. Consider the fact that a point on an insert is rotating about an axis (the cutter center). If the cutter is stationary, the insert traces a true circle. If the cutter translates, the path becomes elongated, so that it is no longer circular. Deriving an expression for the path of an insert is an interesting but advanced problem in kinematics.

**24.46 In describing the broaching operations and the design of broaches, we have not given equations regarding feeds, speeds, and material removal rates, as we have done in turning and milling operations. Review Fig. 24.21 and develop such equations.**

There are many forms for these expressions, and the simple derivation below should be recognized as an example of an acceptable solution. Referring to Fig. 24.21a on p. 743, we note that the volume of material removed by each tooth is

$$V_i = t_i w l$$

where $t_i$ is the depth of cut for tooth $i$, $w$ is the broach width, and $l$ is the length of cut. We can take the derivative with respect to time to obtain the metal removal rate per tooth as

$$\text{MRR}_i = t_i w v$$

We can say that the total metal removal rate is simply the sum of all tooth actions, or

$$\text{MRR} = \sum_{i=1}^{n} t_i w v = w v \sum_{i=1}^{n} t_i$$

If we divide the broach into roughing, semifinishing, and finishing zones (see Fig. 24.23 on p. 744),

$$\text{MRR} = w v \left( \sum_{i=1}^{n_r} t_{ri} + \sum_{i=1}^{n_s} t_{si} + \sum_{i=1}^{n_f} t_{fi} \right)$$

where an $r$ subscript denotes a roughing cut, $s$ for semifinishing, and $f$ for finishing. A simplification can be obtained if one assumes that the depth of cut for all but the roughing zones can be neglected.

## SYNTHESIS, DESIGN, AND PROJECTS

**24.47 The part shown in Fig. 24.1f is to be machined from a rectangular blank. Suggest the machine tool(s) required, the fixturing needed, and the types and sequence of operations to be performed. Discuss your answer in terms of the workpiece material, such as aluminum versus stainless steel.**

By the student. This is an open-ended problem and a number of solutions are acceptable. The main challenge with the part shown is in designing a fixture that allows all of the operations to be performed. Clearly, a milling machine will be required for milling the stepped cavity and the slots; the holes could be done in the milling machine as well, although a drill press may be used instead. Note that one hole is drilled on a milled surface, so drilling and tapping have to follow milling. If the surface finish on the exterior is not critical, a chuck or vise can be used to grip the surface at the corners, which is plausible if the part height is large enough. The grips usually have a rough surface, so they will leave marks which will be more pronounced in the aluminum than in stainless steel.

**24.48 Referring to Fig. 24.1f, would you prefer to machine this part from a preformed blank (near-net shape) rather than a rectangular blank? If so, how would you prepare such a blank? How would the number of parts required influence your answer?**

By the student. This is an open-ended problem and a number of solutions are acceptable. Although starting with a near-net shape blank is always preferable for machining, it can sometimes be difficult or expensive to obtain a near-net shape, especially when production quantities are low. Regardless, obtaining a near-net shaped blank is challenging in this case because of the slots and stepped cavity. This shape is very difficult to forge, and the cross-section is not uniform to be extruded and cut to length; however, a blank can be cast fairly easily. The tapped holes are features that would be very difficult cast, but a dimple for the drill bit (in order to avoid the drill bit wandering from the intended spot) can be incorporated into the cast part. Proper machining allowances should be incorporated on all surfaces and features that have stringent surface finish or dimensional tolerance requirements.

**24.49 Assume that you are an instructor covering the topics described in this chapter, and you are giving a quiz on the numerical aspects to test the understanding of the students. Prepare several quantitative problems and supply the answers.**

By the student. This is an outstanding, open-ended question that requires considerable focus and understanding from the students, and has been found to be a very valuable homework problem.

**24.50 Suggest methods whereby milling cutters of various designs (including end mills) can incorporate carbide inserts.**

By the student. This is an open-ended problem and various solutions would be acceptable. There are several ways to incorporate carbide inserts, some of which are depicted in the text. In Fig. 24.5 on p. 729, for example, inserts are shown mounted on a face-milling cutter, and inserts for ball-nose end mills are shown in Fig. 24.10 on p. 733. These figures show inserts being installed in place with screws, but clamps or brazing also are options for affixing inserts as well, although brazing of carbide inserts is not usually done (see Problem 23.41).

**24.51 Some handbooks include tables of "do and don'ts" regarding machining operations and the equipment used. Survey the available literature and prepare such a table for milling operations.**

By the student. This is an open-ended problem and a number of solutions are acceptable. This question can be directed towards safety rules, material selection rules, or performance rules. For example, the following are acceptable answers:

- Counterboring/countersinking speed = 1/3 of drilling speed.
- When hand tapping, turn in 1/4 - 1/2 of a turn, then out 3/4 turn.
- When boring, drill 1/32 - 1/16 in. undersize, then bore.
- When fly cutting, take off 0.025 to 0.100 in./pass, with a spindle speed of 1500-2000 rpm. Higher speeds will produce a better surface finish, but use 1200 rpm or so with plastics because otherwise the material will melt. Also, having a large radius on the tool tip will improve surface finish.
- When designing a three-edge inside corner (See Fig. 24.2c on p. 725) one of the inside edges must have the radius of the end mill. Also, a separate hole can serve to allow relief for a male 90° corner to fit. The hole must be drilled first since drills cannot withstand significant side loading.
- Where possible, allow inside radii to be determined by the manufacturing personnel; this practice will allow for flexibility to use tools that are easily obtained and maintained.
- For machined surfaces with a high degree of flatness, bosses should be used. This clearly defines what areas need to have flatness control, and also simplifies painting and other finishing operations.
- For outside corners, chamfers are preferable over radii. An outside radius requires a form-relieved cutter and a precise setup, both of which are expensive.
- Always use a cutting fluid when reaming except with brass or cast iron.

**24.52 Make a comprehensive table of the process capabilities of the machining processes described in this chapter. Using several columns, list the machines involved, type of tools and tool materials used, shapes of blanks and parts produced, typical maximum and minimum sizes, surface finish, dimensional tolerances, and production rates.**

By the student. This is an open-ended problem and a number of responses are acceptable. For example, the following can be a portion of a more complete table:

| Machine tool | Tool materials | Typical part shapes | Typical surface finish ($\mu$m) | Typical production rates (parts/hr) |
|---|---|---|---|---|
| Milling machine, column and knee type | Carbide, coated carbide, cermets, SiN, PCD, etc. (see Table 24.2 on p. 736) | No limit; typically moderate aspect ratio | 1-2 | 1-20 |
| Broaching machines | High speed steels, carbide inserts | Short width, constant cross-sections, linear surface lay | 1.5 | 20-200 |
| Gear generator | Carbide | Gears | 1 | 10-30 |

**24.53 Based on the data developed in Problem 24.52, describe your thoughts regarding the procedure to be followed in determining what type of machine tool to select when machining a particular part.**

By the student. In this open-ended problem, the discussions should include the part shape as well as the material, the surface finish and dimensional tolerances required, the production quantity and production rate specified. Also, in practice, this determination is usually constrained by machine or vendor availability, as well as machine backlog.

**24.54 Using the Internet, obtain specifications on the smallest and largest milling machines available and compare your results with the results obtained by your classmates.**

By the student. This is an open-ended problem and a number of solutions are acceptable. The smallest milling machines are novel research tools used for meso-scale manufacturing (see Fig. V.1 on p. 866). Some large milling machines, such as the one depicted below, have a workspace of 20 ft $\times$ 14 ft $\times$ 5 ft.

Source: Ratech Machine, Inc., www.ratechmachine.com

**24.55 Make a list of all the processes that can be used in manufacturing gears, including those described in Parts II and III of this text. For each process, describe the advantages, limitations, and the quality of gears produced.**

By the student. This is an open-ended problem and an example of an acceptable answer would be:

- Form cutting: The advantages are the relatively simple design of machinery and tooling, and the ability to rapidly produce spur gears; However, surface finish is limited.
- Hobbing: Allows production of a wide variety of gears including worm gears; surface finish is limited.
- Grinding: Produces superior surface finish, but is a relatively slow process.

**24.56 If expanded honeycomb panels (see Section 16.12) were to be machined in a form-milling operation, what precautions would you take to keep the sheet metal from buckling due to tool forces? Think up as many solutions as you can.**

By the student. This is an open-ended problem can be interpreted in two ways: That the honeycomb itself is being pocket machined, or that a fabricated honeycomb is being contoured. Either problem is a great opportunity to challenge students to develop creative solutions. Acceptable approaches include:

(a) high-speed machining with properly chosen processing variables,

(b) using alternative processes such as chemical machining,

(c) filling the cavities of the honeycomb structure with a low-melting-point metal (to provide strength to the thin layers of material being machined) which is then melted away after the machining operation has been completed, and

(d) filling the cavities with wax, or with water which is then frozen, and melted after the machining operation.

# Chapter 25

# Machining Centers, Advanced Machining Concepts and Structures, and Machining Economics

## QUALITATIVE PROBLEMS

**25.12 Explain the technical and economic factors that led to the development of machining centers.**

Machining centers (p. 761), as a manufacturing concept, serve two purposes: (a) save time by rapid tool changes and eliminating part handling and mounting in between processes, and (b) rapid changeover for new production runs. The text gives the example of automobile engine blocks which require drilling, boring, tapping, etc., to be performed. Normally, much time would be spent transferring and handling the workpiece between different machine tools. Machining centers eliminate or reduce the need for part handling and, consequently, reduce manufacturing time and costs. Also, a variety of parts can be produced in small lots.

**25.13 We have noted that spindle speeds in machining centers vary over a wide range. Explain the reasons, giving specific applications.**

Spindle speeds vary over a wide range for a number of reasons; the most obvious is the optimization of cutting time. A small drill, for example, is operated at higher spindle speeds than for larger drills to obtain the same surface cutting speed. Since the speed of the cutting operation is important (because different workpiece materials require different cutting speeds for optimum tool life and surface finish) spindles must therefore be capable of operating in a wide range of rotational speeds.

**25.14 Explain the importance of stiffness and damping of machine tools. How are they accomplished?**

High stiffness in machine tools results in lowering the dynamic force/excitation ratios, thus it is important in reducing, or at least controlling, chatter. Also, stiffness is important to minimize tool deflections during machining. By minimizing deflections, one can improve dimensional accuracy and reduce dimensional tolerances. Stiffness typically can be improved by using materials with high elastic modulus, optimizing the section moduli of components, and by improving the type of joints and sliding machine elements. (See Section 25.4 on p. 775.)

**25.15 Are there machining operations described in Chapters 23 and 24 that cannot be performed in machining and turning centers? Explain, with specific examples.**

By the student. Machining centers can easily perform operations which involve a rotating tool (milling, drilling, tapping, and honing) and not the workpiece (other than during indexing or positioning). Consequently, it would be difficult to perform operations such as turning, broaching, sawing, or grinding on a machining center. The students are encouraged to investigate further the machining processes in the two chapters for their suitability for machining centers.

**25.16 Describe how the touch probes shown in Fig. 25.6 operate.**

Touch probes (p. 766) can have different levels of sophistication. The simplest probes are basically limit switches that detect the presence or absence of an object; these can be used to make sure, for example, that a cutting tool is in place, that is, that it hasnt broken. The same simple limit switch concept can be used with a properly positioned probe or probes to also check dimensions or the presence or absence of a workpiece. More elaborate probes measure dimensions. These probes are typically resistance or capacitance-based; the farther the probe is depressed, the larger the changes in resistance or capacitance. This signal is then used by the controlling hardware and software to make appropriate compensations. The students may further investigate such probes as a project.

**25.17 How important is the control of cutting-fluid temperature in operations performed in machining centers? Explain.**

The control of cutting-fluid temperature is very important in operations where high dimensional accuracy is essential. As expected, the fluid heats up during its service throughout the day (due to the energy dissipated during machining), its temperature begins to rise. This, in turn, raises the temperature of the workpiece and fixtures, and adversely affects dimensional accuracy. Temperature-control units are available for maintaining a constant temperature in cutting-fluid systems. (See also Section 22.12.)

**25.18 Review Fig. 25.10 on modular machining centers and explain workpieces and operations that would be suitable on such machines.**

By the student. The main advantages to the different modular setups shown in Fig. 25.10 on p. 769 are that various workpiece shapes and sizes can be accommodated can be changed, and the tool support can made stiffer by minimizing the overhang. (See Section 25.2.4 for the benefits of reconfigurable machines.)

**25.19 Describe the adverse effects of vibration and chatter in machining regarding both the workpiece and the cutting tool.**

By the student. The adverse effects of chatter are discussed on p. 775 and are summarized briefly below:

- Poor surface finish, as shown in the right central region of Fig. 25.13 on p. 775.
- Loss of dimensional accuracy of the workpiece.
- Premature tool wear, chipping, and failure, a critical consideration with brittle tool materials, such as ceramics, some carbides, and diamond.
- Possible damage to the machine-tool components from excessive vibration and chatter.
- Objectionable noise, particularly if it is of high frequency, such as the squeal heard when turning brass on a lathe with a less rigid setup.

**25.20 We know that we may be able to decrease machining costs by changing the cutting speed. Explain which costs are likely to change and how, as the cutting speed is changed.**

By the student. Refer to Section 25.8 on p. 783. Increasing the cutting speed will decrease the machining cost per part. On the other hand, as the cutting speed increases, tool life decreases and thus tool cost increases. When tool life decreases, the tool has to be changed or indexed more often, thus tool changing cost will increase. Note that the determination of the optimal conditions to minimize the overall cost requires considerable quantitative data, which may not always be available.

**25.21 Explain the differences in the functions of a turret and a spindle in turning centers.**

By the student. A turret (see Figs. 23.9 and 23.10 on pp. 692-693) accommodates multiple tools which can be indexed quickly. Spindles (see Fig. 25.8 on p. 767) typically accommodate the workpiece, although they can be equipped with drill bits depending on the design of the machine. The students may investigate this topic further as a project.

**25.22 Explain how the pallet arrangements shown in Fig. 25.4a and b would be operated in the use of these machines.**

In Fig. 25.4a on p. 764, the pallets are taken from the cue in a first in, first out (FIFO) manner. The pallet pool can have individual pallets added, or else the gray shaded region shown with a number of pallets can be added at one time. In Fig. 25.4b, the pallets service two machining centers. These can be arranged identically to Fig. 25.4a, where dedicated pallets are assigned to each machine. However, another approach is to have both machines operate on the same pallet cue. This makes the machining process less susceptible to delays due to machine service.

**25.23 Review the tool changer shown in Fig. 25.5 and explain any constraints to making their operations faster, thus reducing the tool changing time.**

By the student. This question would make a good design project. Tool changers (Fig. 25.5 on p. 765) are very fast for the obvious reason of reducing the noncutting time in machining (see p. 764). Making them faster can involve significant costs by virtue of the more powerful motors required to overcome inertial forces, the adverse effects of these dynamic forces on machine components, and the higher wear rates of the components. The larger motors and the design changes will also increase the bulk of the automatic tool changers as well, making them more difficult to place in the machine where space is a premium.

**25.24 In addition to the number of joints in a machine tool (see Fig. 25.15), what other factors influence the rate at which damping increases?**

In addition to the number of joints and components in a machine tool (as shown in Fig. 25.15 on p. 777) other factors that influence damping is the nature and roughness of the joint interfaces, clamping force, and the presence of lubricants and other fluids at the interfaces.

**25.25 Describe workpieces that would not be suitable for machining on a machining center. Give specific examples.**

By the student. There are few workpieces that cannot be produced on machining centers, as by their nature they are very flexible. Some of the acceptable answers would be:

- Workpieces that are required in much higher quantities than can be performed economically on machining centers.
- Parts that are too large for the machining-center workspace, such as large forging or castings.
- Parts that need specialized machines, such as rifling of gun barrels.

**25.26 Other than the fact that they each have a minimum, are the overall shapes and slopes of the total-cost and total-time curves in Fig. 25.18 important? Explain.**

By the student. Note that the shape of the total cost curve can be sharper or shallower than that shown in Fig. 24.18a on p. 786. If sharper, a small difference in the cutting speed can make a large difference in cost because of the steeper slopes of the curve. If shallower, the cutting speed would have less influence. With numerical data obtained, students can determine the extent of these effects.

**25.27 In Section 21.3, we stated that the thrust force in cutting can be negative at high rake angles and/or low friction at the chip-tool interface. This can have an adverse effect on the stability of the cutting process. Explain why.**

This is a challenging problem and suitable for those specializing in vibration. It should be noted that if the thrust force can be negative (see p. 621) and varies periodically between negative and positive (as it can do with even small variations in the depth of cut), the system will develop a forcing frequency. In that case, there can be vibrations developed, the frequency and amplitude of which will depend on the machine-tool characteristics, the workpiece, and the fixturing.

**25.28 Explain the advantages and disadvantages machine-tool frames made of gray iron castings?**

The advantages of cast machine-tool frames are that it is easy and relatively inexpensive to produce complex and large structures. Gray irons have high internal damping capacity (see pp. 126 and 336). Because of lower elastic modulus, these structures have relatively low stiffness compared to welded-steel frames; however, using larger cross-sections will greatly improve this situation (as is the common practice). Also, the very limited ductility and toughness of cast irons (see Fig. 12.4f on p. 333) may make them unsuitable for high impact situations.

**25.29 What are the advantages and disadvantages of welded-steel frames? Bolted- steel frames? Using adhesive bonding to assemble components of machine tools.**

By the student. This problem can be an interesting project for students, requiring considerable efforts in literature search. Briefly:

(a) The advantages of welded-steel frames (see Part VI) are their high stiffness (due to the high elastic modulus of steels) as well as ease of fabrication since various components can be welded into complex shapes and the overall stiffness can be optimized. However, welded structures cannot be disassembled and thermal distortions during welding can present difficulties.

(b) The advantage to bolted frames is their fairly high stiffness, with some damping capability associated with a bolted joint (see also Fig. 25.15 on p. 777). The disadvantages include the time required for preparation of surfaces to be joined, holes, and fasteners, and possible corrosion at interfaces by time (crevice corrosion).

(c) Adhesive bonding (see Section 32.4 on p. 1014) has major advantages of ease of assembly, fewer problems with corrosion at the interfaces of assembled components, and some capacity for damping vibrations. Among disadvantages are the time required for assembly, reliability of the joints, and the difficulty of disassembly.

**25.30 Why have concrete or polymer concretes been used in some machine tools?**

Concrete and polymer concretes (see p. 771) can play an important role in reducing vibration in steel-framed machine tools. Concrete is poured inside the machine frame in various configurations (including sandwich construction) to provide damping as well as mass, thereby reducing vibrations. Also, vibration-isolating machine supports also can be produced which are very effective. (Note also that concrete canoes have been built.) Among disadvantages are relatively low stiffness and poor thermal conductivity of these materials (important in reducing thermal distortions in machine tools).

**25.31 Describe the economic considerations involved in selecting machining and turning centers.**

Economics plays an obvious and major role in all such decisions. With machining and turning centers, cost increases with workspace size, power requirements, speeds, features, and complexity (see also Section 40.9). A detailed analysis is therefore required to examine the intended (and possible future) uses and match these requirements with the least expensive, commercially available machinery.

**25.32 Give examples of forced vibration or self-excited vibration in general engineering practice.**

Examples of forced vibration are a punching bag, a pogo stick, vibrating pagers, and timing clocks in computers. Examples for self-excited vibration include a whistle made with a blade of grass, music from a bugle, speech, and the collapse of the Tacoma Narrows Bridge in Washington State in 1940. (See also engineering texts on vibration.)

**25.33 Explain specific situations where thermal distortion of machine-tool components would be important.**

When high precision is required (see, for example, Fig. 25.17 on p. 782), thermal distortion is very important and must be eliminated or minimized. As shown in Problem 25.36, this is a serious concern, as even a few degrees of temperature rise can cause sufficient thermal expansion to compromise dimensional accuracy.

**25.34 What are the workpiece requirements that would make a machining center preferable to conventional milling machines, lathes, and drill presses?**

Machining centers are suitable for complex parts requiring machining on different surfaces and in different orientation (for details, see Section 25.2 on p. 761). They are economical for production in small or moderate quantities, a situation that is very common in industry today. Conventional machine tools would be appropriate in transfer lines (not the type and variety of machine tools shown in Fig. 37.5 on p. 1152) for high volume or mass production, or if the parts to be machined are relatively simple. This topic would make a fine project for students.

**25.35 Explain how you would go about reducing each of the cost factors in machining operations. What difficulties would you encounter in doing so?**

By the student. As can be seen on p. 784, the total machining cost per piece consists of four factors (see also Chapter 40 for further details):

(a) Nonproductive cost. This includes labor, overhead, and setup costs. These costs can be reduced through application of automation to reduce labor, especially using CNC machines and machining centers to reduce setup time and costs.

(b) Machining cost. This cost can be reduced not only by automation to reduce labor, but also by selection of appropriate cutting-tool materials, cutting fluids, and machining parameters.

(c) Tool-change cost. This can be reduced through the application of automatic tool changers and fixtures which allow rapid exchange of tools, thus eliminating or reducing manual labor.

(d) Cost of cutting tool. Advanced tool materials are more expensive, thus the tool cost can be reduced through use of more conventional materials. However, the use of less expensive tool materials will likely result in higher tool wear, more frequent tool changes, and the need for lower cutting speeds, thus increasing the machining costs and tool-change costs.

## QUANTITATIVE PROBLEMS

**25.36 A machining-center spindle and tool extend 12 in. from its machine-tool frame. What temperature change can be tolerated to maintain a tolerance of 0.0001 in. in machining? A tolerance of 0.001 in.? Assume that the spindle is made of steel.**

The extension due to a change in temperature is given by

$$\Delta L = \alpha \Delta T L$$

where $\alpha$ is the coefficient of thermal expansion which, for carbon steels, is $\alpha = 6.5 \times 10^{-6}/°\text{F}$. If $\Delta L = 0.0001$ in. and $L = 12$ in., then $\Delta T$ can easily be calculated to be 1.28°F; also for $\Delta L = 0.001$ in., we have $\Delta T = 12.8°\text{F}$. Noting that the temperatures involved are quite small, this example clearly illustrates the importance of environmental controls in precision manufacturing operations, where dimensional tolerances are extremely small (see Fig. 25.17).

**25.37 Calculate the time to manufacture the parts in Example 25.1 using conventional machining and high-speed machining, using the data in Case Study 25.1.**

This is an open-ended problem and various answers would be acceptable because the number of roughing and finishing cuts have not been specified in the statement of the problem. The following would be examples of calculations:

1. Finish turning. The outer diameter is given as 91 mm, so to obtain a cutting speed of 95 m/min, the required rotational speed is

$$N = \frac{V}{\pi D_o} = \frac{95}{\pi(0.091)} = 332 \text{ rpm}$$

For determining the feed, we review Table 23.4 on p. 682 and note that for high-carbon steel the low value of typical feeds is 0.15 mm/rev, which we can use since this is a finishing operation. Thus, using $l = 25$ mm, we have

$$t = \frac{l}{fN} = \frac{25}{(0.15)(332)} = 0.50 \text{ min}$$

2. Boring on inside diameter. Here the ID is 75.5 mm, so to obtain a linear speed of 95 m/min requires a rotational speed of

$$N = \frac{V}{\pi D_o} = \frac{95}{\pi(0.0755)} = 400 \text{ rpm}$$

Therefore, the time required using the same feed of $f = 0.15$ mm/rev is

$$t = \frac{l}{fN} = \frac{25}{(0.15)(400)} = 0.41 \text{ min}$$

The students are encouraged to obtain estimates for the remaining machining steps and investigate incorporating roughing and finishing cuts into each step.

**25.38 In the production of a machined valve, the labor rate is \$19.00 per hour, the tool-grinder labor rate is \$25.00 per hour, and the general overhead rate is \$15.00 per hour. The tool is made of high-speed steel and costs \$25.00, takes five minutes to change, and can be reground four times before it needs to be replaced. The workpiece is a free-machining aluminum. Estimate the optimum cutting speed from a cost perspective.**

The optimum cutting speed is given by Eq. (25.11) on p. 785 as

$$V_o = \frac{C\left(L_m + B_m\right)^n}{\left\{\left(\frac{1}{n} - 1\right)\left[T_c\left(L_m + B_m\right) + T_g\left(L_g + B_g\right) + D_c\right]\right\}^n}$$

For a high-speed-steel cutting tool, lets take $n = 0.14$ to represent a mean value, taken from Table 21.3 on p. 628. Note that $T_c = 5$ min $= 0.0833$ hr and $T_g = 0.1667$ hr. Therefore, substituting these values into Eq. (25.11) yields

$$V_o = \frac{(100)(19+15)^{0.14}}{\left\{\left(\frac{1}{0.14} - 1\right)\left[(0.0833)(19+15) + (0.1667)(25+15) + \frac{25}{4}\right]\right\}^{0.14}}$$

Solving this equation, we find that $V_o = 86.3$ m/min.

## SYNTHESIS, DESIGN, AND PROJECTS

**25.39 If you were the chief engineer in charge of the design of machining and turning centers, what changes and improvements would you recommend on existing models?**

By the student. Among several others, the following research topics are suggested:

(a) Expansion of tool-magazine capabilities.

(b) Development of hardware and software to facilitate programming without sacrificing reliability, as discussed further in Part IX, including holonic manufacturing integration.

(c) Improving the stiffness of the machine tool but without compromising the damping capability of the machine frame.

(d) Alternate materials and optimum structural designs. (See also Section I.11 on p. 41.)

**25.40 Study the technical literature and outline the trends in the design of modern machine tools. Explain why there are those trends.**

By the student. The trend in machine tools is towards increased computer control and increased stiffness, while attempting to maintain good damping characteristics. Note that stiffness and damping are mutually exclusive when using conventional materials. Gray cast iron, which has been used on machine structures for hundreds of years, has good damping characteristics. Steel is being used more and more because of stiffness considerations, but it lacks the inherent damping capability of gray iron. The increase in the use of steel is based upon the need to increase the stiffness of the machine tool for improved dimensional accuracy and reduction of chatter, and also offering greater flexibility in design. Research and development efforts are being directed at utilizing stiffer materials in the construction of machine tools as well as improving damping. Communication between machines and host computers is being continually improved and expanded to allow for better control of the manufacturing enterprise. (See also Section I.11 on p. 41.)

**25.41 Make a list of components of machine tools that could be made of ceramics and explain why ceramics would be suitable.**

By the student. To review the characteristics of ceramics and their processing, refer to Sections 8.2 and 8.3 on pp. 220 and 224, and Section 18.2 on p. 514. Typical candidates are members that reciprocate at high speeds or members that move at high speeds and are brought to rest in a short time. Bearing components are also suitable applications by virtue of the hardness, resistance, and low density (hence low inertial forces) of ceramics.

**25.42 Survey the literature from various machine-tool manufacturers and prepare a comprehensive table, indicating the capabilities, sizes, power, and costs of machining and turning centers. Comment on your observations.**

By the student. This is a challenging project. To obtain costs, students should identify machinery dealers and not manufacturers, because in practice it is rare that a manufacturer will have cost data readily available. It is advisable that the instructor assign a number of machines, such as five machines with different capabilities, since a wide variety of equipment and capacities are commercially available.

**25.43 As you can appreciate, the cost of machining and turning centers is considerably higher than for traditional machine tools. Since many operations performed by machining centers can also be done on conventional machines, how would you go about justifying the high cost of these centers? Explain with appropriate examples.**

By the student. This is an open-ended problem and a variety of answers would be acceptable. The justification needs to be economic, and it is usually tied to increased capabilities, flexibility, and production rates that can be achieved with machining centers. Also, modern machines have much better capabilities to integrate into a computer-controlled manufacturing enterprise, so that part-description recollection and inventory control can be better accomplished. (See also Table 40.9 on p. 1263.)

**25.44 Perform a literature search or contact manufacturers to describe the details of how hexapod machines operate.**

By the student. Details of hexapods are described on pp. 773-774.

**25.45 In Part III of this text, we described forming and shaping processes for metallic and nonmetallic materials. Based on this knowledge, explain whether it would be feasible to design a machine that could be named a "forming center," capable of performing two or more different shaping processes. Give specific examples of parts that can be made and describe your ideas on the design of such a machine or machines.**

By the student. This is an open-ended problem, with many acceptable answers. There are several researchers working on such forming centers. Some concepts, for example, use sheet metal with a roller attachment whereby the roller forces the sheet to form a desired contour. This topic would be a good project for students to investigate.

**25.46 Explain if it could be possible to design and build machining centers without computer controls.**

By the student. Machining centers rely on the rapid decision-making capability of computer controls, with important economic implications. Technically, one could have machine operators change the tools and operate such machines, but it would take significantly longer time to perform all the operations required. The students are encouraged to comment further.

**25.47 In your experience using tools or other devices, have you come across situations where you experienced vibration and chatter? If so, give details and explain how you would go about minimizing them.**

By the student. The particular answers will vary based on the students experience. A student answering "no" to this question obviously is not being sufficiently creative because vibrations are commonly experienced, such as in sounds produced by string and percussion instruments, automobile suspensions, and trampolines (see also Problem 25.49). Chatter has, for example, been commonly experienced by all students in the way of the annoying scratching sound of a chalk while writing on a chalkboard. Minimizing vibration and chatter can be accomplished in several ways, including increasing damping (as in replacing faulty struts on an automobile), and increasing stiffness or process parameters.

**25.48 Describe your thoughts on whether or not it is feasible to include grinding operations (see Chapter 26) in machining centers. Explain the nature of any difficulties that may be encountered.**

By the student. This is a challenging problem for students who have not yet read Chapter 26, although may have been exposed to grinding of a kitchen knife or scissors. It can be a good problem when an instructor is covering these two chapters in an assignment. Note, however, that grinding would be difficult to incorporate into machining centers primarily because the processing parameters are different and the debris from the grinding operation would cause serious damage and wear of the machine components. On the other hand, it is quite conceivable that a "grinding center" could be developed, as has been done in die-sinking machining centers (see p. 848).

**25.49 The following experiment is designed to better appreciate the effect of tool overhang in vibration and chatter. With a sharp tool, scrape the surface of a piece of soft metal by holding the tool with your arm fully stretched. Repeat the experiment by holding the tool with your hand as close to the metal as possible. Describe your observations regarding the tendency for the tool to vibrate. Repeat the experiment with different types of metallic and nonmetallic materials.**

By the student. This would be an interesting experiment to perform. This clearly shows the effect of stiffness on chatter. The same experiment can be demonstrated in a classroom with chalk on a chalkboard.

**25.50 A large bolt is to be produced from extruded hexagonal stock by placing the hex stock into a chuck and machining the cylindrical shank of the bolt by turning.**

**List the difficulties that may be encountered in this operation.**

By the student. There will be several difficulties. This operation obviously will involve interrupted cutting, with repeated impact between the cutting-tool and the surface, and the associated dynamic stresses which, in turn, could lead to tool chipping and breakage. Even if the tool survives, chatter may be unavoidable in the early stages when the depth of cut variations are at their maximum (depending on the characteristics of the machine-tool and of the fixtures used). Note that the ratio of length-to-cross-sectional area of the bolt also will have an influence on vibration and chatter.

# Chapter 26

# Abrasive Machining and Finishing Operations

## QUALITATIVE PROBLEMS

**26.19 Why are grinding operations necessary for components that have previously been machined by the processes described in Chapters 23 and 24?**

The grinding processes described in this chapter are necessary for a number of reasons, as stated at the beginning of Section 26.1 on p. 790. Students are encouraged to articulate further, giving specific examples. Basically, the answer is that the processes described cannot produce the required dimensional accuracy and surface finish for a part.

**26.20 Explain why there are so many different types, shapes, and sizes of grinding wheels.**

By the student. There are many different types and sizes of grinding wheels because of numerous factors: The shape and type of a grinding wheel depend upon the workpiece material and its shape, the surface finish and geometry desired, rate of production, heat generation during the process, economics of wheel wear, and type of grinding fluids used. Each grinding wheel must be chosen for a particular application while considering all of these factors.

**26.21 Explain the reasons for the large difference between the specific energies involved in machining (Table 21.2) and in grinding (Table 26.2).**

Specific energies in grinding as compared to machining (see pp. 602 and 801) are much higher principally due to the presence of wear flats (causing high friction) and due to the large negative rake angles typically found in abrasives (hence the chips formed during grinding must undergo more deformation, and therefore require more energy). Also, since the chips in grinding are very small, there is more surface area for frictional losses per volume of material removed when compared with machining. Size effect (due to very small chips produced) also may be a contributing factor. Students may investigate this topic further as a project.

**26.22 We have stated that ultrasonic machining is best suited for hard and brittle materials. Explain why.**

In ultrasonic machining (p. 818) the stresses developed from particle impact should cause damage sufficient to spall the workpiece, which involves fracture on a very small scale. If the workpiece is soft and ductile, the impact force will simply deform the workpiece locally (as does the indenter in a hardness test), instead of causing fracture.

**26.23 Explain why parts with irregular shapes, sharp corners, deep recesses, and sharp projections can difficult to polish.**

By the student. Students are likely to have had some experience relevant to this question. The basic reason why these shapes may be difficult to polish is that it is difficult to have a polishing medium to properly follow an intricate surface, to penetrate depths, or be able apply equal pressure on all surfaces for uniform polishing.

**26.24 Explain the reasons why so many deburring operations have been developed over the years.**

By the student. There are many deburring operations because (as described on pp. 825-826) of the wide variety of workpiece materials, characteristics, shapes, and surface features and textures involved. There is a also the requirement for different levels of automation in deburring.

**26.25 What precautions should you take when grinding with high precision? Make comments about the machine, process parameters, the grinding wheel, and grinding fluids.**

When grinding for high precision (see also Fig. 25.17 on p. 782), it is essential that the forces involved remain low so that workpiece and machine deflections are minimal. As can be seen from Eq. (26.3) on p. 800, to minimize grinding forces, hence minimize deflections, the wheel speed should preferably be high, the workpiece speed should be low, and the depth of cut should be small. The machine used should have high stiffness with good bearings. The temperature rise, as given by Eq. (26.4) on p. 803, should be minimized. (In comparing the two equations cited, note how the processing parameters have contradicting effects; this is situation where the parameters have to be optimized.)

The grinding wheel should also have fine grains and the abrasive should be inert to the workpiece material to avoid any adverse reactions. The grinding fluid should be selected to provide low wheel loading and wear, and also to provide for effective cooling. Automatic dressing capabilities should be included and the wheel should be dressed often.

**26.26 Why does grinding temperature decrease with increasing work speed (Eq. 26.4)? Does this mean that for a work speed of zero, the temperature is infinite? Explain.**

We should consider the types of heat flow in grinding: There is a heat source at the wheel/workpiece interface (see p. 799), caused primarily by plastic deformation in producing chips and by friction (as it is in metal cutting). Heat is removed through the following mechanisms:

(a) Heat is removed by the chips leaving the ground surface, which is a form of convection or convective heat transfer.

(b) Heat is also removed by conduction through the workpiece.

(c) A moving workpiece removes heat by convection; the heat is being physically moved with the workpiece material.

(d) Heat is also removed by convection by the grinding fluid (if present).

(e) There can be radiation as well, but this is usually smaller than the other forms of heat transfer in the system.

Increasing the work speed will improve the convection of the heat through the workpiece, thus lowering the temperature. However, as the work speed approaches zero, the temperature cannot be infinite because there are still the other forms of heat transfer listed above.

**26.27 Describe the similarities and differences in the action of metalworking fluids in machining versus grinding.**

By the student. Compare the contents of Section 22.12 on p. 665 and pp. 816-817 of Section 26.4. From a functional standpoint, the purposes of these fluids are primarily cooling and lubricating role to reduce temperature, wear, and power requirements. There are many similarities between the two groups, including chemical, rheological, and tribological properties (see also Sections 33.6 and 33.7 on pp. 1050 and 1052, respectively). As for differences: Note that the dimensions in grinding are much smaller than those in machining, and consequently the fluids must be able to penetrate the interfaces. Hence, properties such as viscosity and wetting and surface-tension characteristics can be more important.

**26.28 What factors could contribute to chatter in grinding? Explain why.**

Grinding chatter (see p. 817) is similar to chatter in machining and the factors involved are similar to those discussed in Section 25.4 on p. 775. Factors that contribute to chatter are: stiffness of machine tool and damping of vibration, irregular grinding wheels, dressing techniques, uneven wheel wear, high-grade wheels, high material-removal rates, eccentricity in wheels and or in mounting them on machine spindles, vibrations from nearby machinery, and inadequate support of the workpiece. Sources of regenerative chatter, such as material inhomogeneity and surface irregularities in wheels also can cause chatter in grinding.

**26.29 The grinding ratio, $G$, depends on the following: the type of grinding wheel, workpiece hardness, wheel depth of cut, wheel and workpiece speeds, and the type of grinding fluid. Explain why.**

By the student. The grinding ratio, $G$, decreases as the grain force increases (see Section 26.3.2 on p. 805) and is associated with high attritious wear of the wheel. The type of wheel will have an effect on wheel wear; for example, vitrified wheels generally wear slower than resinoid wheels. Workpiece hardness will reduce $G$ because of increased wear, if all other process parameters are kept constant. Depth of cut has a similar effect. Wheel and workpiece speed affect wheel wear in opposite ways; higher wheel speeds and lower workpiece speeds reduce the force on the grains (see Eq. (26.3) on p. 800) which, in turn, reduces wheel wear.

**26.30 Generally, it is recommended that, when grinding hardened steels, the grinding wheel should be of a relatively soft grade. Explain the reason.**

By the student. The use of a soft wheel on hardened steels is effective because when the abrasive grains develop wear flats (see Fig. 26.8b on p. 799), the wheels should be sufficiently soft so that the grains can be dislodged, thereby reducing workpiece surface damage. By using softer wheels, adverse effects such as burning and heat checking of the workpiece surface and residual stresses can be controlled. Note, however, that soft wheels will wear faster, but this is acceptable as long as workpiece quality is improved. Soft wheels would also reduce the tendency for chatter.

**26.31 In Fig. 26.4, the proper grinding faces are shown with an arrow for each type of wheel. Explain why the other surfaces of the wheels should not be used for grinding, and what the consequences may be in doing so.**

By the student. The proper grinding faces, identified in Fig. 26.4 on p. 795, should be utilized because the wheels are designed to resist grinding forces on these faces. Note, for example, that if grinding forces act normal to the plane of a thin straight wheel (Type 1 in the figure), the wheel will flex and may eventually fracture. Thus, from a functional standpoint, grinding wheels are more made stiff in the directions in which they are intended to be used. There are serious safety and functional considerations involved. For example, an operator who grinds with the side surface of a flared-cup wheel causes wear to take place such that the flange thickness is significantly reduced. It may eventually fracture, exploding with violent force and potentially causing serious injury or death.

**26.32 Explain the factors involved in selecting the appropriate type of abrasive for a particular grinding operation.**

Abrasives (see p. 793) should be inert to the workpiece material so that it does not react with the abrasive grain, thus reducing the effectiveness of the abrasive. The abrasives should also be of proper size and even shape for the application. Applications with better surface finish require smaller grains, while those where surface finish is a secondary consideration (such roughing passes) should utilize larger grains. The grinding wheel should provide for heat removal from the cutting zone, either through the chips produced (acting as heat sink) or using effective grinding fluids.

**26.33 Describe the effects of a wear flat on the overall grinding operation.**

By the student. Refer also to Problems 21.23 and 21.34. A wear flat (see Figs. 26.3 and 26.8 on pp. 794 and 799, respectively) causes dissipation of frictional energy and thus increases the temperature of the operation. Wear flats are undesirable because they provide no useful action (they play no obvious role in deforming the chip) but they increase the frictional forces at the wheel-workpiece interface and cause surface damage. Recall that in orthogonal cutting, flank wear (see Fig. 21.15a on p. 627) is equivalent to a wear flat in grinding.

**26.34 What difficulties, if any, could you encounter in grinding thermoplastics? Thermosets? Ceramics?**

Refer to Section 26.3.4 on p. 808 on grindability of materials and wheel selection, and also compare with Section 21.7.3. Some of the difficulties encountered are:

(a) Thermoplastics (p. 208) have a low melting point and have a tendency to soften (and become gummy) and thus tend to bond to grinding wheels (by mechanical locking). An effective coolant, including cool air jet, must be used to keep temperatures low. Furthermore, the low elastic modulus of thermoplastics (see Table 7.1 on p. 192) can make it difficult to hold dimensional tolerances during grinding.

(b) Thermosets (p. 211) are harder and do not soften with temperature (although they decompose and crumble at high temperatures), consequently grinding, using appropriate wheels and processing parameters, is relatively easy.

(c) Grinding of ceramics (p. 224) is now relatively easy, using diamond wheels and appropriate processing parameters, and implementing ductile-regime grinding (see p. 808). Note also the development of machinable ceramics.

**26.35 Are there any similarities among grinding, honing, polishing, and buffing? Explain.**

By the student. All of these processes use abrasive particles of various types, sizes, and shapes as well as various equipment to remove material, most by very small amounts. Based on the details of each process, described in this chapters, the student can elaborate further.

**26.36 Is the grinding ratio important in evaluating the economics of a grinding operation? Explain.**

If the grinding ratio, $G$, is high, it means that much material is removed with relatively little wear of the grinding wheel. Note, however, that this is not always desirable because it could indicate that abrasive grains may be dulling and possibly causing surface damage. Low grinding ratios, on the other hand, indicate high wheel-wear rate, leading to the need to dress wheels more frequently and eventually replacing the whole wheel. This procedure involves the cost of the wheel, as well as the costs involved in replacing the wheel and the economic impact of having to interrupt the production run. Consequently, as in all aspects of manufacturing, an optimum set of parameters have to be established to minimize adverse economic impact.

**26.37 We know that grinding can produce a very fine surface finish on a workpiece. Is this necessarily an indication of the quality of a part? Explain.**

The answer is no because surface integrity includes factors in addition to surface finish (which is only a geometric feature). As stated in Section 33.2 on p. 1038, surface integrity includes several mechanical and metallurgical parameters which, in turn, can have adverse effects on the performance of a ground part, such as its strength, hardness, and fatigue life. The students are encouraged to explore this topic further.

**26.38 What are the consequences of allowing the temperature to rise during grinding?**

Refer also to Problem 21.19. Temperature rise can have major effects in grinding, including:

(a) If excessive, it can cause metallurgical burn and heat checking.

(b) The workpiece may distort due to thermal gradients.

(c) With increasing temperature, the part will expand and hence the actual depth of cut will be greater; thus, upon cooling, the part will contract and the dimensional tolerances will not be within the desired range.

**26.39 If not done properly, honing can produce holes that are bell-mouthed, wavy, barrel-shaped, or tapered. Explain how this is possible.**

If the honing tool is mounted perfectly on its center and the axis of the tool is aligned with the hole axis, the hole will be cylindrical. However, if these are not the case, the path followed by the hone will not be circular. Its shape will depend on the geometric relationships of the axes involved. This topic could be a further, interesting exercise in solid geometry; refer also to the literature on honing practices.

**26.40 Jewelry applications require the grinding of diamonds into desired shapes. How is this done, since diamond is the hardest material known?**

By the student. Grinding is done with fine diamond abrasives on polishing wheels, and very high quality diamond surfaces can be generated in this manner. This topic could be made into a project.

**26.41 Why are speeds so much higher in grinding than in cutting?**

Grinding is an operation that typically involves very small chips being removed from the workpiece surface by individual grains along the grinding surface of the wheel (see pp. 799-780). Consequently, to remove material at a reasonably high rate for productivity, wheel speeds have to be very high. Note also that high wheel speeds have no particularly adverse effects on the overall grinding operation (unless the wheels cannot withstand the stresses developed). In fact, the trend has been to increase spindle speeds on grinders and develop wheels with higher burst strengths. Recall also that higher removal rates are typically obtained in creep-feed grinding, which is an important industrial process (see p. 815).

## QUANTITATIVE PROBLEMS

**26.42 Calculate the chip dimensions for the following process variables: $D = 8$ in., $d = 0.001$ in., $v = 100$ ft/min, $V = 6000$ ft/min, $C = 500$ per in$^2$, and $r = 20$.**

The undeformed chip length, $l$, is given approximately by the expression

$$l = \sqrt{Dd} = \sqrt{(8)(0.001)} = 0.089 \text{ in.}$$

and the undeformed chip thickness, $t$, is given by Eq. (26.2) on p. 799. Thus,

$$t = \sqrt{\left(\frac{4v}{VCr}\right)\sqrt{\frac{d}{D}}} = \sqrt{\left[\frac{4(100)}{(6000)(500)(20)}\right]\sqrt{\frac{0.001}{8}}} = 0.00027 \text{ in.}$$

Note that these quantities are very small compared to those in typical machining operations.

**26.43 If the strength of the workpiece material is doubled, what should be the percentage decrease in the wheel depth-of-cut, $d$, in order to maintain the same grain force, all other variables being the same?**

Using Eq. (26.3) on p. 800, we note that if the workpiece-material strength is doubled, the grain force is doubled. Since the grain force is dependent on the square root of the depth of cut, the new depth of cut would be one-fourth of the original depth of cut. Thus, the reduction in the wheel depth of cut will be 75%.

**26.44 Assume that a surface grinding operation is being carried out under the following conditions: $D$ = 200 mm, $d$ = 0.1 mm, $v$ = 40 m/min, and $V$ = 3000 m/min. These conditions are then changed to the following: $D$ = 150 mm, $d$ = 0.1 mm, $v$ = 30 m/min, and $V$ = 2500 m/min. How different is the temperature rise from the rise that occurs with the initial conditions?**

The temperature rise is given by Eq. (26.4) on p. 803. We can obtain a relative change even if we dont know a constant of proportionality in the equation, which we will identify as $A$. Thus, for the initial cutting conditions, we have

$$\Delta T = AD^{1/4}d^{3/4}\left(\frac{V}{v}\right)^{1/2} = A(200)^{1/4}(0.1)^{3/4}\left(\frac{3000}{40}\right)^{1/2} = 5.79A$$

and for the new conditions, we have

$$\Delta T = AD^{1/4}d^{3/4}\left(\frac{V}{v}\right)^{1/2} = A(150)^{1/4}(0.1)^{3/4}\left(\frac{2500}{30}\right)^{1/2} = 5.68A$$

Therefore, the modified conditions have a temperature rise which is slightly below (by about 2%) the original temperature rise.

**26.45 Estimate the percent increase in the cost of the grinding operation if the specification for the surface finish of a part is changed from 63 $\mu$in. to 16 $\mu$in.**

Referring to Fig. 26.34 on p. 828, we note that changing the surface finish from 63 $\mu$in. to 16 $\mu$in. would involve an increased cost of about 400%. This is a very significant increase in cost, and is a good example of the importance of the statement made on p. 40 and throughout the book that dimensional accuracy and surface finish should be specified as broadly as is permissible in order to minimize manufacturing costs (see also Fig. 40.5 on p. 1255).

**26.46 Assume that the energy cost for grinding an aluminum part with a specific energy requirement of 8 W-s/mm$^3$ is \$0.90 per piece. What would be the energy cost of carrying out the same operation if the workpiece material is T15 tool steel?**

From Table 26.2 on p. 801 we note that the power requirement for T15 tool steel ranges from 17.7 to 82 W-s/mm$^3$. Consequently, the costs would range from 2.5 to 11.7 times that for the aluminum. This means an energy cost between \$2 and \$9.36 per part.

**26.47 On the basis of the information given in Chapter 23 and this chapter, comment on the feasibility of producing a 10 mm hole that is 100 mm deep in a copper alloy (a) by conventional drilling and (b) by internal grinding.**

By the student. Note that this is a general question and it can be interpreted as either a through hole or a blind hole (in which case it does not specify the shape of the bottom of the hole). Furthermore, the quality of the hole, its dimensional accuracy and the surface finish of the cylindrical surface are not specified. It is intended that the students be observant and resourceful to ask such questions so as to give appropriate answers.

Briefly, a through hole with the dimensions specified can easily be drilled; if the dimensional accuracy and surface finish are not acceptable, the hole can subsequently be reamed and honed. Holes can be internally ground (see Fig. 26.21 on p. 813), depending on workpiece shape and accuracies required; note, however, that there has to be a hole first in order to be ground internally.

For blind holes, the answers will depend on the required shape of the hole bottom. Drills typically will not produce flat bottom, and will require a process such as end milling. Internal grinding is possible on an existing hole, noting also the importance of internal corner features (relief) as stated in the last item of grinding design considerations on p. 818. See Fig. 26.21b for a method of plunge grinding blind holes.

**26.48 In describing grinding processes, we have not given the type of equations regarding feeds, speeds, material removal rates, total grinding time, etc., as we have done in turning and milling operations in Chapters 23 and 24. Study the quantitative relationships involved and develop such equations for grinding operations.**

By the student. This is a challenging problem and a good topic for a project. The students should refer to various texts in the Bibliography, including texts by S. Malkin and M.C. Shaw.

**26.49 What would be the answers to Example 26.1 if the workpiece were high-strength titanium and the width-of-cut is $w$= 0.75 in.? Give your answers in newtons.**

By the student. Refer to Example 26.1 on p. 802. For high-strength titanium, lets assume that the specific energy from Table 26.2 on p. 801 is 20 hp-min/in$^3$. Since the width, $w$, is now 0.75 in., the MRR will be (0.002)(0.75)(60)=0.09 in$^3$/min. The power is then (20)(0.09)=1.8 hp, which is that same as that in the example; hence the answer to be unchanged, that is, $F_c = 5.7$ lb. (25 N), and $F_t = 7.4$ lb. (32 N).

**26.50 It is known that, in grinding, heat checking occurs when grinding with a spindle speed of 4000 rpm, a wheel diameter of 10 in., and a depth-of-cut of 0.0015 in. for a feed rate of 50 ft/min. For this reason, the standard operating procedure is to keep the spindle speed at 3500 rpm. If a new, 8-in. diameter wheel is used, what spindle speed can be used before heat checking occurs? What spindle speed should be used to keep the same grinding temperatures as those encountered with the existing operating conditions?**

To solve this problem, lets assume that the workpiece initial temperature is the same for both cases. The temperature rise for heat checking to occur is given by Eq. (26.4) on p. 803 (and using $A$ as the constant for proportionality) as

$$\Delta T = AD^{1/4}d^{3/4}\left(\frac{V}{v}\right)^{1/2} = A(10)^{1/4}(0.0015)^{3/4}\left[\frac{(4000)\pi(5/12)}{50}\right]^{1/2} = 0.14A$$

The temperature rise for the "safe" operating condition with the 10-in. wheel is

$$\Delta T = AD^{1/4}d^{3/4}\left(\frac{V}{v}\right)^{1/2} = A(10)^{1/4}(0.0015)^{3/4}\left[\frac{(3500)\pi(5/12)}{50}\right]^{1/2} = 0.13A$$

With a new, 8-in. wheel and the same depth of cut and feed, heat checking occurs at

$$\Delta T = 0.14A = AD^{1/4}d^{3/4}\left(\frac{V}{v}\right)^{1/2} = A(8)^{1/4}(0.0015)^{3/4}\left[\frac{N\pi(5/12)}{50}\right]^{1/2}$$

or, solving for $N$ we obtain $N = 4550$ rpm. To maintain the same surface temperatures, we need

$$\Delta T = 0.13A = A(8)^{1/4}(0.0015)^{3/4}\left[\frac{N\pi(5/12)}{50}\right]^{1/2}$$

or $N = 3900$ rpm.

**26.51 It is desired to grind a hard aerospace aluminum alloy. A depth of 0.003 in. is to be removed from a cylindrical section 10 in. long and 4 in. in diameter. If each part is to be ground in not more than one minute, what is the approximate power requirement for the grinder? What if the material is changed to a hard titanium alloy?**

The volume to be removed is

$$V = \pi D_{\text{avg}} dl = \pi(4 - 0.003/2)(0.003)(10) = 0.377 \text{ in}^3$$

and therefore, the minimum metal removal rate is 0.377 in$^3$/min. Taking the specific energy requirement as 10 hp-min/in$^3$ (see Table 26.2 on p. 801), the power requirement is

$$P = (10 \text{ hp-min/in}^3)(0.377 \text{ in}^3/\text{min}) = 3.77 \text{ hp}$$

For the hard titanium, we have $u = 20$ hp-min/in$^3$, hence the power requirement will be 7.54 hp.

**26.52 A grinding operation takes place with a 10 in. grinding wheel with a spindle speed of 3000 rpm. The workpiece feed rate is 60 ft/min and the depth-of-cut is 0.002 in. Contact thermometers record an approximate maximum temperature of 1800 °F. If the workpiece is steel, what is the temperature if the speed is increased to 4000 rpm? What if the speed is 10,000 rpm?**

Assuming that the workpiece is at room temperature, Eq. (26.4) on p. 803 can be used to calculate the temperature rise. The temperature rise for the initial state lets one calculate the proportionality constant as

$$\Delta T = AD^{1/4}d^{3/4}\left(\frac{V}{v}\right)^{1/2} = A(10^{1/4}(0.002)^{3/4}\left[\frac{(3000)\pi(5/12)}{60}\right]^{1/2} = 1800$$

which is solved as $A = 13,200$. If the speed is 4000 rpm, then

$$\Delta T = AD^{1/4}d^{3/4}\left(\frac{V}{v}\right)^{1/2} = (13,200)(10^{1/4}(0.002)^{3/4}\left[\frac{(4000)\pi(5/12)}{60}\right]^{1/2} = 2070^\circ\text{F}$$

If the speed is 10,000 rpm, the same equation gives 3278 °F; note however that steel melts at around 2500°F (see Table 3.1 on p. 103). When the steel melts, the grinding process mechanics change dramatically, hence this temperature should be regarded as the maximum temperature rise.

**26.53 Derive an expression for the angular velocity of the wafer, as shown in Fig. 26.30b, as a function of the radius and angular velocity of the pad in chemical-mechanical polishing.**

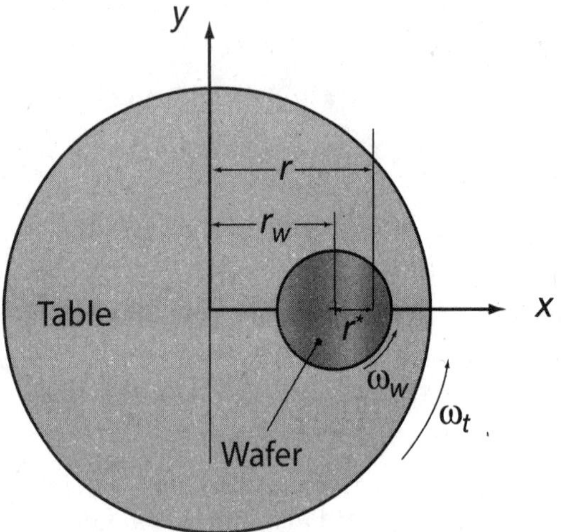


By the student. Refer to the figure above and consider the case where a wafer is placed on the $x$-axis as shown. Along this axis there is no velocity in the $x$-direction. The $y$-component of the velocity has two sources: rotation of the table and the rotation of the carrier. Considering the table movement only, we can express the velocity distribution as

$$V_y = r\omega_t$$

and for the carrier

$$V_y = r^*\omega_w$$

where $r^*$ can be positive or negative, and is shown positive in the figure. Note that $r = r_w + r^*$, so that we can substitute this equation into $V_y$ and combine the velocities to obtain the total velocity as

$$V_{y,\text{tot}} = (r_w + r^*)\omega_t + r^*\omega_w$$

If $\omega_w = -\omega_t$, then $V_{y,\text{tot}} = r_w\omega_t$. Since the location of the wafer and the angular velocity of the carrier are fixed, it means that the $y$-component of velocity is constant across the wafer.

## SYNTHESIS, DESIGN, AND PROJECTS

**26.54 List and explain factors that contribute to poor surface finish in the processes described in this chapter.**

By the student. Various factors can contribute to poor surface finish, including the following (noting also that a wide variety of abrasive processes are described in the chapter):

- Improper selection of type and size of abrasives.
- Improper selection of process variables.
- Heat checking that can occur if the temperatures become excessive.
- A loaded wheel that will smear surfaces and cause damage, instead of remove material effectively.
- Unbalanced grinding wheels.
- Chatter that can lead to objectionable marks on the workpiece surface (somewhat similar to that shown in Fig. 25.13 on p. 775).

**26.55 With appropriate sketches, describe the principles of various fixturing methods and devices that can be used for the processes described in this chapter.**

By the student. This is an open-ended problem that would also be suitable for a project. The students are encouraged to conduct literature search on the topic a well as recalling the type of fixtures used and described throughout the chapters. See especially Section 37.8 starting on p. 1176 and Case Study 37.1 on pp. 1178-1179.

**26.56 Explain the major design guidelines for grinding.**

By the student. These guidelines are described in Section 26.5 on p. 818.

**26.57 Which of the processes described in this chapter are particularly suitable for workpieces made of (a) ceramics, (b) thermoplastics, and (c) thermosets? Why?**

By the student. The processes are listed in terms of their applicability to these material classes as follows:

| Ceramics | Thermoplastics | Thermosets |
|---|---|---|
| Grinding | Belt grinding | Grinding |
| Ultrasonic machining | Wire brushing | Belt grinding |
| Lapping | Deburring | Wire brushing |
| Chemical-mechanical polishing | Polishing | Ultrasonic machining |
| Abrasive-flow machining | | Lapping |
| | | Barrel finishing |

The basic reasons that processes are suitable for a material class depends on the mechanics of the process and the properties of the material. For example, note that ultrasonic machining is effective on hard and brittle workpieces; it is thus well-suited for ceramics but not thermoplastics.

**26.58 Make a comprehensive table of the process capabilities of abrasive-machining processes. Using several columns, describe the machines involved, the type of abrasive tools used, the shapes of blanks and parts produced, typical maximum and minimum sizes, surface finish, tolerances, and production rates.**

By the student. This is a very challenging problem. The following should be considered as an example of the kinds of information that can be contained in such a table.

| **Process** | **Abrasives used** | **Part shapes** | **Maximum size** | **Typical surface finish ($\mu$m)** |
|---|---|---|---|---|
| Grinding | $Al_2O_3$ SiC, cBN Diamond | Flat, round or circular | Flat: no limit. Round: 12 in. Circular: 12 in. | 0.2 |
| Barrel finishing | $Al_2O_3$, SiC | Limited aspect ratio | 6 in. | 0.2 |
| Chemical-mechanical polishing | $Al_2O_3$, SiC | Flat surfaces | 13 in. | 0.05 and lower |
| Shot blasting | Sand, $SiO_2$ | All types | No limit | 1-10 |

**26.59 Based on the data developed in Problem 26.58, describe your thoughts regarding the procedure to be followed in determining what type of machine tool to select for a particular part to be machined by abrasive means.**

By the student. This is an open-ended problem. Basically, the discussion should include a consideration of process capabilities, abrasives used and their suitability for the subject material, and costs. For example, while chemical-mechanical polishing produces excellent surface finish, it is highly developed only for some materials, and is not suitable for tool steels.

**26.60 Vitrified grinding wheels (also called ceramic wheels) use a glass-like bond to hold the abrasive grains together. Given your understanding of ceramic part manufacture (as described in Chapter 18), list methods of producing vitrified wheels.**

By the student. The students should refer to the literature on wheel production, as a project on this topic. The basic process involves blending the abrasive grains with powdered glass, pressing the mixture into various wheel shapes (see Fig. 26.4 on p. 795), firing the green wheels, cooling them (which, for large wheels such as those used in foundries, can take hours to eliminate residual stresses and possible cracking), and truing and balancing the wheel.

**26.61 A somewhat controversial subject in grinding is size effect; that is, there is an apparent increase in the strength of a workpiece when the depth of penetration by grinding abrasives is reduced. Design an experimental setup whereby this size effect can be examined.**

By the student. Refer to various books listed in the bibliography. The experiments can be macro-scaled by measuring power consumption as a function of chip thickness (see Eq. (26.2) on p. 799 for the important parameters affecting chip thickness). The experiments could also use an effective system on a microscale, such as indenters mounted on piezo-electric load cells and dragged across a surface.

**26.62 Describe as many parameters as you can that could affect the final surface finish in grinding. Include process parameters as well as setup and equipment effects.**

By the student. For this is an open-ended problem the students are encouraged to think creatively. The following are some typical answers:

- Grinding-wheel condition, such as shape, whether or not it is loaded or has freshly dressed abrasives, will have an effect on the grinding operation and the surface finish produced.
- Grain size and shape.
- Temperature, since excessive heat can lead to heat checking. Equation (26.4) on p. 803 indicates that major process parameters that are important include wheel diameter, depth of cut, feed, and wheel and workpiece speeds.
- The quality of the equipment and the fixturing also are important as their characteristics such as stiffness and damping can influence the overall operation.

**26.63 Assume that you are an instructor covering the topics described in this chapter, and you are giving a quiz on the numerical aspects to test the understanding of the students. Prepare three quantitative problems and supply the answers.**

By the student. This is an challenging, open-ended question and has been found to be a very valuable homework problem.

**26.64 Conduct a literature search and explain how observing the color, brightness, and shape of sparks produced in grinding can be a useful guide to identifying the type of material being ground and its condition.**

By the student. Various charts, showing photographs or sketches of the type and color of sparks produced, have been available for years as a useful but general guide for material identification at the shop level, especially for steels. Some of these charts can be found in textbooks, such as in Fig. 24.15 on p. 458 of *Machining Fundamentals*, by J.R. Walker.

**26.65 Review Fig. 26.4 and give possible grinding applications for each type of wheels shown in the figure.**

By the student. This is an open-ended problem, and students should be encouraged to develop answers based on their experience and whatever they can research. Both the cylindrical cup in part (b) and the flared cup in part (d) are used on large flat surfaces. The mounted wheel is available in a large size range, and can be used for die repair, marking and flash removal. Straight grinding wheels can be used for plunge grinding.

**26.66 Visit a large hardware store and inspect the grinding wheels on display. Make a note of the markings on the wheels and, based on the marking system shown in**

**Fig. 26.6, comment on your observations, including the most common types of wheels available in the store.**

By the student. This is a good opportunity to encourage students to gain some exposure to grinding wheels. The markings on the grinding wheels will have the type of information shown in Fig. 26.6 on p. 796. It will also be noted that the most common grinding wheels are basically the same as those shown in Fig. 26.4 on p. 795. Those shown in Fig. 26.5 are less common and also more expensive.

**26.67 Obtain a small grinding wheel or a piece of a large wheel. (a) Observe its surfaces using a magnifier or a microscope and compare these with Fig. 26.9. (b) Rub the abrasive wheel pressing it hard against a variety of flat metallic and nonmetallic materials. Describe your observations regarding the surface produced.**

By the student. This is a good project, and can become a component of a laboratory course.

**26.68 Explain how you would produce the steel balls that are subsequently ground on the type of setups shown in Fig. 26.15.**

By the student. There are two basic methods: closed-die forging and skew rolling. Both processes are shown in Fig. 13.14 on p. 362; the students are encouraged to review them and comment on them.

**26.69 In reviewing the abrasive machining processes in this chapter, you will note that some use bonded abrasives while others involve loose abrasives. Make two separate lists for these processes, and comment on your observations.**

By the student. This is an open-ended problem and the following table should be regarded as only an illustration of an answer. The students should give further details, based on a study of each of the processes cover in the chapter.

| Process | Comments |
|---|---|
| **Bonded abrasives** | |
| Grinding<br>Belt grinding<br>Sanding<br>Honing<br>Superfinishing | These processes are basically similar to each other and with a wide range abrasive sizes, the material removal rates, surface finish, and lay (see Fig. 33.2 on p. 1039). |
| **Loose abrasives** | |
| Ultrasonic machining<br>Chemical-mechanical polishing<br>Barrel finishing<br>Abrasive-flow machining | A random surface lay is most common for these processes. |

**26.70 Do you think the plunge grinding operation shown in Fig. 26.17 could compete with a turning operation to produce the same type of part? Explain.**

By the student. Plunge grinding is successfully applied to cylindrical parts with varying diameters and corner radii (see Fig. 26.17 on p. 811). This process can accurately control perpendicularity of side. Plunge grinding is a relatively costly process, typically done on large dual-angle-head machines, using 0.75-m diameter aluminum-oxide grinding wheels, or on straight plunge grinders with 1-m diameter wheels. To maintain dimensional accuracy and surface finish, dressing is frequently done typically after each part is ground.

**26.71 Observe the cycle patterns shown in Fig. 26.20 and comment on why they follow those particular patterns.**

By the student. It should be noted, fore example, that critical surfaces have undergone multiple passes (as clearly shown in sketches 7 and 8 on p. 813), while simple surfaces are subjected to only one or two single pass (as in sketches 1, 11, and 12). Factors that affect the cycles include surface finish ad economic consideration, often requiring considerable experience on the shop floor. The students should elaborate further on these cycle patterns and their logic behind them.

**26.72 Obtain a piece each of sand paper and emery cloth of different coarseness. Using a magnifier or a microscope, observe its surface features and compare them with Fig. 26.25.**

By the student. This is a valuable exercise and simple to perform. The illustration in Fig. 26.25 on p. 820 is only a cross-section (side view) of the coated abrasive. The top view should also be viewed, which can be done easily using a magnifier or a simple microscope. The students should comment on the shape and distribution of the abrasives grains and other features that they could observe of the product.

**26.73 In Chapter 25, we described the principles of machining and turning centers, and we will describe similar centers in Chapter 27 on advanced machining operations. Based on the contents of this chapter, describe your thought on whether or not it would be possible to design and build a "grinding center." Explain if such a center could perform all types of grinding operations or would be confined to specific types. Comment also on any difficulties that have to be dealt with in such machines and operations.**

By the student. There are now grinding centers commercially available, although the distinction between a machine and a center is not a clear as it is in machining centers. A study of grinding centers and their features would be an interesting topic for a student project.

# Chapter 27

# Advanced Machining Processes

## QUALITATIVE PROBLEMS

**27.13 Give possible technical and economic reasons why the processes described in this chapter might be preferred over those described in the preceding chapters, or even necessary.**

The reasons for these considerations are outlined in the introduction to Section 27.1 on p. 835. Students are encouraged to give specific examples after studying each of the individual processes.

**27.14 Why has electrical-discharge machining become so widely used in industry?**

With increasing strength and toughness and various other properties of advanced engineering materials, there was a need to develop processes that were not sensitive to these properties. Because EDM basically involves electrical properties and is capable of removing material in a variety of configurations, it was one of the most important developments and continues to do so. As in all other processes, it has its advantages as well as limitations, regarding particularly the material-removal rate and possible surface damage which could significantly reduce fatigue life.

**27.15 Explain why the mechanical properties of workpiece materials are not significant in most of the processes described in this chapter.**

Mechanical properties such as hardness, yield strength, ultimate strength, ductility, and toughness are not important because the principles of these operations do not done involve mechanical means, unlike traditional machining processes. For example, hardness (which is an important factor in conventional machining processes) is unimportant in chemical machining because it does not adversely affect the ability of the chemical to react with the workpiece and remove material. The students should give several other examples of properties and their relevance to specific advanced processes.

**27.16 In which types of products or parts is the wire EDM process most applicable?**

The wire EDM process is most suitable for flat parts, with or without constant thickness. The machines (see p. 850) most commonly have two-degree or three-degree freedom, with the latter capable of producing tapered walls and complex die contours. The major competing process is blanking (see Section 16.2 on p. 625), provided the workpiece is sufficiently thin.

**27.17 Why may different advanced machining processes affect the fatigue strength of materials to different degrees?**

Fatigue is a complex phenomenon which accounts for the vast majority of component failures, including dies and tooling (see Section 2.7 on p. 83). Fatigue failures are known to initiate and propagate as cracks through the part. Because these cracks usually (but not necessarily) start at the workpiece surface and grow with repeated cyclic loadings, the surfaces should be as smooth as possible (see Fig. 2.28 on p. 93). As described throughout the chapter, various chemical, electrical, and thermal mechanisms are involved in each process (with some mechanical interactions as in electrical-discharge grinding and abrasive water-jet machining). Thus, as expected, each process will produce a surface with its own texture and characteristics, and hence the fatigue life of a component will depend on the particular process employed.

**27.18 Explain why it is difficult to produce sharp profiles and corners with some of the processes described in this chapter.**

By the student. Note, for example, that in water-jet machining the minimum radius that can be produced will depend on the ability to focus the water jet precisely in a certain location. This phenomenon can easily be appreciate when observing how a water jet begins to spread around when hitting an obstacle. With wire EDM, the minimum radius depends on the wire diameter and the kerf developed (see Fig. 27.12 on p. 849). In laser-beam machining, radii are adversely affected by the high temperatures developed, causing the material to melting away from the cutting zone. Similar problems exist in chemical machining as the chemical tends to attack a wider area than required for producing sharp profiles.

**27.19 Which of the advanced machining processes causes thermal damage? What is the consequence of such damage to workpieces?**

The advanced machining processes which cause thermal damage are obviously those that involve high levels of heat, that is, EDM, and laser-beam and electron-beam machining. The thermal effect is to cause the material to develop a heat-affected zone, thus adversely affecting hardness and ductility (see also pp. 960-961). For the effects of temperature in machining and grinding, see pp. 623-624 and pp. 802-803.

**27.20 In abrasive water-jet machining, at what stage is the abrasive introduced in the water jet? Survey the available literature, then draw a schematic illustration of the equipment involved.**

The abrasive water-jet machining process is shown in Fig. 27.17 on p. 857 which also indicates the location where the abrasive powder is introduced. Further information can be obtained by surveying manufacturers on the Internet. A very good site is www.waterjets.org; the figure below is from this site.

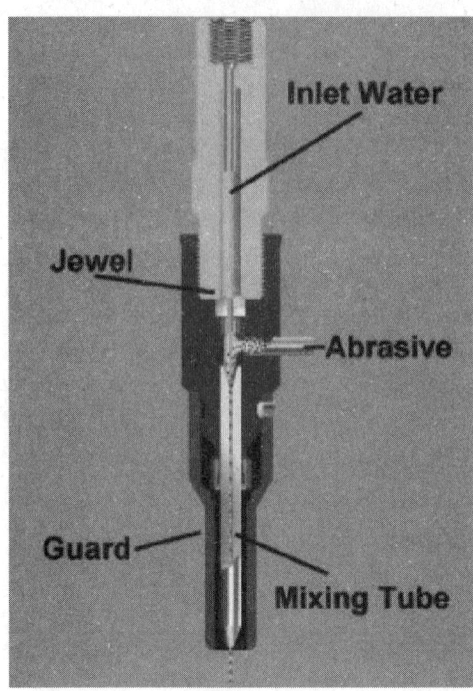


**27.21 Describe your thoughts regarding the laser-beam machining of nonmetallic materials. Give several possible applications, including their advantages as compared to other processes.**

By the student. Most nonmetallic materials, including polymers and ceramics, can be laser-beam machined (see p. 853) using different types of lasers. The presence of a major heat source and its various adverse effects on a particular material and workpiece must of course be considered. Some materials can have additional concerns; wood, for example, is flammable and may require an oxygen-free environment.

**27.22 Why is the preshaping or premachining of parts sometimes desirable in the processes described in this chapter?**

By the student. Most of the processes described in this chapter are slow and costly, thus they are economically feasible if the volume to be removed is low. Consequently, preshaping of the parts is very important. Note also the concept of net- or near-net shape manufacturing described on p. 31.

**27.23 Are deburring operations necessary for parts made by advanced machining processes? Explain and give several specific examples.**

By the student. Deburring operations, described on Section 26.8 on p. 825, may be necessary for many of the advanced machining processes described in this chapter. This would be a good topic for the student to conduct research and write a paper. A good reference is *Deburring and Edge Finishing Handbook* by L. Gillespie.

**27.24 Do you think it should be possible to produce spur gears by advanced machining processes, starting with a round blank? Explain.**

By the student. It is appropriate to assume here that such gears would be in high demand (hence large production quantities) and that they should have good dimensional accuracy and surface finish. Very small spur gears (see Fig. 24.29 on p. 749), such as those in wrist watches and clocks, can be suitable for production using the processes described in this chapter (such as by photochemical blanking, electrochemical machining, and EDM). However, stamping such gears (at much higher rates than achievable in these processes) is a far more economical process. Larger spur gears cannot be produced economically through advanced machining processes, with the possible exception of wire EDM (see, for example, Fig. 27.10b on p. 847 for similar geometric features produced by this process). Furthermore, the surface finish developed may not be acceptable for such gears (see, for example, Figs. 24.34 and 27.4 on pp. 755 and 839, respectively), control of dimensional tolerances would be difficult, and material-removal rate is low.

**27.25 List and explain factors that contribute to poor surface finish in the processes described in this chapter.**

By the student. Many factors are involved in poor surface finish, depending on the particular process used, each of which has its own set of parameters. A brief outline of the major factors is as follows:

(a) Chemical machining: preferential etching and intergranular attack.

(b) Electrochemical machining and grinding: improper selection of electrolyte, process variables, and abrasives.

(c) Electrical-discharge machining: high rates of material removal and improper selection of electrodes, dielectric fluids, and process variables.

(d) Laser-beam and electron-beam machining: improper selection of process variables, development of heat-affected zones,

(e) Water-jet and abrasive water-jet machining: machining: improper selection of process variables.

**27.26 Conduct a survey of the available technical literature and describe the types of surfaces produced by electron-beam, plasma-arc, and laser cutting.**

By the student. This is a good opportunity for a literature and Internet search. It should be noted that the surface finish varies widely depending on the material and process parameters in these three operations. In addition, some of these processes have been developed to produce tailored surface textures (for tribological or aesthetic purposes). Examples of surface textures produced are given below (from Hector, L.G., and Sheu, S., "Focused Energy Beam Work Roll Surface Texturing Science and Technology," *J. Materials Processing & Materials Science*, v. 2, 1993, pp. 63-117).

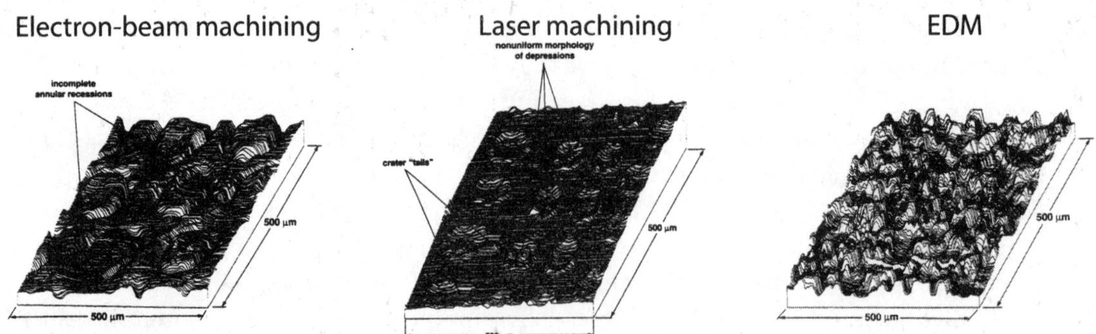


**27.27 It was stated that graphite is the preferred material for EDM tooling. Would graphite be useful in wire EDM? Explain.**

It is presently impossible to produce graphite wires, although significant effort has been directed towards impregnating tungsten wire with graphite to improve its performance in EDM. An important consideration is their lack of ductility, which is essential in the wire EDM process (note the spools and wire guides in Fig. 27.12 on p. 849). Such hybrid wires have considerable promise, but to date have not yielded sufficient utility, especially when compared to their cost.

**27.28 What is the purpose of the abrasives in electrochemical grinding?**

The purpose of the abrasives in electrochemical grinding are described on p. 845; namely, they act as insulators and, in the finishing stages, produce a surface with good surface finish and dimensional accuracy.

**27.29 Why are lasers increasingly used to mark parts?**

Lasers are being increasingly used to mark parts because the laser beam is easy to manipulate with computer-controlled machinery, allowing intricate patterns to be easily programmed. Furthermore, the laser beam can be focused precisely and it restricts material removal to sub-millimeter depth. The marking process does not require hard tooling, or any preparation and subsequent cleaning. Since marking only requires a very shallow depth of cut, low-powered lasers are capable of marking most materials, making this approach very cost-effective.

**27.30 Which of the processes described in this chapter are suitable for producing very small and deep holes? Why?**

The answer depends on what is meant by the relative terms "small" and "deep." Tungsten-wire electrodes as small as 0.1 mm in diameter have been used in EDM, producing depth-to-hole diameter ratios of up to 400:1 (see p. 848 and Fig. 27.10d on p. 847). Laser beams can also be used, and are capable of producing holes at ratios as high as 50:1 (see p. 853). Sub-micron deep holes can only be produced through reactive ion etching.

**27.31 Is kerf width important in wire EDM? Explain.**

The kerf developed in wire EDM is important primarily because it affects dimensional tolerances, as can be seen in Fig. 27.12 on p. 849.

**27.32 Are there similarities between photochemical machining and solid ground curing (see Section 20.3.6)?**

By the student. There are similarities between photochemical machining or blanking (p. 840) and solid-ground curing (p.592) in that both processes layers of material are produced through the action of a lightsource to cure a thermosetting polymer. In both cases, the entire image is developed at one time, instead of requiring a step-by-step exposure as in stereolithography. Several layers with varying profiles can then be assembled to produce a part.

## QUANTITATIVE PROBLEMS

**27.33 A 100-mm deep hole that is 20 mm in diameter is being produced by electrochemical machining. A high production rate is more important than machined surface quality. Estimate the maximum current and the time required to perform this operation.**

From Table 27.1 on p. 837 we find that the maximum current density is 8 A/mm$^2$. The area of the hole is

$$\text{Area} = \frac{\pi D^2}{4} = \frac{\pi(20 \text{ mm})^2}{4} = 314 \text{ mm}^2$$

The current is the product of the current density and the cathode area. Thus,

$$(8 \text{ A/mm}^2)(314 \text{ mm}^2) = 2513 \text{ A}$$

From Table 27.1, we also find that the maximum material-removal rate (given in terms of penetration rate) is 12 mm/min. Since the hole is 100 mm deep, the machining time is 100/12 = 8.33 min.

**27.34 If the operation in Problem 27.33 were performed on an electrical-discharge machine, what would be the estimated machining time?**

Refer to the volume and area calculations in Problem 27.33. With electrical-discharge machining, the maximum material-removal rate is typically 0.15 cm$^3$/min = 150 mm$^3$/min. Since the problem states that high production rate rather than surface quality is important, lets assume that the material-removal rate is twice this amount, that is, 300 mm$^3$/min. The volume to be removed is

$$V = \pi \left[\frac{20^2}{4}\right](40) = 12,560 \text{ mm}^3$$

Therefore, the machining time is

$$\text{Time} = \frac{12,560}{300} = 42 \text{ min.}$$

**27.35 A cutting-off operation is being performed with a laser beam. The workpiece being cut is $\frac{3}{4}$ in. thick and 8 in. long. If the kerf is $\frac{5}{32}$ in. wide, estimate the time required to perform this operation.**

From Table 27.1 on p. 837, the range of cutting speeds for laser-beam machining is found to range between 0.5 and 7.5 m/min. Because the workpiece is rather thick, only large capacity lasers will be suitable for this operation, but we will calculate the range of speeds. The time to traverse 8 in. (0.203 m) is between 0.4 min (24 s) and 0.02 min (1.6 s).

**27.36 A 1.0-in.-thick copper plate is being machined through wire EDM. The wire moves at a speed of 5 ft/min and the kerf width is What is the required power? Note that it takes 1550 J (2100 ft-lb) to melt one gram of copper.**

The metal-removal rate is calculated as MRR=(1/16 in.)(1 in.)(60 in./min)=3.75 in$^3$/min. Since the density of copper is 8970 kg/m$^3$ (from Table 3.1 on p. 103), the mass removal rate is

$$\dot{m} = \rho(\text{MRR}) = \left(8970\ \text{kg/m}^3\right)\left(3.75\ \text{in}^3/\text{min}\right)\left(\frac{1\ \text{m}}{39.37\ \text{in.}}\right)^3 = 0.55\ \text{kg/min}$$

Therefore, the power required is

$$P = (1550\ \text{J/g})\dot{m} = (1550\ \text{J/g})(0.55\ \text{kg/min}) = 852\ \text{kJ/min} = 14.2\ \text{kJ/s}$$

## SYNTHESIS, DESIGN, AND PROJECTS

**27.37 Would you consider designing a machine tool that combines (in one machine) two or more of the processes described in this chapter? Explain. For what types of parts would such a machine be useful? Make a preliminary sketch for such a machine.**

By the student. This is a challenging but valuable exercise. It will be noted that, in some respects, processes such as chemical-mechanical polishing and electrochemical machining satisfy the criteria stated in this problem in that they apply one or more processes in the chapter.

**27.38 Repeat Problem 27.37, combining processes described in (a) Chapters 13 through 16, (b) Chapters 23 and 24, and (c) Chapters 26 and 27. Give a preliminary sketch of a machine for each of the three groups. How would you convince a prospective customer of the merits of such machines?**

By the student. This is an open-ended and challenging but valuable exercise. The particular answer will depend on the individual processes selected for a combination. As an expanded project, students could be encouraged to develop such a design and prepare a brochure, describing the characteristics and capabilities of the machine (as well as its limitations) to venture capitalists, requesting funds to begin producing such machines.

**27.39 Make a list of machining processes that may be suitable for each of the following materials: (a) ceramics, (b) cast iron, (c) thermoplastics, (d) thermosets, (e) diamond, and (f) annealed copper.**

By the student. It will be noted that, as described in Chapters 23 through 26, most of these materials can be machined through conventional means. Restricting our attention to the processes described in Chapter 27 (although the student is encouraged to extend the discussion to previous chapters), the following processes would be suitable:

(a) Ceramics: water-jet machining, abrasive-jet machining, chemical machining (see etching of silicon, p. 885).

(b) Cast iron: chemical machining, electrochemical machining, electrochemical grinding, EDM, laser-beam and electron-beam machining, and water- and abrasive-jet machining.

(c) Thermoplastics: water-jet and abrasive-jet machining; electrically-conducting polymers (see p. 206) may be candidates for EDM processing.

(d) Thermosets: similar consideration as for thermoplastics.

(e) Diamond: None, because diamond would not be responsive to any of the methods described in this chapter (see also Problem 26.40).

(f) Annealed copper: Chemical and electrochemical processes, EDM, and laser-beam machining.

**27.40 Which of the processes described in this chapter require a vacuum? Explain why.**

By the student. It will be noted from Table 27.1 on p. 837 that the only process that requires a vacuum is electron-beam machining. This is because the electron-beam gun, shown in Fig. 27.15 on p. 855, requires a vacuum to operate.

**27.41 How would you manufacture a large-diameter, conical, round disk with a thickness that decreases from the center outward?**

By the student. The following methods would be suitable.

(a) Machine the part on a CNC milling machine, and supporting it (if thin) with a backup plate or fixture.

(b) Electrochemical machining is a simple method, although it would take longer to produce the part. Take a round blank with a constant thickness and supported at its center, and insert it fully into the tank containing the electrolyte (see p. 841 and the figure below). Begin to withdraw the blank slowly at a constant rate, whereby the outer portions of the part will remain in the tank longer and thus become thinner.

(c) A version of chemical etching can be used, as shown in the figure below. In this setup, a constant-thickness disk is immersed into a chemical etching solution, and is rotated as it is slowly withdrawn from the tank. A mask is applied to the blank periphery to ensure that the outside diameter doesn't change.

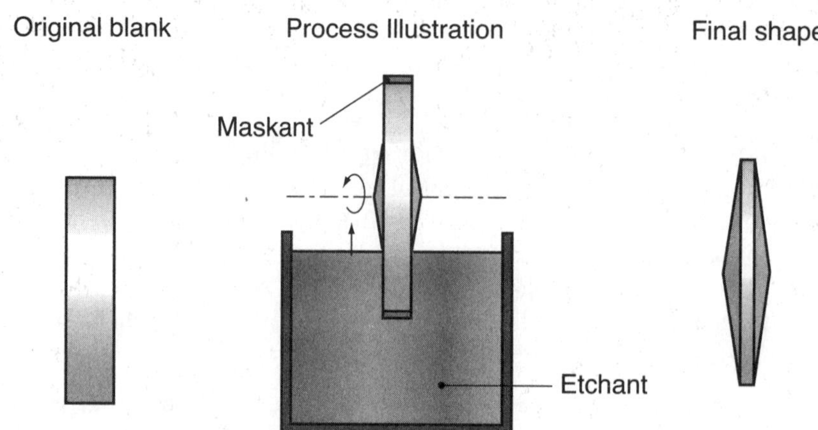


**27.42 Describe the similarities and differences among the various design guidelines presented in this chapter.**

By the student. The major guidelines are listed on pp. 841, 843, 846, 849, 853, and 855.

**27.43 Describe any size limitations in advanced machining processes. Give examples.**

By the student. As expected, size limitations vary from process to process, and the students are encouraged to investigate this topic based on data from various sources. For example, processes such as water-jet machining (Fig. 27.16b on p. 856) and laser-beam machining is limited only by the material handling equipment (Fig. 27.14d on p. 852), and sheet size can be quite large. As an actual illustration, bulldozer manufacturers use laser-beam machining of the plate that forms the support of an operators cab; it measures approximately 20 ft x 15 ft with a 3 in. thickness. In a process such as chemical machining workpiece sizes are limited by tank size, which can be as large as 5 ft x 10 ft x 10 ft, but more commonly are about 2 ft x 4 ft x 4 ft. In electrical-discharge machining, workpiece sizes can be large so as to accommodate large dies for various metalworking operations. Conversely, in electron-beam machining, the vacuum chamber size is limited, and, thus, large workpieces cannot be accommodated. This topic would make a good student project.

**27.44 We have seen that there are several hole-making methods. Based on the topics covered in Parts III and IV, make a comprehensive table of hole-making processes. Describe the advantages and limitations of each method, comment on the quality and surface integrity of the holes produced, and give examples of specific applications.**

By the student. This is an ambitious and challenging problem topic for students. The problem implies that holes are to generated on a sheet or a block of solid material, and that it does not include finishing processes for existing holes. From the contents of Parts II and IV, it can be seen that hole-making processes include (a) piercing, (b) punching, (c) drilling and boring, (d) chemical machining, (e) electrochemical machining, (f) electrical-discharge machining, (g) laser-beam and electron-beam machining, and (h) water-jet and abrasive water-jet machining. The students can prepare a comprehensive answer, based on the study of these processes in the chapter.

**27.45 An example of combining laser cutting and the punching of sheet metal is given in Example 27.1. Considering the relevant parameters involved, design a system whereby both processes can be used in combination to produce parts from sheet metal.**

By the student. Since punching capability will be a feature of such a machine, the main advantage is the use of a laser beam to soften the workpiece material prior to punching, thereby reducing the punch force. Another possibility is nibbling of flat sheets (see bottom of p. 430) to produce contoured sections, in which the laser beam reduces forces, can remove burrs from the punching operation (see Fig. 16.2 on p. 427), and provide means for markings while the part is being processed. The students are encouraged to further develop these concepts.

**27.46 Marking surfaces with numbers and letters for part identification purposes can be done not only with labels but by various mechanical and nonmechanical methods. Based on the processes described throughout this book thus far, make a list of these methods, explaining their advantages, limitations, and typical applications.**

By the student. Some methods include

(a) laser beams (where the laser path is computer controlled to produce the desired shapes of marks),

(b) etching (where a droplets of an etchant are placed in a fashion similar to ink jet printers),

(c) machining with a small end mill on a CNC milling machine,

(d) embossing (see bottom of p. 457, provided that the material is thin), and

(e) using punches with numbers and letters, in a punching operation, similar to coining, as has been done traditionally.

**27.47 Precision engineering is a term that is used to describe manufacturing high-quality parts with close dimensional tolerances and good surface finish. Based on their process capabilities, make a list of advanced machining processes with decreasing order of quality of parts produced. Include a brief commentary on each method.**

By the student. Refer also to Fig. 25.17 on p. 782. The order in such a listing will depend on the size of the parts to be produced, the quantity required, the workpiece materials, and the dimensional tolerances and surface finishes. An approximate ranking would be as follows: (1) Chemical etching, (2) Electrochemical grinding, (3) Electrochemical machining, (4) Chemical blanking, (5) Electron-beam machining, (6) Laser-beam machining, (7) Electrical-discharge machining, (8) Abrasive-jet machining, and (9) Water jet machining. The students should add comments on each of these items.

**27.48 With appropriate sketches, describe the principles of various fixturing methods and workholding devices that can be used for the processes described in this chapter.**

By the student. This important and challenging topic can be discussed in several ways. For example, specific fixture designs with strategies of fixturing of flanges versus holes can be examined, or the fixture material and its compatibility with the workpiece material and the process can be explored. The fixturing approach as a function of workpiece shape is also important. Fixturing can involve flexible devices, powered devices, or hard fixtures constructed for a particular workpiece shape. This topic would be a good project, based also on the contents of Section 37.8 on p. 1176.

**27.49 Make a table of the process capabilities of the advanced machining processes described in this chapter. Use several columns describing the machines involved, the type of tools and tool materials used, the shapes of blanks and parts produced, the typical maximum and minimum sizes, surface finish, tolerances, and production rates.**

By the student. This is an ambitious problem, as locating the sources of dimensional tolerance and production rate data can be particularly difficult. Students should be allowed some leeway in the numbers that are generated, and it is probably reasonable to restrict their consideration to a subset of processes discussed in the chapter. An example of an answer is as follows:

| Process | Tool material | Workpiece material | Typical shape | Typical part thickness and size |
|---|---|---|---|---|
| Chemical etching | None (chemical etchant) | Any | Any; most commonly etched cavities on silicon. | No limit; usually < 12 in. |
| Laser-beam machining | None (light source) | Any, mostly metals | Usually planar blanks | No limit; usually < 1 in. |
| Wire EDM | Tungsten or copper | Electrically-conducting, mostly metals | Usually planar blanks | No limit; typical workspace is 4 ft × 4 ft |
| Plunge EDM | Tungsten or graphite | Electrically-conducting, mostly metals | Complex die cavities | Typical workspace is 4 ft × 4 ft |

**27.50 One of the general concerns regarding advanced machining processes is that, in spite of their many advantages, they generally are slower than conventional machining processes. Make a survey of the speeds, machining times, and production rates involved, and prepare a table comparing their respective process capabilities.**

By the student. This is a good opportunity to perform an Internet search for machinery suppliers. It should be noted that it is difficult to obtain consistent numbers for comparison purposes because of the differences in material, dimensional tolerances required, etc. Nevertheless, a benchmark for all of these processes can be found in Table 27.1 on p. 837.

**27.51 We have seen that several of the processes described in Part IV of this book can be employed (either singly or in combination) to make or finish dies for metalworking**

**operations. Write a brief technical paper on these methods, describing their advantages and limitations, and typical applications.**

By the student. This is a valuable exercise for students, and should include the latest technical innovations including rapid prototyping and rapid tooling (see Chapter 20). Traditionally, plunge EDM was most commonly used for these applications, although electrochemical grinding can be used for near-net-shape parts to improve their surface finish. Laser-beam and electrical-discharge machining is sometimes performed to roughen the tool and die surfaces for improved material formability (by virtue of its effects on tribological behavior at workpiece-die interfaces; see bottom of p. 1051).

**27.52 Would the processes described in this chapter be difficult to perform on various nonmetallic or rubberlike materials? Explain your thoughts, commenting on the influence of various physical and mechanical properties of workpiece materials, part geometries, etc.**

By the student. Some materials will be difficult for some of the processes. For example, a chemically inert material will obviously be difficult to machine chemically. An electrically-insulating material is impossible for EDM; a tough material can be difficult to cut with a water jet; and a shiny or transparent material is difficult to machine by laser beams. Note that it is rare that a workpiece material has all of these properties simultaneously.

**27.53 Make a list of the processes described in this chapter in which the following properties are relevant: (a) mechanical, (b) chemical, (c) thermal, and (d) electrical. Are there processes in which two or more of these properties are important? Explain.**

By the student. Because "relevant" is a subjective term, the students should be encouraged to deviate from this answer if they can articulate a rationale for their decisions. Also, the problem can be interpreted as properties that are important in the workpiece or the phenomenon that is the basic principle of the advanced machining process. An acceptable answer is shown below:

| | |
|---|---|
| Mechanical: | Electrochemical grinding, water-jet machining, abrasive-jet machining. |
| Chemical: | Chemical machining, electrochemical machining, electrochemical grinding. |
| Thermal: | Chemical machining, electrochemical machining, electrochemical grinding, plunge EDM, wire EDM, laser-beam machining, electron-beam machining. |
| Electrical: | Electrochemical machining, electrochemical grinding, plunge EDM, wire EDM, electron-beam machining. |

Clearly, there are processes (such as chemical machining) where two properties that are important: the chemical reactivity of workpiece and reagents, and the corrosion processes (which is the principle of chemical machining) which are temperature dependent.

# Chapter 28

# Fabrication of Microelectronic Devices

## QUALITATIVE PROBLEMS

**28.15 In a horizontal epitaxial reactor (Fig. P28.15), the wafers are placed on a stage (susceptor) that is tilted by a small amount, usually 13°. Why is this done?**

The stage in the horizontal epitaxial reactor is usually tilted by a small amount to provide equal amounts of reactant gases in both the front and back of the chamber. If the stage were not tilted, the reactant gases would be partially used up (on the wafers in the front of the chamber) before reaching the wafers at the back end of the chamber, causing a nonuniformity in the film deposition.

**28.16 The table below describes three wafer manufacturing changes: increasing the wafer diameter, reducing the chip size, and increasing the process complexity. Complete the table by filling in "increase," "decrease," or "no change," indicating the effect that each change would have on the wafer yield and on the overall number of functional chips.**

The effects of manufacturing changes are tabulated below:

| Change | Wafer yield | Number of functional chips |
|---|---|---|
| Increase wafer diameter | No change | Increase |
| Reduce chip size | Increase | Increase |
| Increase process complexity | Decrease | Decrease |

**28.17 The speed of a transistor is directly proportional to the width of its polysilicon gate: a narrower gate results in a faster transistor, and a wider gate results in a slower transistor. Knowing that the manufacturing process has a certain variation for the gate width (say $\pm$ 0.1 $\mu$m), how might a designer alter the gate sizing of a critical circuit in order to minimize its speed variation? Are there any negative effects of this change?**

In order to minimize the speed variation of critical circuits, gate widths are typically designed at larger than the minimum allowable size. As an example, if a gate width is 0.5 ?m and the process variation is $\pm 0.1\ \mu$m, a $\pm 20\%$ variation in speed would be expected. However, if the gate width is increased to 0.8 $\mu$m, the speed variation reduces to $\pm 12.5\%$. The penalty for this technique is a larger transistor size (and in turn a larger die area) and a slower transistor.

**28.18 A common problem in ion implantation is channeling, in which the high-velocity ions travel deep into the material via channels along the crystallographic planes before finally being stopped. What is one simple way to stop this effect?**

A simple and common method of stopping ion channeling during implantation is to tilt the crystal material by a few degrees (typically 4 to 7°) so that the incident ion beam is not coincident with the crystallographic planes of the material.

**28.19 Examine the hole profiles in Fig. P28.19 and explain how they might be produced.**

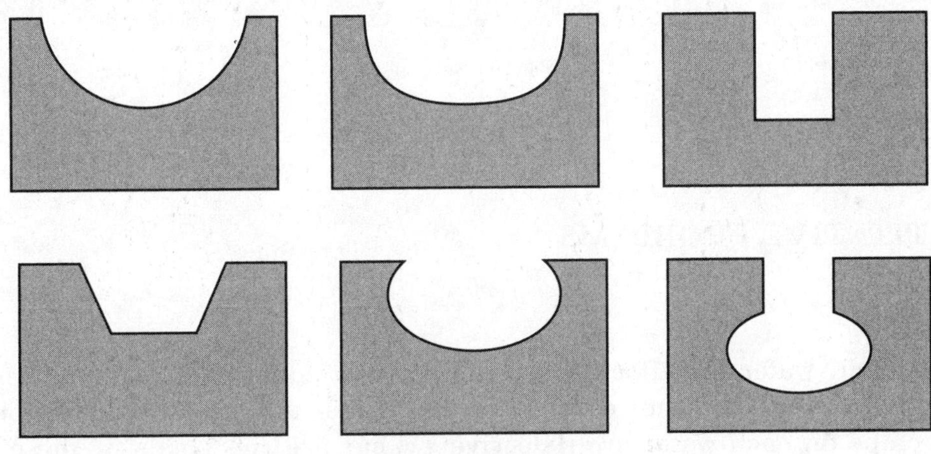

FIGURE P28.19

The figures will be referred to by letter (a)-(f), where (a)-(c) are in the top row.

(a) This profile shows an isotropic etch with no preferential etch direction; this type occurs in wet etching for polycrystalline materials.

(b) This profile shows an almost isotropic etch; note, however, the extended flat region. This can be done with wet etching on a polycrystalline material, where the hole did not have an initial circular profile.

(c) The vertical sidewalls in this profile suggest that ion etching was performed (see Fig. 28.18 on p. 890).

(d) This type is indicative of wet etching on a single-crystal workpiece by sputtering.

(e) This profile is indicative of wet etching, possibly on a dry-etched hole. Note that the surface is undercut, which requires an isotropic etchant.

(f) This profile can be explained as a hole produced with ion etching with an inhibitor layer, followed by isotropic (wet) etching.

**28.20 Referring to Fig. 28.20, sketch the holes generated from a circular mask.**

The challenge to this problem is that conical sections are difficult to sketch. Note, however, that some etching processes will expose crystallographic planes, resulting in an undercut of the circular mask in places. The sketches are given below.

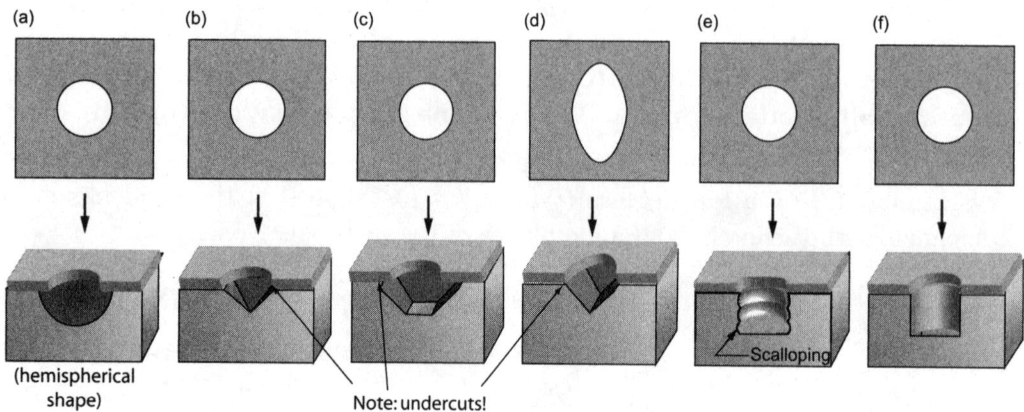


## QUANTITATIVE PROBLEMS

**28.21 A certain wafer manufacturer produces two equal-sized wafers, one containing 500 chips and the other containing 300 chips. After testing, it is observed that 50 chips on each wafer are defective. What are the yields of these two wafers? Can any relationship be drawn between chip size and yield?**

The yield for the 500 chip wafer is (500-50)/500 = 90.0%, and for the 300 chip wafer it is (300-50)/300 = 83.3%. Thus, given the same number of defects per wafer, the wafer with smaller chips (more chips per wafer) will have a higher yield because the same number of defects are spread over a larger number of chips, making the number of unacceptable chips a smaller percentage. The relationship between chip size and yield is for this circumstance is

$$\text{Yield} = \frac{N - x}{N}$$

where $N$ is the number of chips on the wafer and $x$ the number of defects per wafer. If a chip has a certain size, $l$, then the number of chips on a wafer of diameter $d$ is given by

$$N \sim \frac{A_{\text{wafer}}}{A_{\text{chip}}} = \frac{\left(\frac{\pi}{4}d^2\right)}{l^2} = C\left(\frac{d}{l}\right)^2$$

where $C$ is a constant that takes into account the fact that there will be wasted space on a wafer. For a wafer of a given diameter, it can be seen that the number of chips that can be placed on the wafer is approximately inversely proportional to its size.

**28.22 A chlorine-based polysilicon etch process displays a polysilicon-to-resist selectivity of 4:1 and a polysilicon-to-oxide selectivity of 50:1. How much resist and exposed oxide will be consumed in etching 3500 Å of polysilicon? What would the polysilicon-to-oxide selectivity have to be in order to reduce the loss to only 40 Åof exposed oxide?**

The etch rate of the resist is 1/4 that of polysilicon; therefore, etching 3500 Å of polysilicon will result in (3500)(1/4) = 875 Å of resist being etched. Similarly, the amount of exposed oxide etched away will be (3500)(1/50) = 70 Å. To remove only 40 Å of exposed oxide, the polysilicon-to-oxide selectivity would be 3500/40 = 88:1.

**28.23 During a processing sequence, three silicon-dioxide layers are grown by oxidation to: 2500 Å, 4000 Å, and 1500 Å. How much of the silicon substrate is consumed?**

The total oxide thickness = 2500 Å+ 4000 Å+ 1500 Å= 8000 Å. From Section 28.6 on p. 877, the ratio of oxide to the amount of silicon consumed is found to be 1:0.44. Therefore, to grow 8000 Å of oxide, approximately (0.44)(8000 Å) = 3520 Å of the silicon substrate will be consumed.

**28.24 A certain design rule calls for metal lines to be no less than 2 $\mu$m wide. If a 1-$\mu$m-thick metal layer is to be wet-etched, what is the minimum photoresist width allowed (assuming that the wet etch is perfectly isotropic)? What would be the minimum photoresist width if a perfectly anisotropic dry-etching process is used?**

A perfectly isotropic wet-etch process will etch equally in the vertical and horizontal directions. Therefore, the wet-etch process requires a minimum photoresist width of 2 $\mu$m, plus 1 $\mu$m per side, to allow for the undercutting, hence a total width of 4 $\mu$m. The perfectly anisotropic dry-etch process displays no undercutting and hence requires a photoresist width of only 2 $\mu$m.

## SYNTHESIS, DESIGN, AND PROJECTS

**28.25 Inspect various electronic and computer equipment, take them apart as much as you can, and identify components that may have been manufactured by the techniques described in this chapter.**

This is a good problem and one that can be inexpensively performed, as most schools and individuals have obsolete electronic devices that can be harvested for their components. Some interesting and fun projects also can arise from this experiment. One fun project would be to microscopically examine the chips to observe the manufacturers logos, as graphical icons are often imprinted on chip surfaces. See http://www.microscopy.fsu.edu/micro/gallery.html.

**28.26 Do any aspects of this chapters contents and the processes described bear any similarity to the processes described throughout previous parts of the book? Explain and describe what they are.**

There are, as to be expected, some similarities. For example, the principles of etching processes are the same as chemical machining (see Section 27.2 on p. 836). Also, there are polishing and grinding applications (as in finishing the wafers and grinding the sides) that are similar to the polishing and grinding processes, described in Chapter 26. Producing silicon wafers involves the Czochralski (CZ) process (see p. 313). Printed circuit boards are stamped and the holes are drilled, as described in previous chapters. Packaging involves potting and encapsulation of polymers (see p. 559). The students are encouraged to comment further.

**28.27 Describe your understanding of the important features of clean rooms, and how they are maintained.**

Clean rooms are described in Section 28.2. Students should be encouraged to search for additional information, such as the design features of HEPA filters, the so-called bunny suits, and humidity controls. It should be noted, however, that any discussion of clean rooms has to recognize the sources of contaminants (mostly people and their clothing) and the strategies used to control them.

**28.28 Describe products that would not exist without the knowledge and techniques described in this chapter. Explain.**

By the student. This topic would be a good project. Clearly, a wide variety of modern products could not exist without using the processes described in this chapter. Certainly, the presence of the integrated circuit has had a profound impact on the lives of everyone, and any product that contains an integrated circuit would either not exist or it would be more expensive and less reliable. Personal computers, television sets, and cellular phones are other major examples of products that could not exist (or exist in a vastly different form) without integrated circuits are televisions, automobiles, and music players. The students are encouraged to comment further, with numerous other examples.

**28.29 Review the technical literature and give more details regarding the type and shape of the abrasive wheel used in the wafer-cutting process shown in Step 2 in Fig. 28.2.**

By the student. The main source for such information would be manufacturers and distributors of abrasive wheels. It should be noted that the wheel is contoured, hence the wafer does not have a vertical wall. This means that the wafer will have a barrel shape, which is beneficial for avoiding chipping.

**28.30 As you know, microelectronic devices may be subjected to hostile environments (such as high temperature, humidity, and vibration) as well as physical abuse (such as being dropped on a hard surface). Describe your thoughts on how you would go about testing these devices for their endurance under these conditions.**

By the student. This is a good topic for students to study and develop testing methods for electronic devices. It will be helpful to have students refer to ASTM standards and various other sources to find standardized test procedures, and evaluate if they are sufficient for the difficulties encountered.

**28.31 Review the specific devices indicated in Fig. V.2. Choose any one of these devices and investigate what they are, their characteristics, how they are manufactured,**

**and at what costs.**

By the student. This is an open-ended problem and the answer will of course vary depending on which component the student wishes to study. Note that the air bag sensor, for example, is described in Case Study 29.1 on p. 928.

# Chapter 29

# Fabrication of Microelectromechanical Devices and Systems (MEMS)

## QUALITATIVE PROBLEMS

**29.15 What is the difference between isotropic and anisotropic etching?**

In isotropic etching, material is chemically machined in all directions at the same rate, as shown in Fig. 13.16a on p. 776. Anisotropic etching involves chemical machining where one direction etches faster than another, with the extreme being vertical etching (Fig. 13.16f) where material is only removed in one direction.

**29.16 Lithography produces projected shapes, so that true three-dimensional shapes are more difficult to produce. What lithography processes are best able to produce three-dimensional shapes, such as lenses?**

Making three dimensional shapes is very difficult. A shape with a smooth surface is especially challenging, since a stepped surface can be produced by multilayer lithography. Three-dimensional objects can be produced by isotropic etching, but the surface wont necessarily have the desired contour. The best lithography-based process for producing three dimensional surfaces is stereolithography or microstereolithography, which can be combined with electroforming (see p. 1072) or other processes (such as LIGA, see p. 920).

**29.17 What is the difference between chemically reactive ion etching and dry-plasma etching?**

Chemically assisted ion etching is one type of dry plasma etching. In chemically assisted ion-etching, described on pp. 890-891, a chemically reactive species is used along with the impact of ions onto a surface to remove material. This is a form of dry-plasma etching because no liquids are used in the process. However, the general category of 'dry plasma etching' also includes processes such as sputter etching (see p. 889) and cryogenic dry etching (see p. 892).

**29.18 The MEMS devices discussed in this chapter apply macroscale machine elements, such as spur gears, hinges, and beams. Which of the following machine elements can and cannot be applied to MEMS and why? (a) ball bearings, (b) bevel gears, (c) worm gears, (d) cams, (e) helical springs, (f) rivets, and (g) bolts.**

Although, in principle, most of these machine elements can be manufactured, it is extremely difficult to manufacture ball bearings, helical springs, worm gears, and bolts (and use them in micromechanical systems). The main reason is that these components are three dimensional, and the current MEMS manufacturing processes are best suited for 2D, or at best, 2-1/2 D devices.

**29.19 Referring to Fig. 28.20, sketch the holes generated from a circular mask.**

The challenge to this problem is that conic sections are difficult to sketch. Note however that some etching processes will expose crystallographic planes, resulting in an undercut of the circular mask in places.

**29.20 Explain how you would produce a spur gear if its thickness was one-tenth its diameter and its diameter was (a) 10 $\mu$m, (b) 100 $\mu$m, (c) 1 mm, (d) 10 mm, and (e) 100 mm.**

The answer depends on the material, but lets assume the material is silicon.

(a) 10-$\mu$m spur gear could be produced through surface micromachining.

(b) 100 $\mu$m spur gear could be produced through micromachining (p. 909). If silicon is not the desired material, LIGA is an option (p. 920).

(c) 1-mm gear can be produced through LIGA, chemical blanking or chemical etching from foil (p. 836).

(d) 10 mm gear can be blanked or chemically blanked.

(e) 100 mm gear should be machined or hobbed (p. 752).

**29.21 List the advantages and disadvantages of surface micromachining compared to bulk micromachining.**

By the student. This is an open-ended problem and the students should be encouraged to develop answers that may deviate from this partial list.

Advantages of surface micromachining:

- Multilayer objects can be produced.
- Very good dimensional tolerances can be maintained.
- Complex shapes can be produced in multiple layers.
- A mature technology which is fairly robust.
- Not restricted to single-crystal materials.

Disadvantages of surface micromachining:

- Additional manufacturing steps are required to deposit and remove spacer layers.
- The process is effectively limited to silicon as the substrate material.

- Wet etchants can result in structures that fail to separate from surfaces, as shown in Fig. 29.5 on p. 912.

**29.22 What are the main limitations to the LIGA process?**

LIGA is an acronym from the German *X ray Lithographie, Galvanoformung und Abformung* (meaning x-ray lithography, electroforming and molding, as shown in Fig. 13.38 on p. 795). LIGA has the capability of producing MEMS and micromechanical devices with very large aspect ratios, and it also allows the production of polymer MEMS devices and the mass production of these devices (since the LIGA-produced structure is a mold for further processing). The main limitations of LIGA are cost-based: collimated x-rays are obtained only with special equipment, currently available only at selected U.S. National Laboratories; thus, the cost of parts produced is very high.

**29.23 What other process can be used to make the microtweezers in Fig. 29.22 other than HEXSIL?**

The HEXSIL tweezers shown in Fig. 29.22 on p. 927 are difficult, but not impossible, to produce through other processes. The important features to be noted in these tweezers are the high aspect ratios and the presence of lightening holes in the structure, resulting in a compliant and lightweight structure. Although processes such as SCREAM can be used, the required aspect ratio will be difficult to achieve. LIGA also can be used, but it is expensive. For each of these processes, the tweezers shown in Fig. 29.22 would require redesign of the microtweezers. For example, in LIGA, it would be desirable to have a draft in the vertical members to aid in molding. However, a structure that serves the same function can be produced, even though vertical sidewalls cannot be produced.

## QUANTITATIVE PROBLEMS

**29.24 A polyimide photoresist needs 100 mJ/cm$^2$ per micrometer of thickness to develop properly. How long does a 150 $\mu$m film need to develop when exposed by a 1000 W/m$^2$ light source?**

It is useful to convert units to avoid confusion in making the calculations. Note that the polyimide photoresist requires the following power density:

$$P = 100\frac{\text{mJ}}{\text{cm}^3(\mu\text{m})t}h = \frac{1000 \text{ Nm}}{t \text{ m}^2}\frac{h}{(\mu\text{m})}$$

where $t$ is the exposure time and $h$ is the film thickness. Since the power available is 1000 W/m$^2$, we can calculate the time as

$$1000\frac{\text{W}}{\text{m}^2} = \frac{1000 \text{ Nm}}{t \text{ m}^2}\frac{h}{(\mu\text{m})} \quad \rightarrow \quad t = \left(\frac{1000 \text{ Nm}}{1000 \text{ W}}\right) h = 150 \text{ s}$$

**29.25 Calculate the undercut in etching a 10-$\mu$m deep trench if the anisotropy ratio is (a) 200, (b) 2, and (c) 0.5. What is the sidewall slope for these cases?**

The anisotropy ratio, AR, is given by Eq. (28.1) on p. 888 as the ratio of etch rates in the desired and undesired directions. We can now write

$$\text{AR} = \frac{E_1}{E_2} = \frac{(10\ \mu\text{m}/t)}{x/t} = \frac{10\ \mu\text{m}}{x} \quad \rightarrow \quad x = \frac{10\ \mu\text{m}}{\text{AR}}$$

Note that the dimensions are as shown in the sketch below, namely, that $x$ is the undercut and $t$ is the time required to produce a 10-$\mu$m deep trench. Also, the sidewalls are as shown; a vertical wall is taken as 90°. Therefore,

(a) For AR = 200, $x = 10\ \mu\text{m}/200 = 0.05\ \mu\text{m}$; and $\theta = \tan^{-1}(10/0.05) = 89.7°$

(b) For AR=2, $x = 10\ \mu\text{m}/2 = 5\ \mu\text{m}$; and $\theta = \tan^{-1}(10/2) = 78.7°$

(c) For AR=0.5, $x = 10\ \mu\text{m}/0.5 = 20\ \mu\text{m}$; and $\theta = \tan^{-1}(10/20) = 26.5°$

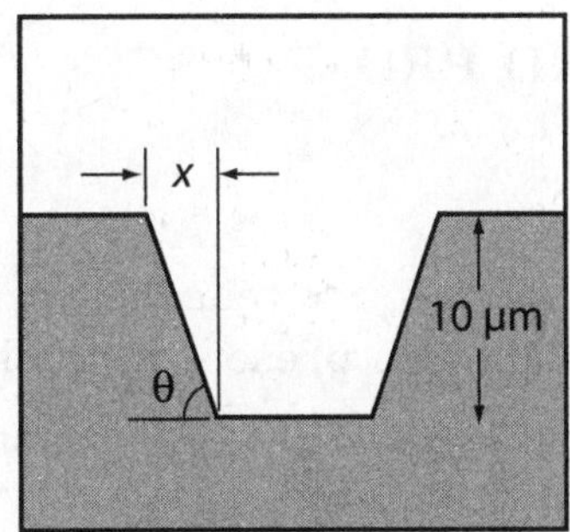


**29.26 How many levels are needed to produce the micromotor shown in Fig. 28.19d?**

At a minimum, the following layers are needed:

- Base for rotor
- Rotor
- Pin or bearing (it must protrude past the rotor)
- Lip on bearing to retain rotor.

This list assumes that the electrical connections can be made on the same layers as the MEMS features, as otherwise an additional layer is required.

**29.27 Conduct an Internet search and determine the smallest diameter hole that can be produced by the following processes: (a) drilling, (b) punching, (c) water-jet cutting, (d) laser machining, (e) chemical etching, and (f) EDM**

By the student. This is a good and challenging problem and requires an understanding of the capabilities and limitations of each process. Note that the problem doesnt specify the type of material or hole depth; there will therefore be variations in the answers given. The following are some approximate values as obtained from various sources:

(a) The smallest drill bit is about 0.34 m=13.6 in. (Source: www.micro100.com)

(b) The smallest punch diameter commercially available is about 1.59 mm=0.0625 in. (Source: Small Parts Inc., http://www,smallparts.com/)

(c) The smallest hole in water-jet cutting varies by material and depth, but is on the order of 1 mm=0.04 in. Jet-nozzle diameters can be as small as 0.05 mm=0.002 in..

(d) In laser-beam machining, the smallest hole depends on material, depth and aspect ratio desired. For vertical sidewalls and with a 10:1 aspect ratio, the smallest hole produced is about 1 $\mu$m=40 $\mu$in..

(e) Dimensional tolerance depends on hole diameter; for example, for nonferrous alloys and for 0.005 to 0.0032 in. diameter holes, tolerances up to 10% of diameter can be maintained, so that the smallest hole is 8.8 $\mu$m in diameter.

(f) In EDM the smallest hole is 100 $\mu$m=0.004 in. (*Source:* AMI Machining, www.wireedm.com)

## SYNTHESIS, DESIGN, AND PROJECTS

**29.28 List similarities and differences between IC technologies covered in Chapter 28 and miniaturization technologies presented in this chapter.**

By the student. There are many similarities, and the student is encouraged to produce more than given in the short list provided here.

- Microelectronics and MEMS both depend on etching, wet and dry.
- Both use predominantly silicon as the main substrate material.
- Both use similar packaging strategies.
- Both require clean rooms for manufacture.
- Both use batch production techniques.

**29.29 Figure I.11 in the General Introduction shows a mirror which is suspended on a torsional beam and which can be inclined through electrostatic attraction by applying a voltage on either side of the mirror at the bottom of the trench. Make a flow chart of the manufacturing operations required to produce this device.**

The device shown in Fig. I.11b on p. 30 was produced at the University of California at Berkeley Sensor and Actuator Center. As can be seen, the layer below the mirror is very deep and has near vertical sidewalls, so clearly this device was produced through a dry (plasma) etching approach. Note also that the device was machined from the top since the sidewall slope is slightly inclined. However, a high-quality mirror cannot be produced in this manner. The only means of producing this micromirror is (a) to perform deep reactive ion etching on the lower portion, (b) traditional surface micromachining on the top layer, and (c) joining the two layers through silicon fusion bonding. (See Fig 13.35 on p. 793 for further examples of this approach.)

**29.30 Referring to Fig. 29.5, design an experimental study to find the critical dimensions of an overhanging cantilever which will not stick to the substrate.**

By the student. There are several potential solutions and approaches to this problem. An experimental investigation, pursued by K. Komvopolous, Department of Mechanical Engineering at the University of California at Berkeley, is to produce a series of cantilevers of different aspect ratios on a wafer. After production through surface micromachining followed by rinsing, some of the cantilevers attach to the substrate while others remain suspended. The figure below shows the transition. Based on beam theory from the mechanics of solids, a prediction of the adhesive forces can be determined.

**29.31 Design an accelerometer using the (a) SCREAM process and (b) HEXSIL process.**

By the student. This is an open-ended problem and thus many solutions are possible. The students should draw upon the manufacturing sequence shown in Figs. 29.26 through 29.28 on pp. 930-932, and consider the capability of the SCREAM and HEXSIL processes to produce large, overhanging structures.

**29.32 Design a micromachine or device that allows the direct measurement of the mechanical properties of a thin film.**

By the student. This is an interesting problem, and since it does not specify a length scale, there are a number of designs. Currently, a number of devices, including nanoindenters and atomic force microscopes are used to obtain the mechanical properties (such as stiffness and strength) of thin films. The student should consider the very small lengths involved; actuators must be extremely sensitive and hence their proper control is essential.

**29.33 Perform a literature search and write a one-page summary of applications in biomems.**

By the student. This is an interesting problem and is open-ended because there are numerous biomems (MEMS in biology) applications. Some of the topics that could be considered by the students are:

- Drug manufacturing (macromolecules).

- Chemical analysis, as, for example, in laboratory-on-a-chip sensors that can perform several tests on a small sample of blood.
- Miniature implants for treatment of Parkinsons disease and other applications such as nerve repair.

# Chapter 30

# Fusion-Welding Processes

## QUALITATIVE PROBLEMS

**30.15 Explain the reasons why so many different welding processes have been developed.**

A wide variety of welding processes have been developed for several reasons (see also top of p. 937). Among these are:

(a) There are many types of metals and alloys with a wide range of mechanical, physical, and metallurgical properties and characteristics.

(b) There are numerous applications involving a wide variety of part shapes and thicknesses. For example, small or thin parts which cannot be arc welded can be resistance welded, and for aerospace applications, where strength-to-weight ratio is a major consideration, laser-beam welding or diffusion bonding are attractive processes.

(c) The workpiece is often not suitable for in-plant welding, and the welding process and equipment must be brought to the site, such as in large construction. When the workpiece is available for in-plant welding, less mobile welding processes are necessary.

**30.16 What is the effect of the thermal conductivity of the workpiece on kerf width in oxyfuel-gas cutting?**

In oxyfuel-gas cutting, it is desirable to melt as small a width (kerf) as possible. If the workpiece has high thermal conductivity (see Table 3.1 on p. 103), the heat will be dissipated throughout the workpiece more rapidly, resulting in a wider kerf. Low thermal conductivity results in a more localized heating and, hence, a smaller kerf. For this reason, processes that involve a highly localized application of heat, such as laser-beam or electron-beam welding, can be used with much smaller kerfs than other processes. (See, for example, Fig. 30.16 on p. 959.)

**30.17 Describe the differences between oxyfuel-gas cutting of ferrous and of nonferrous alloys. Which properties are significant?**

In oxyfuel-gas cutting of ferrous alloys, the cutting process takes place mainly by oxidation and burning of the ferrous metal, with some melting also taking place. In nonferrous alloys, on the other hand, the cutting action is mainly by melting; oxidation and burning are usually less important factors; in fact, iron fluxes are often introduced in the flame to localize the melting zone. This method is not effective with ferrous alloys because iron fluxes consume some of the available oxygen and actually hinder the cutting process. The temperature at which welding takes place varies significantly among ferrous and nonferrous alloys, and is it usually higher for ferrous alloys. This phenomenon affects the selection of process parameters such as fuel and oxygen flow rates and welding speed.

**30.18 Could you use oxyfuel-gas cutting for a stack of sheet metals? (Note: For stack cutting, see Fig. 24.25e.) Explain.**

A major problem in cutting a stack of sheet metal is that if the cutting is predominantly through melting, the sheets may be welded together. To minimize this effect, the cutting speed should be as high as possible and at as high a heat-input rate as possible. To further limit the welding of the individual sheets, oxyfuel-gas cutting should be limited to ferrous alloys where the welding is predominantly through oxidation and burning, and not melting. Another problem with stack cutting is that the cut size of the top and bottom sheets can be different (depending on how many layers there are and their thickness, as well as how well the process parameters are controlled) because the heat source is maintained after the top sheets have been cut.

**30.19 What are the advantages of electron-beam and laser-beam welding when compared to arc welding?**

The main advantages of these processes are associated with the very small weld kerf, and the localized energy input and small heat-affected zone. Weld failures, especially by fatigue, occur in the heat-affected zone; thus, minimizing this volume reduces the likelihood of large flaws and rapid crack growth. Also, the low energy input means that thermal distortions and warping associated with these processes will be much lower than with arc welding (see also Figs. 30.23 and 30.25 on pp. 966-967).

**30.20 Discuss the need for and role of fixtures for holding workpieces in the welding operations described in this chapter.**

By the student. Fixtures are important to ensure that parts maintain their proper location and orientation prior to and after joining. If the pieces are joined incorrectly through welding, they must be separated (or even scrapped), unlike bolted connections which can easily be disassembled. Fixture design is thus an important consideration to ensure maximum dimensional accuracy and repeatability in welded parts.

**30.21 Describe the common types of discontinuities in welds and explain the methods by which they can be avoided.**

Discontinuities in welds are discussed on pp. 962-968. Some of the common defects are porosity, inclusions, incomplete fusion/penetration, underfilling, undercutting, overlaps, and cracks (see Fig. 30.21 on p. 964). The methods by which they can be avoided are discussed on p. 965. Basically, they involve modifying the process parameters (usually modifying welding speed) or preheating the workpiece.

**30.22 Explain the significance of the stiffness of the components being welded on both weld quality and part shape.**

The effect of stiffness on weld defects is primarily through the thermal stresses that develop during heating and cooling of the weld joint. As shown in Fig. 30.22 on p. 965, for example, not allowing contraction (such as due to a very stiff system) may cause cracks in the joint due to thermal stresses. (See also Section 30.9.1 on p. 962.)

**30.23 How would you go about detecting underbead cracks in a weld?**

By the student. Underbead cracks are difficult to detect because they are not at the surface and cannot be detected visually or with penetrants or probes. Instead, nondestructive techniques such as x-ray or acoustical test methods must be used, as described on p. 971 and in Section 36.10 on p. 1132.

**30.24 Could plasma-arc cutting be used for nonmetallic materials? If so, would you select a transferred or a nontransferred type of arc? Explain.**

Plasma arc cutting can be applied to nonmetallic materials. The heating mechanism is pure conduction/convection, with no chemical reactivity because heat transfer takes place in an inert-gas atmosphere. However, few nonmetallic materials require a welding process of this complexity. Plastics could conceivably be welded with this process. Obviously, such applications would require different process parameters than for welding metals, due to the difference in the melting points of plastics and their relatively low thermal conductivity.

**30.25 What factors influence the size of the two weld beads shown in Fig. 30.14?**

The important factor is the intensity and rate of energy supplied to the workpiece. Other important factors are the shape of the weld bead, and, of course, the thermal conductivity of the material.

**30.26 Which of the processes described in this chapter are not portable? Can they be made so? Explain.**

While some welding processes are very portable, and this is extremely valuable for field repairs, other processes are not portable. Examples are plasma arc welding, submerged arc welding, electrogas welding, and laser-beam and electron-beam welding. These processes are difficult to make into portable versions, mostly because of the bulkiness of the power supplies required. However, since there are so many portable processes, there is little need to adapt these approaches to make them portable.

**30.27 Describe your observations concerning the contents of Table 30.1.**

By the student. There are many possible answers to this question, depending on the interpretation and experiences of the student. This problem and others like it have been found to be useful aides in lectures; it can be modified by asking the students to list additional advantages, or the possibility of extending operation from manual to automatic for some processes. Students should be encouraged to develop an answer to this problem that demonstrates they read and studied the information.

**30.28 What determines whether a certain welding process can be used for workpieces in horizontal, vertical, or upside-down positions (or any position)? Explain your answer and give examples of appropriate applications.**

Note the contents of Table 30.1 on p. 941. Submerged arc welding is the only process listed that requires a flat and horizontal surface, and this is because the flux would not remain in place otherwise. This problem can be repeated as Chapters 31-32 are covered as well to increase the number of operations that are limited in terms of their position.

**30.29 Explain the factors involved in electrode selection in arc-welding processes.**

By the student. Electrodes are chosen for the particular process and workpiece. For example, with high-strength workpieces, a stronger electrode may be desired (such as an E110XX series) while for ductile, low-carbon steels, an E60XX series would be adequate. The alloy content can be selected to closely match the alloys being welded to improve fusion.

**30.30 In Table 30.1, there is a column on the distortion of welded components that is ordered from lowest distortion to highest. Explain why the degree of distortion varies among different welding processes.**

By the student. The main reason distortion varies greatly between processes is the amount of heating involved. Some processes, such as laser-beam machining, apply heat to a very small volume and, therefore, there is much less distortion than, say, oxyacetylene welding where a large volume is heated.

**30.31 Explain the significance of residual stresses in welded structures.**

By the student. This is an open-ended problem, and students should be encouraged to develop additional or expanded solutions compared to the one given here. Residual stresses (see p. 966) are important for several reasons, including:

- They can lead to warpage, especially if a portion of the weldment is later machined or ground.
- Tensile residual stresses usually result in a reduction of fatigue life.
- Residual stresses require larger dimensional tolerances in design.

**30.32 Comment on your observations regarding the shape of the weld beads shown in Fig. 30.5. Which ones would you recommend for thin sheet metals?**

By the student. For very thin sheet metals, none of these would be suitable, but mash seam welds (see Fig. 31.11 on p. 991) and other equivalents would be better suited. For moderately thick sheets, a deep penetration is advisable, since the cross-section of the weld is very small (if the weld is only a surface weld on the sheet material). Hence, the bead shown in Fig. 30.5a on p. 945 is the best choice of those presented.

**30.33 Why is oxyacetylene welding limited to rather thin sections?**

Oxyacetylene welding is limited to thin sections because the heat generated is much less intense than for arc welding. Therefore, thick cross-sections would require a long time to heat through, which would make oxyacetylene welding not practical or economical.

**30.34 Rank the processes described in this chapter in terms of (a) cost and (b) weld quality.**

By the student. Refer to Table 30.1 on p. 941. It will be noted that the weld quality and process costs follow the same trends. Also, cost data given in Table 30.1 relates to equipment costs. While the cost per weld will follow the same trends as the equipment costs, it should be noted that high production rates can justify higher capital equipment expenditures, whereas low production rates cannot make this justification. Geometry and material to be welded also have an effect on economy and quality. Thus, for one weld, the lowest cost process could be shielded metal arc or oxyfuel welding, depending on the material. For higher production rates, an automatic process such as laser welding may actually cost less per weld, even though the capital equipment costs are much higher.

**30.35 What are the sources of weld spatter? How can spatter be controlled?**

Weld spatter arises from a number of sources. If the filler metal is a powder, errant particles can strike the surface and loosely adhere to the surface, similar to the thermal spraying process (see Section 34.5 on p. 1063). Even a continuous electrode will spatter, as a violently evolving or pumped shielding gas can cause the molten metal to emit droplets, which then adhere to the workpiece surface near the weld zone.

**30.36 Must the filler metal be of the same composition as the base metal to be welded? Explain your response.**

It is not necessary for the filler metal, rod, or wire to be the same as the base metal to be welded. Many filler metals are chosen for the favorable alloying properties that they impart to the weld zone. The only function the filler metal must fulfill is to fill in the gaps; whether it diffuses into the base metal is not a requirement, although it is usually beneficial. The filler metal is typically an alloy of the same metal, due to the fact that the workpiece and the filler should melt at reasonably close temperatures. To visualize why this is the case, consider a copper filler used with a material with a much higher melting temperature, such as steel. When the copper melts, the steel workpiece is still solid, and the interface will be adhesion-based, with no diffusion between the copper and steel.

**30.37 Describe your observations concerning Fig. 30.18.**

By the student. Many observations can be made, such as:

(a) The microstructures can be explained by drawing upon the principles of metal casting, as discussed in Chapter 10.

(b) The hardness contours match the volumes that are expected to be significantly heated as a result of the welding process.

(c) See the solution to Problem 30.45 for a plot of the hardness as a function of distance from the surface.

**30.38 In Fig. 30.24b, assume that most of the top portion of the top piece is cut horizontally with a sharp saw. The residual stresses will now be disturbed and the part will undergo shape change, as was described in Section 2.11. For this case,**

**how do you think the part will distort: curved downward or upward? Explain your response. (See also Fig. 2.29d).**

The part will bow upward (that is, it will hold water), with the center of curvature above the part. Recall that the internal forces in a part have to achieve a state of static equilibrium. The top layer of material (which is under tension) has the tendency to bend the bar downward. When this stress is relieved, such as by removing the top layer by machining or grinding, the bar will compensate by bending upward. Such residual stress systems can be modeled with a set of horizontal tension and compression springs (see also Section 2.11 on p. 94).

**30.39 Describe the reasons that fatigue failures generally occur in the heat-affected zones of welds instead of through the weld bead itself.**

Fatigue failure and crack propagation theory suggests that cracks are slower to grow in a harder material than a soft one. In general, the weld bead itself is highly alloyed and has a higher hardness than the workpiece. The base metal of the workpiece is often rolled or extruded, and has a high degree of cold work and, therefore, high hardness. The heat-affected zone is annealed or partially annealed; it has a lower hardness and therefore a lower fatigue strength than the base metal or the weld bead.

**30.40 If the materials to be welded are preheated, is the likelihood for porosity increased or decreased? Explain.**

Weld porosity arises from a number of sources, including micropores similar to those found in castings, entrained or evolved gases, and bridging and cracking. If the part is preheated, bridging and cracking are reduced and the cooling rate is lower, therefore large shrinkage pores are less likely. However, since cooling is slower with preheat, soluble gases may be more likely to be entrained unless effective shielding gases are used (see Problem 29.25).

**30.41 Make a list of welding processes that are suitable for producing (a) butt joints (where the weld is in the form of a line or line segment), (b) spot welds, and (c) both butt joints and spot welds.**

By the student. Butt welds can be produced by any of the processes listed in Table 30.1 on p. 941 and described in this chapter. Spot welds (shown in Fig. 31.6b on p. 987) are more difficult for the processes described in this chapter. Note that the weld is developed between two overlapping pieces of metal, and this is difficult with spot welding. However, laser-beam and electron-beam welding are well-suited for producing spot welds.

## QUANTITATIVE PROBLEMS

**30.42 A welding operation takes place on an aluminum-alloy plate. A pipe 50-mm in diameter with a 4-mm wall thickness and a 60-mm length is butt-welded onto a section of 15 x 15 x 5 mm angle iron. The angle iron is of an L-shape and has a length of 0.3 m. If the weld zone in a gas tungsten-arc welding process is**

**approximately 8 mm wide, what would be the temperature increase of the entire structure due to the heat input from welding only? What if the process were an electron-beam welding operation with a bead width of 6 mm? Assume that the electrode requires 1500 J and the aluminum alloy requires 1200 J to melt one gram.**

For the first part of the problem, assume that the electrode is placed around the entire pipe, so that the weld length is $\pi D = \pi(50 \text{ mm}) = 0.157$ m. If the weld cross-section is triangular, its volume is approximately

$$V = \frac{1}{2}bhL = \frac{1}{2}(0.008 \text{ m})^2(0.157 \text{ m}) = 5.02 \times 10^{-6} \text{ m}^3$$

The electrode material should be matched to aluminum, so it will likely be an aluminum alloy in order to roughly match melting temperatures and compatibility. The density should therefore be around 2700 kg/m$^3$ (see Table 3.1 on p. 103, where it is also noted that $C = 900$ J/kg-K). Therefore, the energy input is (1500 J/g)(2700 kg/m$^3$)($5.02 \times 10^{-6}$ m$^3$) = 20.3 kJ. The total volume of the aluminum is

$$V = \frac{\pi}{4}(d_o^2 - d_i^2)L + 2btl = \frac{\pi}{4}(50^2 - 42^2)(60) + 2(15)(5)(300) = 79,683 \text{ mm}^3$$

or $V = 7.968 \times 10^{-5}$ m$^3$. The temperature rise is then calculated as:

$$E = \rho VC\,\Delta T \quad \rightarrow \quad \Delta T = \frac{E}{\rho VC} = \frac{20,300 \text{ J}}{(2700 \text{ kg/m}^3)(7.968 \times 10^{-5} \text{ m}^3)(900 \text{ J/kg-K})}$$

Or $\Delta T = 104°$C. For the second part of the problem, the change to be made is in the input energy. Using the same approach as above, we have

$$V = \frac{1}{2}bhL = \frac{1}{2}(0.006 \text{ m})^2(0.157 \text{ m}) = 2.826 \times 10^{-6} \text{ m}^3$$

However, here the weld material is aluminum, so that the input energy is (1200 J/g)(2700 kg/m$^3$)($2.826 \times 10^{-6}$ m$^3$)=9.16 kJ. The temperature rise is therefore

$$\Delta T = \frac{E}{\rho VC} = \frac{9,160 \text{ J}}{(2700 \text{ kg/m}^3)(2.826 \times 10^{-6} \text{ m}^3)(900 \text{ J/kg-K})} = 1333°\text{C}$$

**30.43 A welding operation will take place on carbon steel. The desired welding speed is around 0.7 in./s. If an arc-welding power supply is used with a voltage of 10 V, what current is needed if the weld width is to be 0.2 in.?**

Note that inconsistent units are provided; the product of volts and amperes is Joules, whereas the length units are in the English standard measurement system. Special care will be needed to make sure the units used are consistent. Note that $v$ = 0.7 in./s = 0.0178 m/s. Also, assuming that we have a T-joint (see Fig. VI.4 on p. 939), the weld cross-sectional area is

$$A = \frac{1}{2}bh = \frac{1}{2}(0.2 \text{ in.})(0.2 \text{ in.}) = 0.02 \text{ in}^2 = 1.29 \times 10^{-5} \text{ m}^2$$

which assumes that the cross-section is triangular. If all the energy is used to melt the weld metal, we can write,

$$H = \frac{\rho V C\, \Delta T}{l}$$

Also, From Eq. (30.3) on p. 946, $H = EI/v$. Therefore, we can now write, noting that $V = Al$, where $l$ is the weld length,

$$\frac{EI}{v} = \frac{\rho V C\, \Delta T}{l} = \frac{\rho ALC\, \Delta T}{l} = \rho AC\, \Delta T$$

So that the current required is solved as

$$l = \frac{\rho ACv\, \Delta T}{E}$$

From Table 3.1 on p. 103, $\rho = 7860$ kg/m$^3$, $C = 460$ J/kg-K, and $T_{\text{melt}} = 1450°$C (using mid-range values for steels). Therefore, $\Delta T = 1425°$C. The current is then obtained as

$$I = \frac{(7860)(1.29 \times 10^{-5})(460)(1425)(0.01778)}{(10)} = 118 \text{ A}$$

**30.44 In oxyacetylene, arc, and laser-beam cutting, the processes basically involve melting of the workpiece. If an 80-mm-diameter hole is to be cut from a 250-mm-diameter and 12-mm-thick plate, plot the mean temperature rise in the blank as a function of kerf. Assume that one-half of the energy goes into the blank.**

The volume melted is

$$V = (\pi D)th = \pi(0.08 \text{ m})(0.012 \text{ m})t = 0.0030t$$

where $t$ is the kerf width. The energy input is then $E = FrV/2 = 0.0015tF\rho$, where $F$ is the energy required to melt one kg of workpiece and $\rho$ is the workpiece density. Note above that we have divided the energy by two because only one-half of the energy goes into the blank. The volume of the blank is

$$V = bwh = \frac{\pi}{4}d^2h = \frac{\pi}{4}\left[(0.250 \text{ m})^2 - (0.08 \text{ m})^2\right](0.012 \text{ m}) = 5.29 \times 10^{-4} \text{ m}^3$$

The temperature rise in the blank is $\Delta T = E/\rho V C_p$, so substituting for the input energy, we have

$$\Delta T = \frac{0.0015tF\rho}{\rho C_p(5.29 \times 10^{-4})} = 2.83t\left(\frac{F}{C_p}\right)$$

It can be seen that the plot of temperature rise is a linear function of kerf width, $t$.

**30.45 Plot the hardness in Fig. 30.18d as a function of the distance from the top surface and discuss your observations.**

The plot is shown below:

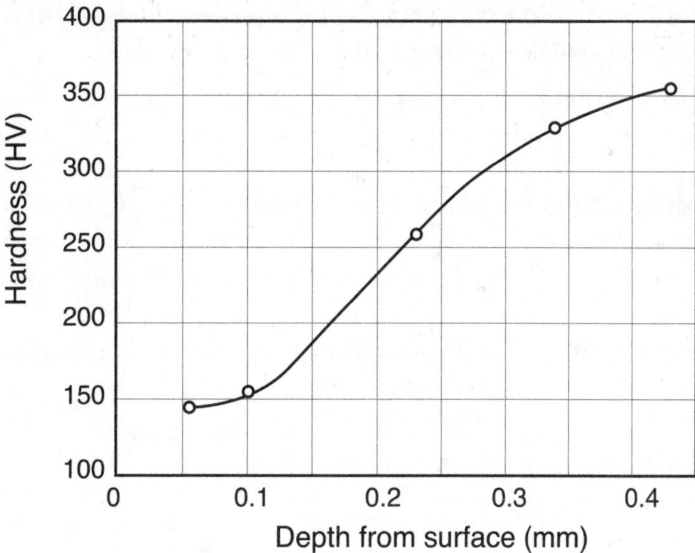


## SYNTHESIS, DESIGN, AND PROJECTS

**30.46 Comment on workpiece size and shape limitations (if any) for each of the processes described in this chapter.**

By the student. Some obvious examples are that oxyacetylene welding requires thin workpieces, stick welding requires shapes that allow access to the intended area, and in electron-beam welding workpieces must be small enough to fit into the vacuum chamber.

**30.47 Review the types of welded joints shown in Fig. 30.27 and give an application for each.**

By the student. This is an open-ended problem, with various possible answers based on the experience of the students. Some examples are:

- Single square-groove weld: pressure vessel walls, tailor welded blanks.
- Single V-groove weld: pressure vessel walls, ship construction.
- Single-flare, V-groove weld: crane booms and lattice structures.

**30.48 Comment on the design guidelines given in this chapter.**

By the student. This is an open-ended problem, and several acceptable answers can be given based on the experience of the students. The design guidelines given on pp. 971-974 are fairly straightforward, but the students are encouraged to develop creative answers of their own to this problem.

**30.49 Make a summary table outlining the principles of the processes described in this chapter, together with examples of their applications.**

By the student. As this is an open-ended problem, students should be encouraged to develop their own answers. An acceptable answer, for example, will be similar to the table below:

| Welding process | Underlying principle | Typical applications |
|---|---|---|
| Shielded metal-arc | Electrical arc melts sacrificial consumable electrode within a shielding gas | Wide variety of applications, including automotive and aerospace |
| Submerged-arc | Electrical arc melts sacrificial electrode beneath a powder flux | Thick plate for shipbuilding or pressure vessels |
| Gas metal-arc | Electrical arc melts filler metal within an inert-gas shield | Robotic welding systems, widely used in metal fabrication |
| Gas tungsten-arc | Electrical arc between workpiece and tungsten electrode melts filler metal within a gas shield | Applicable to a wide variety of workpiece materials; high quality welds |
| Fluxed-cored arc | Similar to gas metal-arc, but flux is inside electrode | Robot welding systems |
| Oxyfuel | Combustion of acetylene in oxygen | Widely applied, especially for field repairs |
| Electron-beam | Electron stream melts workpiece | Hermetically-sealed containers for MEMS |
| Laser-beam | Light source melts workpiece | Tailor-welded blanks, razor blades |

**30.50 Prepare a table of the processes described in this chapter and give the range of welding speeds as a function of workpiece material and thicknesses.**

By the student. This is an open-ended problem, with various answers based on the experience of the students. Students should be encouraged to develop their own answers to this problem.

**30.51 Assume that you are asked to inspect a welded structure for a critical application, Describe the procedure that you would follow.**

By the student. Refer to Sections 36.10 and 36.11 on pp. 1132 and 1136, respectively. Visual examination can detect some defects such as undercuts and toe cracks; however, underbead cracks or incomplete fusion cannot be detected visually. There are nondestructive techniques for evaluating a weld, acoustic and x-ray techniques being the most common for determining porosity and large inclusions. Proof stressing a weld is a destructive approach, but is certainly suitable since defective welds cannot be placed in service safely.

**30.52 Explain the factors that contribute to any differences in properties across a welded joint.**

There are several factors that can contribute to property differences across a weld joint. The mechanics of casting, covered in Chapter 10, describes clearly that the weld microstructure, which is essentially a cast microstructure, will not be uniform (see Fig. 30.18a and b) and that the alloy element concentration will vary within the weld. Also, porosity will be present due to entrained gases and shrinkage that may be concentrated in local areas of the weld.

**30.53 Explain why preheating the components to be welded is effective in reducing the likelihood of developing cracks.**

Preheating the components prior to welding is helpful because it reduces thermal stresses which could lead to fracture. Consider that the weld solidifies at the melting temperature of the electrode, which can be over 1400°C for steels. When the molten-metal pool solidifies at this temperature, it is stress-free, but the stresses can begin to develop as it contracts, until the part reaches room temperature. However, if the workpiece is preheated, then it will contract with the weld and the resulting built-up stresses will be lower.

**30.54 Review the poor and good joint designs shown in Fig. 30.29 and explain why they are labeled so.**

By the student. This is an open-ended problem, and various answers are acceptable based on the experience of the students. Students should be encouraged to develop their own answers to this problem. However, examples of acceptable answers are:

- In Fig. 30.29a on p. 973, the loading labeled "Poor" is eccentric and causes a bending moment to the weld; the loading labeled "Good" leads to welds that undergo no stress.
- In (b), the loading has similar effects as in (a).
- In (c), the T-joint on the left is not square, hence it will stress the weld more than a vertical member that is cut square.
- In (d), the burr creates the same type of situation as in (c).
- In (e), the purpose of the design change is to move the welds away from the main body so as to reduce the adverse effect of stress concentration, especially in a location within the heat-affected zone.
- In (f), the design change is to avoid having to machine a weld bead, which can present problems.

**30.55 In building large ships, there is a need to weld large sections of steel together to form a hull. For this application, consider each of the welding operations discussed in this chapter and list the benefits and drawbacks of that particular operation for this application. Which welding process would you select? Why?**

By the student. This is an open-ended problem and the students should be encouraged to develop their own opinions. The following are examples of points that can be made:

- Submerged arc welding can be used for joining some sections but is not suitable for assembly of the sections into the hull.
- Electroslag welding is probably best suited for this application because it can produce very thick and high-quality welds in one pass; however, the setup is complicated.

**30.56 Perform a literature search and describe the relative advantages and limitations of $CO_2$ and Nd:YAG lasers.**

By the student. This is a good topic for students to explore, noting that the advantages and limitations of the two types of lasers will depend on the particular application and materials be welded.

- Advantages of $CO_2$ lasers:
  - $CO_2$ lasers offers high processing speeds due to high average powers (e.g., 2.5 kW).
  - The structure of the $CO_2$ laser beam enhances uniformity of cutting.
  - Enhanced images can be produced by $CO_2$ lasers.
- Disadvantages of $CO_2$ lasers:
  - The mechanical pulsing mechanism in $CO_2$ lasers can make their cutting pattern difficult to control.
  - It is difficult to produce especially fine features.
  - Exposure to the laser beam is a serious hazard.
- Advantages of Nd:YAG lasers:
  - These lasers are capable of producing mirror-finished workpieces.
  - The lasers are much lower in cost and are lower-maintenance systems.
- Disadvantages of Nd:YAG lasers:
  - The structure of the laser beam is more difficult to focus than a $CO_2$ laser.
  - The Nd:YAG rod exhibits energy instabilities, so that pulse strength is not uniform.
  - Pulse frequency is limited to the range of 10 to 20 kHz, which is a relatively low pulse rate.
  - Exposure to the laser beam is a serious hazard to personnel.

**30.57 Inspect various parts and components in an automobile and explain if any of the processes described in this chapters has been used in joining them.**

By the student. There are many examples of welding processes described in this chapter that are used in automobiles. Other examples also can be found, depending on the persistence of students (e.g., whether they would crawl under their car and look up). Much of the structure has been arc welded or gas metal arc welded, depending on whether or not robots were used.

**30.58 Similar to Problem 30.57 but for kitchen utensils and appliances. Are there any major differences between two two types of product lines? Explain.**

By the student. For example, many metallic food or beverage containers are seamed from sheet (see pp. 459 and 1025). Knife blades are riveted or bonded to their handles. Pots and pans may have a number of bonded layers of sheet, which are then deep drawn (see p. 453) and formed to desired final shapes. The reason pots have a number of layers is to combine the desirable properties of various materials; for example, the thermal conductivity of copper with the strength and ease of cleaning of stainless steel. (These layers can be observed by inspecting the bottom of some pots and pans.). Kitchen appliances have similar processes involved, with additional features so that (unlike pots and pans) they can be taken apart for maintenance and repair. The mechanical fastening and assembly systems involved are described in Section 32.5 on p. 1023. These processes are used for these applications because other processes which can be technologically feasible but lack economic, functional, or aesthetic advantages.

**30.59 Make an outline of the general guidelines for safety in welding operations. For each of the operations described in this chapter, prepare a poster which effectively and concisely gives specific instructions for safe practices in welding (or cutting). Review the various publications of the National Safety Council and other similar organizations.**

By the student. This is a valuable study by the students, and the preparation of a poster or a flyer is a good opportunity for students to polish their writing and presentation skills. Safety in Welding is a standard published by the American National Standards Institute (ANSI Z49.1) and describes in detail the safety precautions that must be taken; most of the standards are process-specific. For example, some safety guidelines for shielded metal-arc welding are:

- The operator must wear eye and skin protection against radiation.
- Leather gloves and clothing should be warn to prevent burns from arc spatter.
- Welding should be done in properly ventilated areas, where fresh air is available to workers and the work area is not flooded by shielding gases.
- To prevent electric shock, the welder should not weld while standing on a wet surface.
- The workpiece should be positioned to minimize trauma to the back and arms.

**30.60 Are there common factors affecting the weldability, castability, formability, and machinability of metals? Explain with appropriate examples.**

By the student. Note that there are some common factors, involving physical and mechanical properties, energy requirements, thermal considerations, and warping.

**30.61 If you find a flaw in a welded joint during inspection, how would you go about determining whether the flaw is important?**

By the student. This is a challenging task and will require students to search the literature. Some calculations on flaw behavior and crack propagation in metal structures can be attempted, probably with finite-element methods or by using advanced concepts for crack propagation. Proof-testing is another approach. An understanding of the loads and the resulting stresses often determines whether or not a flaw is important. For example, if the defect is on a weld at the neutral axis of a beam in bending, then the stresses are not likely to be high and the flaw is not likely to be critical. On the other hand, a defect in a highly loaded area or in a stress concentration would raise concerns.

**30.62 Lattice booms for cranes are constructed from extruded cross-sections that are welded together. Any warpage which causes such a boom to deviate from straightness severely reduces its lifting capacity. Perform a literature search on the approaches used to minimize distortion due to welding and to correct it, specifically in the construction of lattice booms.**

By the student. Lattice booms are constructed in typically 20-ft sections, are checked with a caliper (see p. 1089) and, if necessary, are bent to straightness over the length of the section before welding them. This approach results in a section that, after welding, is sufficiently straight to properly support the intended loads. This is assured by making certain that welds are done in a proper sequence and are balanced everywhere on the boom.

**30.63 A common practice in repairing expensive broken or worn parts (such as may occur when a fragment is broken from a forging) is to fill the area with layers of weld bead and then to machine the part back to its original dimensions. Make a list of the precautions that you would suggest to someone who uses this approach.**

By the student. Examples are that the weld bead will have different properties than the substrate, so machining may result in vibration and chatter (Section 25.4). The weld material may cause the cutting tools to wear more quickly. The weld material may fracture during machining and compromise the part strength. The weld material may have insufficient ductility for the application.

**30.64 A welded frame needs first to be disassembled and then to be repaired (by rewelding the members). What procedures would you recommend for disassembly of the frame and in preparation for rewelding?**

By the student. Welded frames are very difficult and costly to disassemble, hence it is not usually done. However, it is possible, for example, to cut off the members at the weld joint with a blow torch, and then rewelding them using reinforcing sleeves or angle irons. The reinforcement usually strengthens the weakened location.

**30.65 Assume that you are asked to give a quiz to students on the contents of this chapter. Prepare three qualitative questions and supply the answers.**

By the student. This is a good, open-ended question that requires considerable focus and understanding on the part of the students, and has been found to be a very valuable homework problem.

# Chapter 31

# Solid-State Welding Processes

## QUALITATIVE PROBLEMS

**31.11 Explain the similarities and differences between the joining processes described in this chapter and those described in Chapter 30.**

By the student. The similarities between the processes described in the two chapters are that they all involve permanent joining by the application of heat and/or pressure. The differences are mainly in the power source and the workpiece shapes involved. Chapter 30 deals with chemical reactions and electrical energy sources (including high-energy beams), whereas Chapter 31 deals additionally predominantly mechanical energy sources, and no filler metal is required. The students are encouraged to make a comprehensive table regarding this topic.

**31.12 Explain the reasons why the processes described in this chapter were developed.**

By the student. Not every joining operation is ideally suited for electric-arc or gas welding (Chapter 30), as can be deduced from the various applications described in this chapter. In addition to technological-feasibility considerations, it can be more economical to weld parts utilizing the processes described in this chapter (see also the Introduction to the chapter). For example, cold welding and roll bonding allow using a lower-cost metal or one with certain specific properties (e.g., thermal conductivity) sandwiched between two more expensive alloys or with different properties (e.g., corrosion resistance). The students are encouraged to describe their own observations.

**31.13 Describe your observations concerning Figs. 31.17c and d.**

By the student. The explosion welding operation results in wavy interfaces (as shown in the figures) due to the very high velocities and the pressures involved. The ripples observed are actually due to stress waves in the interface, and help improve joint strength by mechanical interlocking of the mating surfaces. This is a specialized subject and some students may wish to study and elaborate further as to how these waves are formed and how they affect interfacial strength.

**31.14 Would you be concerned regarding the size of the weld beads shown in Fig. 31.16? Explain.**

The size of the weld beam is important; the microstructure is similar to an as-cast structure as shown in Fig. 30.18 on p. 961. Since large defects can be present in a large weld bead, it is helpful to minimize the size of the bead. However, the more important benefit to a small bead is that less energy has been put into the joint. Thus, the heat-affected zone around the bead will be smaller, and it is this zone that is commonly associated with fatigue failure.

**31.15 Discuss the factors that influence the strength of (a) a diffusion-bonded and (b) a cold-welded component.**

The joint strength in diffusion bonding is influenced by the materials being joined, temperature, pressure, and time; the higher these quantities, the more diffusion will take place and the stronger the joint. The cleanliness of the surfaces is also important to make sure there are no lubricants or oxides present on the mating surfaces to interfere with the diffusion process. For this reason, diffusion-bonded joints are commonly prepared by solvent cleaning and/or pickling to remove oxides (see Section 34.16 on p. 1078). The joint strength in cold welding is similarly influenced by the parameters outlined above, except temperature since the process is carried out at room temperature (although the basic process can also be carried out at elevated temperatures, as has been done traditionally by blacksmiths).

**31.16 Describe the sources of heat for the processes described in this chapter.**

The sources of heat for the processes described in this chapter are primarily due to (a) friction, as in friction welding, (b) chemical reactions, as in explosion and Thermit welding, and (c) electromagnetic waves, as in electron-beam and laser-beam welding). It should be noted, however, that some of the processes described in this chapter do not necessarily involve significant heat (e.g., cold welding and ultrasonic welding), while the heat source in diffusion bonding is external heating of the workpieces.

**31.17 Comment on the feasibility of applying explosion welding in a factory environment.**

By the student. As the name implies, there are obvious concerns with explosion welding (p. 995) because explosives develop very high levels of energy (traditionally used for destructive purposes). The process is an inherently dangerous process and can cause serious injury or death. Furthermore, the impacts (shock) are bound to adversely affect nearby machinery due to shock and vibration transfer via the foundation. See also explosive forming of sheet metals on p. 465.

**31.18 Can the roll-bonding process be applied to a variety of part configurations? Explain.**

Roll bonding (p. 981) is mainly used in flat rolling, although there is no reason why it cannot be used in other applications. The important consideration is that the pressure (normal stress) between the sheets to be joined be sufficiently high. To meet this condition for shapes other than flat is likely to be a difficult task (and involve complex tooling), and any significant variation in pressure during rolling can make the bonded structure unreliable. The student is encouraged to search the literature and attempt to find examples of such applications.

**31.19 Why is diffusion bonding (when combined with superplastic forming of sheet metals) an attractive fabrication process? Does it have any limitations?**

By the student. Diffusion bonding combined with superplastic forming (p. 998) can lead to lightweight, strong aerospace structures and with high stiffness-to-weight ratios, as shown in Fig. 31.19. The main drawback is the long production time and the high costs involved, which may be justified for many aerospace applications. The students are encouraged to find other examples of applications for this process.

**31.20 Describe the features of a weld nugget. What does its strength depend on?**

By the student. Noting that the problem states a weld nugget and not a weld bead, refer to Figs. 31.6b and 31.10 on pp. 987 and 990, respectively, for typical weld nuggets. The students are encouraged to search the literature and collect photographs and more details on weld nuggets. This question can be answered from different viewpoints. Thus, for example, one may consider this question as a stress-analysis problem, whereby the joint strength depends on the size of the nugget, its relationship to the surrounding bodies, and the types of materials welded and their mechanical and physical properties. Here, one should of course consider the role of process parameters such as current, pressure, time, and the nature of the faying surfaces. The students are encouraged to explore this topic further and produce an illustrated table of weld nuggets and add comments to each. It would also be interesting and instructional to find weld nuggets that are poorly made.

**31.21 Make a list of some products that can be fabricated by resistance-welding processes.**

By the student. This is an open-ended problem, and the answer depends on the students' initiative in searching for interesting examples in the technical literature and on the Internet. Typical products involve sheet metals and include welding of automotive bodies, the walls of three-piece cans and various containers for household products, and attaching of handles to metal cookware.

**31.22 Give some of the reasons that spot welding is used commonly in automotive bodies and in home appliances.**

By the student. This is an open-ended problem, and the answer depends on the initiative of students in searching for examples in the technical literature and from the Internet (see also Fig. I.13 on p. 34). The most obvious reasons are that spot welding is economically advantageous over other processes, it is very suitable for assembly of sheet-metal components, and it is fast and is easy to automate.

**31.23 Explain the significance of the magnitude of the pressure applied through the electrodes during a spot-welding operation.**

By the student. This is an open-ended problem, and the students are encouraged to carefully view Fig. 31.6a on p. 987 (and similar figures in other references) and to develop their own answers. It is important to note the relationship between pressure and temperature, as it affects weld strength. Note also that the oxides on the surfaces are to be broken up by plastic deformation of the sheets, thus assuring an intimate contact for developing a strong joint.

**31.24 Give some applications for (a) flash welding, (b) stud welding, and (c) percussion welding.**

By the student. This is an open-ended question and many answers are possible, depending on the experience of the student and the effort they make to find applications. The following are some typical applications of each method:

- Flash welding: band-saw blades, joining the ends of coils (produced in rolling mills), tubular parts in brass beds, railroad and overhead crane rails, and MEMS (see Chapter 29).
- Stud welding: attaching flanges, hangers, and bolts on metal frames, cable hangers, and insulation hangers that attach to metal piping.
- Percussion welding: generally restricted to small electrical components, such as welding silver electrodes to copper contacts in switches. This process has also been investigated for MEMS applications.

**31.25 Discuss the need and role of fixtures in holding of workpieces in the welding operations described in this chapter.**

By the student. See also Problem 30.20. Fixturing is essential for most welding operations because the weld bead requires time to cool and develop full strength. Also, the weld bead will hold the components materials together to acquire the desired alignment. Fixturing is required to make sure the welding operation proceeds as intended.

**31.26 Inspect Fig. 31.4 and explain why those particular fusion-zone shapes are developed, as a function of pressure and speed. Comment on the influence of the material's properties.**

Inspecting the fusion zones in Fig. 31.4 on p. 984, it is obvious that higher forces and speeds both result in more pronounced fusion zones. The relevant material properties are strength and ductility, but also physical properties such as thermal conductivity and specific heat. This is because all materials soften at elevated temperatures and the hotter the interface becomes, the more pronounced the fusion zone. Note that a uniform (optimum) zone can be obtained with proper control of the parameters.

**31.27 Discuss your observations concerning the welding design guidelines illustrated in Fig. 31.14d and e.**

By the student. The two design guidelines shown on p. 993 basically point out that it is desirable to place the welds between uniform cross-sections and away from locations of stress concentration. Note in sketch (e) that constant cross-section is achieved by drilling a hole in the part to the left. (See also Problem 30.48.)

**31.28 Can you friction weld if one of the pieces to be welded is noncircular? Explain, giving some examples.**

By the student. The vast majority of friction-welded parts are axisymmetric, it can be done, but the fixturing must be able to accommodate the parts to be joined. Also, when the parts are upset at their ends, the cross-sections may not produce flash that are even. Some examples include electrical connectors and, although rare, automotive-body panels. Note also that friction stir welding is typically performed on sections as shown in Fig. 31.5 on p. 985.

**31.29 Could the process shown in Fig. 31.12 also be applicable to part shapes other than round? Explain your answer and give specific examples.**

The high-frequency butt welding can be performed on products other than tubes; in fact, it can be performed for any application containing butt joints. Applications include a wide variety of structural shapes, such as I-beams and channels, that are fabricated from flat plates, as well as finned tubes such as for heat exchangers.

**31.30 What applications could be suitable for the roll-spot-welding process shown in Fig. 31.11?**

Roll spot welding is suitable for applications where a pressure-tight seal is not required, but a relatively strong and stiff joint is necessary. Suitable applications include assembling car bodies onto frames, food containers (where compression against a seal is required, but not essential in all designs), and some structural shapes.

**31.31 Survey the available technical literature on friction welding and prepare a table of the similar and dissimilar metals and nonmetallic materials that can be friction-welded.**

By the student. This is an open-ended problem and the students are encouraged to develop their own lists. The following is a subset of the materials that have been friction welded.

- Similar metals: all metallic materials which are forgeable can, as a rule, be friction welded, including automotive valve alloys, maraging steels, tool steels, alloy steels, and tantalum. Many castings, powder metals, and metal-matrix composites are also weldable.
- Dissimilar metals: metal combinations not normally considered compatible can be joined by friction welding, such as aluminum to steel, copper to aluminum, titanium to copper, and nickel alloys to steel. Also, polymers and ceramics can be friction-welded to metals.
- Nonmetallic materials: most thermoplastics can be friction welded. The joining of ceramic parts directly to each other by the friction heating and forging process is not practical. However, certain joint configurations can be joined by using an aluminum interlayer. Ceramics can be friction welded to metals as stated above.

**31.32 Could the projection-welded parts shown in Fig. 31.13 be made by any of the processes described in other chapters in this book? Explain.**

The projection-welded parts shown in Fig. 31.13 on p. 992 could possibly be made through resistance welding, although it would require several strokes, whereas resistance projection welding can produce many nuggets in one stroke. Several processes can produce the parts shown, but the joint strength developed or the economics of the processes may not be as favorable. However, the shape can also be achieved through arc or gas welding processes (followed by grinding if necessary), as well as brazing or soldering (see Chapter 32). With a modified interface, mechanical fastening or adhesive bonding also would be suitable processes.

**31.33 Explain the difference between resistance seam welding and resistance spot welding.**

By the student. The difference between resistance seam welding and resistance spot welding is essentially in the spacing of the weld nuggets. If the nuggets overlap, it is a seam weld; if they do not overlap, it is a spot weld.

**31.34 Referring to Fig. 14.11b, could you use any of the processes described in Chapters 30 and 31 to make a large bolt by welding the head to the shank? Explain the advantages and limitations of this approach.**

By the student. Certainly, processes such as arc welding and gas welding can be used to attach the two components. However, the advantage of friction welding is that the weld is over the entire contact area between the two joined components, instead of a small bead along the periphery of the contact location.

## QUANTITATIVE PROBLEMS

**31.35 Two flat copper sheets (each 1.5 mm thick) are being spot welded by the use of a current of 7000 A and a current flow time of 0.3 s. The electrodes are 5 mm in diameter. Estimate the heat generated in the weld zone. Assume that the resistance is 200 $\mu\Omega$.**

This problem is similar to Example 31.2 on p. 989. We note in Eq. (31.1) on p. 986 that the quantities now are $I = 7000$ A and $t = 0.3$ s. Since the material is copper, its electrical conductivity is higher (hence the resistance is lower) than that for the steel sheet given in the example, thus the assumed value of 200 $\mu\Omega$. Therefore,

$$H = (7000)^2(0.0002)(0.3) = 2940 \text{ J}$$

As in the example, we take the weld nugget volume to be 30 mm$^3$. From Table 3.1 on p. 103, the density of copper is found to be 8970 kg/m$^3$, thus the weld nugget has a mass of 0.27 g. The heat required to melt 1 g of copper is 1550 J; therefore, the heat required to melt the weld nugget is $(1550)(0.27) = 420$ J. The remaining heat (that is, 2940-420 J $= 2520$ J) is dissipated into the volume of metal surrounding the weld nugget.

**31.36 Calculate the temperature rise in Problem 31.35 assuming that the heat generated is confined to the volume of material directly between the two round electrodes and the temperature is distributed uniformly.**

The volume of metal directly under the 5-mm electrodes is $(p)(5^2/4)(2) = 39.3$ mm$^3$, and has a mass of $(39.3)(0.00897) = 0.35$ g $= 0.00035$ kg. The specific heat for copper is 385 J/kgK.

Therefore, the theoretical temperature rise is

$$\Delta T = \frac{2940 \text{ J}}{(385 \text{ J/kgK})(0.00035 \text{ kg})} = 21,800 \text{ K}$$

Note that the melting point of copper is 1082°C (1355 K), so far more energy has been provided than is needed for this small volume. Clearly, in practice, very little of the heat is concentrated in this small volume.

**31.37 Calculate the range of allowable currents for Problem 31.35 if the temperature should be between 0.7 and 0.85 times the melting temperature of copper. Repeat this problem for carbon steel.**

This problem can be interpreted as between 0.7 and 0.85 times the melting temperature on an absolute (Kelvin) or a Celsius temperature scale. This solution will use a Celsius scale, so that the final target temperature is between 765 and 925 °C. Using the same approach as in Problem 31.35, the allowable energy for these cases is 100 and 121 J, respectively. With a resistance of 200 $\mu\Omega$, the currents are 1310 and 1420 A, respectively. The solution for carbon steel is left for the student, but uses the same approach.

**31.38 The energy applied in friction welding is given by the formula $E = IS^2/C$, where $I$ is the moment of inertia of the flywheel, $S$ is the spindle speed in rpm, and $C$ is a constant of proportionality (5873, when the moment of inertia is given in lb-ft$^2$). For a spindle speed of 600 rpm and an operation in which a steel tube (3.5 in. OD, 0.25 in. wall thickness) is welded to a flat frame, what is the required moment of inertia of the flywheel if all of the energy is used to heat the weld zone (approximated as the material in. deep and directly below the tube)? Assume that 1.4 ft-lbm is needed to melt the electrode.**

The volume of the weld metal for this case is

$$V = \frac{\pi}{4}\left(d_o^2 - d_i^2\right) h = \frac{\pi}{4}\left(3.5^2 - 3^2\right)(0.25) = 0.638 \text{ in}^3$$

If the electrode has the same density as steel, which from Table 3.1 on p. 103 is 6290 kg/m$^3$ (or 0.227 lbm/in$^3$), then this represents 0.144 lb of electrode; thus the input energy is 0.20 ft-lb. Therefore, the flywheel inertia can be calculated as:

$$E = \frac{IS^2}{C} \quad \rightarrow \quad I = \frac{EC}{S^2} = \frac{(0.2)(5873)}{(600)^2} = 0.0033 \text{ lb-ft}^2$$

**31.39 The energy required in ultrasonic welding is known to be related to the product of the thickness and hardness of the workpiece. Explain why this relationship exists.**

The energy in ultrasonic welding is needed to induce localized heating at the asperities of the surfaces to be joined. Consider each of these parameters: If the workpiece thickness is large, then the workpiece has a comparatively large mass and this large mass must be vibrated to obtain relative motion at the contacting asperities. If the hardness is high, then the real contact area will be small (see Section 33.4 on p. 1043), and the heating will be localized at individual contact patches. A low hardness results in higher fractional contact areas and, therefore, more uniform heating of the interface.

## SYNTHESIS, DESIGN, AND PROJECTS

**31.40 Explain how you would fabricate the structures shown in Fig. 31.19 by methods other than diffusion bonding and superplastic forming.**

By the student. If diffusion bonding cannot be used, one may employ processes such as spot welding or the processes described in Chapter 32 such as adhesive bonding, brazing, and mechanical joining.

**31.41 Comment on workpiece size and shape limitations (if any) for each of the processes described in this chapter.**

By the student. This is an open-ended question, and the students are encouraged to develop their own answers which deviate from the answer here. There are limitations that are often associated with fixturing requirements. Roll bonding is generally used with sheet metals, so parts that do not involve thin layers are difficult to roll bond. Ultrasonic welding is typically restricted to thin foils. Friction welding requires parts that can be mounted into chucks or similar fixtures. Explosion welding is restricted to thick plates, thus thin sheets would not be processed in this manner.

**31.42 Describe part shapes that cannot be joined by the processes described in this chapter. Gives specific examples.**

By the student. This is an open-ended problem with many possible answers. The students are encouraged to develop their own answers based on their experience and training. For example, friction stir welding can be suitable for most geometries as long as the material is aluminum or other similar materials. (This process has not been used to weld steels to date.) If the steel part is a thin-walled tube, it will not be able to withstand the high axial loads involved in friction welding or inertia friction welding.

**31.43 Prepare a table giving the welding speeds (as a function of the relevant parameters) for the processes described in Chapters 30 and 31. Comment on your observations.**

By the student. This is a good problem for students, but can be rather demanding because such extensive data is rarely given, except with a wide range or only for a particular material. Consequently, it can be difficult to compare the processes. Although this difficulty should be explained to the students, they nevertheless should be encouraged to develop such a list as best they can.

**31.44 Make a comprehensive outline of this chapter; include sketches of possible welded-joint designs (other than those given) and of their engineering applications. Give specific examples for each type of joint.**

By the student. Our experience in teaching such a course has been that this type of problem is especially useful because it forces the student to organize their thoughts on classifying the numerous welding processes. The contents on p. 980 are a useful starting point, from which the student can fill in the remaining data. This presentation can also be done as a poster.

**31.45 Using a magnifier, inspect the cross-section of coins (such as the U.S. dime and nickel) and comment on your observations.**

By the student. This is a useful problem to demonstrate the significance of cold welding (see Example 31.1 on p. 982). An example side-view of a U.S. quarter is shown below. Note that the center is a copper alloy; the outer layers are a nickel-based alloy. Coins such as pennies and nickels are typically made of one material (see also Example I.3 on p. 18). The following observations may be made about the coins:

- The core is used to obtain the proper weight and feel, as well as sound.
- The strength of cold-welded joints is very high, as confirmed by the experience with coins in circulation that one never encounters coins that have peeled apart.
- The outer layers, which are made of the more expensive alloy, are thin for cost reduction.

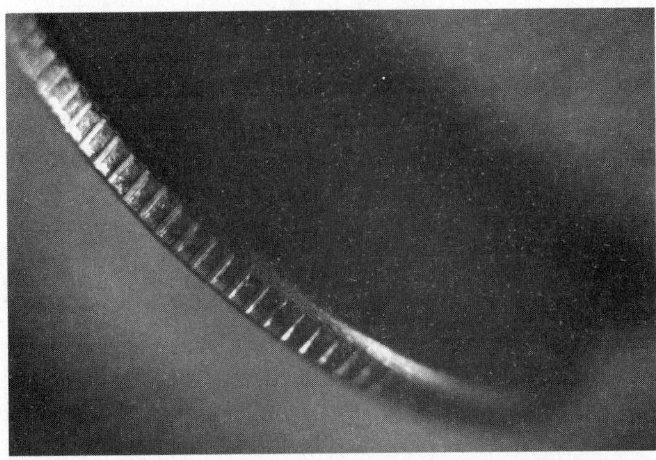

**31.46 In spot-weld tests, what would be the reason for weld failure to occur at the locations shown in Fig. 31.10?**

By the student. The students can analyze these failures by first noting the initial and the deformed shapes of the specimens in these tests. In Fig. 31.10a on p. 990, for example, note that the sheets undergo deformation (because of the force couple present). Thus, the weld is subjected to a combination of a shear force and a bending moment. Failure occurs where the tensile stress (due to bending) is highest, and it propagates across the weld. This situation is also true for tests (b) and (d). Failure in (c) occurs due to the torque on the weld, which shears it along its periphery.

**31.47 Describe the methods you would use for removing the flash from welds, such as those shown in Fig. 31.3. How would you automate these methods for high production rates?**

By the student. This topic would make a fine project for students, noting that there can be various methods to remove the flash from welds, and that the appropriate method would depend on the number of parts. For example, flash removal can be done simply by turning on a lathe; however, turning is in general a low-volume operation but it can be automated, as described in Section 23.3 on p. 686. The flash can also be removed by cylindrical grinding, in a manner similar to those shown in Fig. 26.16 on p. 811, with the welded pieces held in special fixtures. Shearing the flash is a possibility (see, for example, Fig. 14.8 on p. 378), but this method would present difficulties in fixturing the part and producing an acceptable sheared surface.

**31.48 For each of the operations described in this chapter, prepare a poster which effectively and concisely gives specific instructions for safe practices in welding. Consult various publications of the National Safety Council and similar organizations.**

By the student. This is a valuable experience for students. (Note that this problem is similar to Problem 30.59 and requires the same considerations.)

**31.49 In the roll-bonding process shown in Fig. 31.1, how would you go about ensuring that the interfaces are clean and free of contaminants so that a good bond is developed? Explain.**

By the student. Refer also to Section 34.16 on p. 1078. This is a major challenge in roll bonding. Students are encouraged to perform a literature search for particular approaches. The basic procedure has been to (a) wire brushing the surfaces, which removes oxide from the surfaces, and (b) solvent cleaning, which removes residues and organic films from the surface.

**31.50 Inspect several metal containers for household products and for food and beverages. Identify those that have utilized any of the processes described in this chapter. Describe your observations.**

By the student. This is an interesting project for the students. It will be noted that some food or beverage containers are three-piece cans, with a welded seam along the length of the can. These containers are typically used for shaving cream, laundry starch sprays, and various spray cans for paints and other products. Laser-beam welding has been used on shaving razors (see Fig. 30.15 on p. 958) and resistance welding on grills for refrigerators and barbecue grills.

**31.51 Discuss various other processes that can be used in attaching tubes to head plates in boilers.**

By the student. This is an open-ended problem, and various answers are possible, including:

- Shielded metal arc welding can be performed around the periphery of the tube.
- Brazing (described in Section 32.2) can be used.
- Friction welding (including friction stir welding) and laser-beam welding can be used if the part geometry allows it.

**31.52 Describe part designs that cannot be joined by any of the friction-welding processes described in this chapter.**

By the student. Note that friction welding can be suitable for most geometries, including one of the parts not being symmetric. However, if the part is, for example, a thin-walled tube, it may not be able to support the large axial loads involved in this process. The students are encouraged to explore this topic further.

**31.53 Inspect the sheet-metal body of an automobile, and comment on the size and frequency of the spot welds applied. How would you go about estimating the number of welds?**

By the student. This is an interesting topic for students to investigate. It should be relatively easy to inspect the size and and estimate the number of spot welds in the assembled sheet-metal automobile body components. A literature search would also be helpful. Note also the statement on p. 988 that automobile bodies can have as many as 10,000 spot welds.

**31.54 Alclad stock is made from 5182 aluminum alloy and has both sides coated with a thin layer of pure aluminum. The 5182 provides high strength, while the outside layers of pure aluminum provide good corrosion resistance because of their stable oxide film. Hence, Alclad is commonly used in aerospace structural applications. Investigate other common roll-bonded materials and their uses, and prepare a summary table.**

By the student. This could be a challenging project for students. Examples include coinage and a thin coating of metals on workpieces where the coating serves as a metalworking lubricant (see p. 1054).

**31.55 Perform an Internet survey of available spot-welding machines, their capabilities, and their costs. Describe your observations.**

By the student. It will be noted that some spot welding machines are intended for incorporation into automated systems with robotic controls (as in automotive-body assembly; see Fig. I.13 on p. 34). Other machines are manual, for use in shops and small manufacturing facilities.

**31.56 What kind of applications could the structures shown in Fig. 31.19b and c have? Explain.**

By the student. These structures are lightweight but have a very large moment of inertia. Therefore, they are ideal for such applications as floors on aircraft, elevators and the like where weight reduction is important and structural stiffness must be high (see also Problem 31.19). The students are encouraged to explore this important topic further.

# Chapter 32

# Brazing, Soldering, Adhesive Bonding, and Mechanical-Fastening Processes

## QUALITATIVE PROBLEMS

**32.15 Comment on your observations concerning the joints shown in Figs. 32.3 and 32.6.**

By the student. It can readily be seen that it is desirable to have a large contact area between the components for high brazed-joint strength. It will also be noted that the area can be increased by various design changes.

**32.16 How different is adhesive bonding from other joining methods? What limitations does it have?**

By the student. Some obvious differences are the type of materials used, the levels of temperatures required (if any) for the adhesive to develop full strength, and the joint designs. The major limitations of adhesive bonding are the lack of high strength (as, for example, compared to welded joints and mechanical fastening) and the low peel strength (see p. 1018). It should be pointed out that these limitations can be countered by special joint designs.

**32.17 Discuss the need for fixtures for holding workpieces in the joining processes described in this chapter.**

By the student. Refer also to Problems 30.20 and 31.25. Fixtures are generally required for the processes described in this chapter, except in some mechanical fastening operations. Fixture are, for example, needed in some adhesive-bonding operations that require time for curing, as the workpieces may shift or sag during bonding. Interestingly, adhesives are used to hold components together so that welding or equivalent can take place; an adhesive bond serves very well as a fixture in such cases. An example is in reflow soldering of components onto a circuit board, where the component is adhesively bonded to the board and held in place until the paste solder is heated in a furnace and flows onto the leads.

**32.18 Soldering is generally applied to thinner components. Explain why.**

Solders have lower strength than braze metal fillers or weld beads. Therefore, if one is joining members that have to support significant loads (typical of joined members with large thickness), one would normally consider welding, brazing, or mechanical fastening, but not soldering. Soldering is generally applied to joining thin components because much lower temperatures than brazing or welding are required, so that one does not have to be concerned about the workpiece melting due to excessive heating or warping in the joint area.

**32.19 Explain why adhesively bonded joints tend to be weak in peeling.**

Adhesives are weak in peeling because there is a concentrated, high tensile-stress at the tip of the joint when being peeled (see Fig. 32.9 on p. 1018); consequently, their low tensile strength reduces the peeling forces. Note, however, that tougher adhesives require considerable force and energy to peel, as can be appreciated when trying to peel off adhesive tapes. (Recall that this situation is somewhat analogous to crack initiation and propagation in metals under tensile stresses; see Section 2.10 on p. 87.)

**32.20 It is common practice to tin plate electrical terminals to facilitate soldering. Why is it tin that is used?**

Since the solders are usually lead-tin alloys (see p. 1009 and also note the developments in lead-free solders), the surface tension of the tin and the solder will be very low, thus allowing good wetting of the surfaces. Also, since tin is not dissimilar from the solder, it will adhere well and form a good joint.

**32.21 How important is a close fit for two parts that are to be brazed?**

Close fit is important (see Fig. 32.4 on p. 1007); however, it should not be too close because then the braze material may not fully penetrate the joint interface. It should also be noted that a poor fit (such as a rough or wavy interface) will similarly prevent proper penetration. (See also p. 1009.)

**32.22 If you are designing a joint that needs to be strong and yet needs to be disassembled a few times during the product life, what kind of joint would you use? Explain.**

By the student. Disassembly is a difficult feature to assess when using joining methods (see also Section I.3 on p. 14 and p. 1185). If the part has to be disassembled often, bolted connections are likely be the best solution, or else a quick-disconnect clamp or similar devices should be used. If the number of disassemblies over the lifetime of the part is limited (such as automobile dashboards), integrated snap fasteners (see Fig. 32.19 on p. 1026) and even soldering or brazing can be options. However, soldering and brazing are only suitable if the filler metal can be melted without damaging the joint, and if the joint can be resoldered.

**32.23 Loctite® is an adhesive used to keep bolts from vibrating loose; it basically glues the bolt to the nut and threaded hole. Explain how it functions.**

Loctite® is an anaerobic adhesive (see Table 32.4 on p. 1016), meaning that it cures in the absence of oxygen, hence it does not solidify in air. Such a situation exists in the interfaces between threaded fasteners and their nuts, as well as pins and sleeves, so that the adhesive can be applied to the threaded fastener and it does not cure until assembled.

## QUANTITATIVE PROBLEMS

**32.24 Refer to the simple butt and lap joints shown in the top left of Fig. 32.10. (a) Assuming the area of the butt joint is 3 mm x 20 mm and referring to the adhesive properties given in Table 32.3, estimate the minimum and maximum tensile force that this joint can withstand. (b) Estimate these forces for the lap joint assuming that its area is 15 mm x 15 mm.**

Referring to Table 32.3 on p. 1015, we note that the lowest adhesive strength given is for epoxy or polyurethane at 15.4 MPa, and the highest tension-shear strength is for modified acrylic at 25.9 MPa. These values will be used in the solution below.

(a) For a butt joint, and assuming there is strong adhesion between the adhesive and work-piece, the full strength of the adhesive can be developed. In this case, we can calculate the required load-bearing area as

$$A = (3)(20) = 60 \text{ mm}^2 = 6.0 \times 10^{-5} \text{ m}^2$$

Consequently, we have

$$F_{\text{min}} = (15.4 \times 10^6)(6.0 \times 10^{-5}) = 924 \text{ N}$$

and

$$F_{\text{max}} = (25.9 \times 10^6)(6.0 \times 10{-}5) = 1554 \text{ N}$$

(b) For the lap joint, we similarly obtain $A = (15)(15) = 225 \text{ mm}^2 = 2.25 \times 10^{-4} \text{ m}^2$. Note that in this case, the joint is loaded in shear, and the shear strength is one-half the tensile strength, as discussed in courses on mechanics of solids. Therefore,

$$F_{\text{min}} = \frac{1}{2}\left(15.4 \times 10^6\right)\left(2.25 \times 10^{-4}\right) = 1730 \text{ N}$$

$$F_{\text{max}} = \frac{1}{2}\left(25.9 \times 10^6\right)\left(2.25 \times 10^{-4}\right) = 2910 \text{ N}$$

**32.25 In Fig. 32.12a, assume that the cross-section of the lap joint is 20 mm x 20 mm, and that the solid rivet diameter is 5 mm and it is made of copper. Using the**

**strongest adhesive shown in Table 32.3, estimate the maximum tensile force that this joint can withstand.**

In this solution, we calculate each component for the maximum force from the rivet and from the adhesive, then combine them based on the principle of superposition.

(a) Copper rivet: The cross-sectional area is

$$A = \frac{\pi}{4}(5 \text{ mm})^2 = 19.6 \text{ mm}^2 = 1.96 \times 10^{-5} \text{ m}^2$$

From Table 6.6 on p. 177, we can take UTS = 220 MPa. Noting that in shear the material strength is one-half that in tension, we can calculate:

$$F_{\text{min}} = \frac{1}{2}\left(220 \times 10^6\right)\left(1.96 \times 10^{-5}\right) = 2160 \text{ N}$$

(b) Adhesive: We select the modified acrylic because it is the strongest adhesive given in Table 32.3 on p. 1015. Therefore, UTS = 25.9 MPa. The area, $A$, of the adhesive is

$$A = (20)(20) - 19.6 \text{ mm}^2 = 380.4 \text{ mm}^2 = 3.80 \times 10^{-4} \text{ m}^2$$

Therefore, the force carried by the adhesive is

$$F_{\text{min}} = \frac{1}{2}\left(25.9 \times 10^6\right)\left(3.80 \times 10^{-4}\right) = 4920 \text{ N}$$

The total force is then

$$F = 2160 + 4920 = 7080 \text{ N}$$

**32.26 As shown in Fig. 35.15a, a rivet can buckle if it is too long. Referring to Chapter 14 on forging, determine the maximum length-to-diameter ratio of a rivet so that it would not buckle during riveting.**

The riveting process is very similar to heading, for which design rules are described on p. 380 and illustrated in Fig. 14.11 on p. 381. Basically, the design requirement is that the length-to-diameter ratio should be 3 or less. If the heading tool has a controlled geometry, a longer length can be accommodated if the head diameter is not more than 1.5 times the shank diameter.

**32.27 Figure 32.4 shows qualitatively the tensile and shear strength in brazing as a function of joint clearance. Search the technical literature, obtain data, and plot these curves quantitatively. Comment on your observations.**

By the student. A number of different curves are available depending on the materials involved. The curves will very much look like Fig. 32.4.

## SYNTHESIS, DESIGN, AND PROJECTS

**32.28 Examine various household products and describe how their components are joined and assembled. Explain why those particular processes were used.**

By the student. Metallic food containers are generally seamed from sheet (see p. 1025). Knife blades are often riveted/bonded to their handles (see p. 372). Some pots have a number of cold-welded layers of sheet, which are then deep drawn and formed to desired shapes. The reason pots have a number of layers is to combine the desirable qualities of a number of materials; for example, the high thermal conductivity of copper with the strength and ease of cleaning of stainless steel. Handles on pots and pans are typically spot welded, riveted, or assembled with threaded fasteners. All of these processes are used because other processes are technologically feasible but lack economic, functional, or aesthetic advantages.

**32.29 Name several products that have been assembled by (a) seaming, (b) stitching, and (c) soldering.**

By the student. Examples of products (a) assembled by seaming are food containers and tops of beverage cans, (b) made through stitching are cardboard and wooden boxes, insulation and other construction materials, and footwear, and (c) soldered parts are electrical components such as diodes attached to circuit boards, pipe fittings, and electrical terminals.

**32.30 Suggest methods of attaching a round bar (made of a thermosetting plastic) perpendicularly to a flat metal plate. Discuss their strengths.**

By the student. One can attach the plastic rod to the plate by a number of methods, including:

(a) Threading the end of the rod, drilling and tapping a hole into the plate, and screwing the rod in, using lock-titeR if necessary.

(b) Performing a shrink fit, where the metal is drilled, heated, and the plastic rod is inserted; as the metal cools, it contracts, binding against the rod.

(c) Fittings, such as those used in scaffolding, can be employed.

(d) The rod may be riveted in place.

**32.31 Describe the tooling and equipment that are necessary to perform the double-lock seaming operation shown in Fig. 32.17. Start with a flat sheet.**

With the guidance of the instructor, the students should be able to describe designs and equipment that are necessary for performing this operation. Some of the references given in the Bibliography in Chapter 16 will also be helpful.

**32.32 Prepare a list of design guidelines for joining by the processes described in this chapter. Would these guidelines be common to most processes? Explain.**

By the student. The list can be generated by reviewing handbooks such as those cited in the Bibliography. A good starting point for students is to examine the design rules in Sections 34.4.4 on p. 1019 and 32.5.2 on p. 1026.

**32.33 What joining methods would be suitable for assembling a thermoplastic cover over a metal frame? Assume that the cover is removed periodically, like the top of a coffee can.**

By the student. Because the cover has to be removed periodically, the most feasible joining method is simply snapping the lid on, as is done on numerous food products such as shortening or coffee cans. The tight sealing is due to the elastic recovery of the lid after it is stretched over the periphery of the top of the metal or glass container.

**32.34 Answer Problem 32.33, but for a cover made of (a) a thermoset, (b) a metal, and (c) a ceramic. Describe the factors involved in your selection of methods.**

By the student. (a) Snap fastening may be an option for a thermoset cover; a threaded connection could also be used. (b) Metallic lids can be press fit over the container or be attached with threaded fasteners. (c) Ceramics can be press fit or attached using clamps or threaded joints.

**32.35 Comment on workpiece size and shape limitations (if any) for each of the processes described in this chapter.**

By the student. This topic will be a good project. There really are no large parts that cannot be accommodated in these processes. Small parts may be more delicate and hence will require careful handling. Leads for electronic components are generally soldered; the wires are typically much smaller than one mm in diameter.

**32.36 Describe part shapes that cannot be joined by the processes explained in this chapter. Give specific examples.**

By the student. Diamond is difficult to adhesively bond to jewelry (and may not be reliable to do so as it is exposed to various environments), hence it is usually mounted with an interference (mechanical) fit. Structural steels for building frames require strong and reliable welds and, except mechanical fastening (using bolts and rivets), could not utilize the processes described in this chapter.

**32.37 Describe the similarities and differences between the processes described in this chapter and those described in Chapters 30 and 31.**

By the student. Similarities between the processes include the use of fillers (weld metal versus adhesive), the use of heat and pressure, and the requirements for various fixtures. Differences include the specific materials used, the use of electrical arcs in welding only, and the inability of adhesives to withstand peeling forces (which is not a concern with welded joint).

**32.38 Give examples of products in which rivets in a structure or assembly may have to be removed and later replaced by new rivets.**

By the student. Rivets generally are not designed to be removed. Rivets may, however, have to be removed, such as in dismantling steel frames and structures. This can be done by chiseling the rivet head or by drilling it out. In applications such as aircraft where rivets are of suspect strength, a reinforcing patch material is placed over the suspect area, just as a patch is applied to torn cloth. The patch reinforces the area without the need to remove rivets.

**32.39 Using the Internet, investigate the geometry of the heads of screws that are permanent fasteners - that is, ones that can be screwed in but not out.**

By the student. These heads usually present a straight vertical surface for the screwdriver in one direction, but a curved surface in the opposite direction, so that a screwdriver simply slips when turned counterclockwise and is not effective for unscrewing. The sketch on the left was obtained from www.k-mac-fasteners.com, while the photo on the right was obtained from www.storesonline.com.

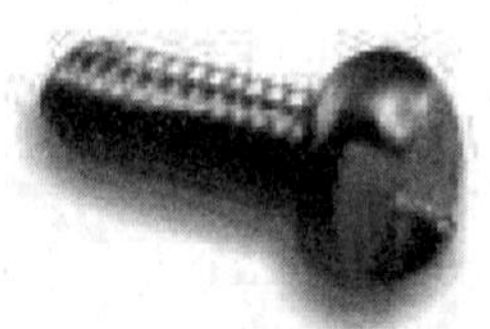

**32.40 Obtain a soldering iron and attempt to solder two wires together. First, try to apply the solder at the same time as you first put the soldering iron tip to the wires. Second, preheat the wires before applying the solder. Repeat the same procedure for a cool surface and a heated surface. Record your results and explain your findings.**

By the student. This is a valuable and inexpensive laboratory experience, and shows the importance of surface tension. With cold wires, molten solder has high surface tension against the wires, and the solder does not wet the surface. At elevated temperatures, the solder has low surface tension and the solder coats the wire surfaces very effectively. Students can be asked to examine this phenomenon further by placing a small piece of solder of known volume (it can be measured in a precision scale) on a steel plate section. When heated, the solder spreads according to the surface temperature of the steel. It will be noted that above a threshold value, the solder will flow freely and coat the surface.

**32.41 Perform a literature search to determine the properties and types of adhesives used to affix artificial hips onto the human femur.**

By the student. Refer also to Example I.5 on p. 26. Sometimes an adhesive is used, but with some designs this is not necessary, as they rely upon *osteointegration* or bone-ingrowth to affix the implant. Usually the cement is polymethylmethacrylate (see acrylics on p. 2-8), or "bone cement," or hydroxyapetite polymer. New materials are constantly being developed and a number of variations can be found in the literature and through an Internet search. A common trend is to develop cements from calcium phosphates, as these are closer matches to the mineral content of bone.

**32.42 Using two strips of steel 1 in. wide and 8 in. long, design and fabricate a joint which gives the highest strength in a tension test in the longitudinal direction.**

By the student. This is a challenging problem and an experimental project as well; it could also be made into a contest among students. It must be noted, however, that the thickness of the strips is not given in the statement of the problem (although the word strip generally indicates a thin material; see Fig. 13.1 on p. 348). The thickness is a factor that students should realize and point out, and supply their answers accordingly. It can also be seen that most of the processes described in Chapters 30 through 32 can be used for such a joint.

Consequently, a wide variety of processes and designs should be considered, thus the response to this question can be extensive.

Using a single bolt through the two strips, for example, it should be apparent that if the bolt diameter is too large, the stresses in the rest of the cross-section may be too high, causing it to fail prematurely. If, on the other hand, the bolt diameter is too small, it will easily shear off under the applied tensile force. Thus, there has to be an optimum to bolt size. The students are encouraged to consider multiple-bolt designs as well as a host of other processes (singly or in combination, as shown in Fig. 32.12).

# Chapter 33

# Surface Roughness and Measurement; Friction, Wear and Lubrication

## QUALITATIVE PROBLEMS

**33.12 Give several examples that show the importance of friction in manufacturing processes.**

By the student. This is an open-ended problem and there are a number of ways of viewing this problem. One can consider situations where friction is present but generally undesired, like in machining, forging, extrusion, or sheet-metal forming. On the other hand, there are operations such as all forms of rolling where some friction is necessary to make the process possible. One can also consider the workpiece features such as surface roughness that then yield desired friction. Also, in friction welding friction between the two members is essential for the process to be successful, and a regulating wheel in centerless grinding needs friction to feed workpieces through the grinding zone. All fixtures and workholding devices need friction as well.

**33.13 What is the significance of the fact that hardness of metal oxides is generally much higher than the base metals themselves?**

This situation would indicate that the hard, oxidized surface can be abrasive when in intimate contact and sliding against another surface, especially if it is softer, as well as against tool and die surfaces. Furthermore, the oxidized surface can, over a period of time, be depleted of hard oxide particles, depending on the contact stress levels and the strength and ductility of the oxidized layer. This, in turn, causes abrasive wear between sliding bodies (causing severe surface damage), known as three-body wear where the third body is the loose oxide particles.

.

**33.14 What factors would you consider in specifying the lay of a surface for a part?**

By the student. Specifying the lay of a surface (see Fig. 33.2b on p. 1039) requires considerations such as the nature of the mating surfaces, direction of sliding, frictional, lubricants and their entrapment, and factors such as appearance and reflectivity of the surface.

**33.15 Explain why identical surface-roughness values do not necessarily represent the same type of surface.**

As can be seen in the figure below [obtained from Hamrock, Schmid and Jacobson, *Fundamentals of Fluid Film Lubrication*, 2nd ed., Marcel-Dekker, 2005, p. 49], there are numerous different surface profiles (as produced by different manufacturing and finishing processes) that could give the same arithmetic mean value, $R_a$, or the root-mean-square roughness, $R_q$. (See also Problem 33.29.) The equations for surface roughness (see p. 1040) represent averages; since the surfaces shown below have a wide range of values for the ordinates a, b, c, etc., it is quite possible that, when they are substituted into the two equations, the averages will be the same.

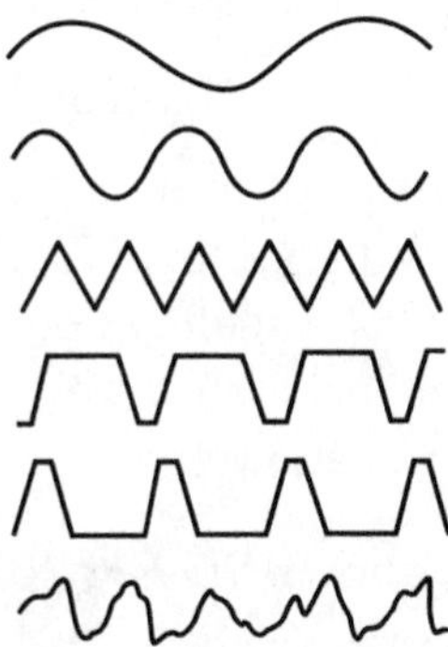

**33.16 How does the wear of molds, tools, and dies affect a manufacturing operation?**

By the student. As in most applications, wear of tools and dies is detrimental. Wear is a progressive loss of material, and hence the more wear, the more the die or tool profile will deviate from its original profile. Thus, the parts produced will become larger and perhaps eventually out of specification. Sometimes this is less influence than others. For example, the use of a wear land in wire drawing or blocking stages in a forging operation can lead to longer tool and die life.

**33.17 Comment on the surface roughness of various parts and components with which you are familiar.**

By the student. The students are encouraged to select a variety of parts and make comments such as, for example: (a) Aluminum foils have one surface that is shiny and the other rough. (b) Stainless-steel pots and pans are shiny, whereas aluminum ones are duller and rougher, as are cast-iron skillets. (c) Ball-bearings are typically shiny, yet piston-rings have rougher surfaces. (d) Reinforced-plastic boat hulls are shinier, but plastic housings for computers and various office equipment have dull surfaces. Note also the importance of not specifying surface roughness on a component any smoother than technologically necessary, since this could add significantly to product cost.

**33.18 What is the significance of the fact that the path of the stylus and the actual profile of the surface are not necessarily the same?**

This situation indicates that profilometer traces are not exact duplicates of actual surfaces and that such readings can be misleading for precise study of surfaces. For example, surfaces with deep narrow valleys will measure smoother than they really are. This can have significant effects on estimating fatigue life, corrosion, friction, wear, and proper assessment of the capabilities of various manufacturing processes described throughout this book.

**33.19 Give two examples for each category in which surface waviness would be (a) desirable and (b) undesirable.**

By the student. This is an open-ended question and the students are encouraged to develop their own answers based on their experience. Waviness would be desirable, for example, for aesthetic and decorative reasons, as well as a means for entrapping lubricants in interfaces. On the other hand, in most applications waviness is generally undesirable, such as mirrors, sheet-metal parts, and for mating interfaces as in airtight containers.

**33.20 Same as Problem 33.19 but for surface roughness.**

By the student. This is an open-ended question and the students are encouraged to develop their own answers based on their experience. A high surface roughness is desirable for applications requiring high friction, such as for safety flooring, or for parts where surface appearance is unimportant, such as cast-iron weights for weightlifting. Smooth surface finish is required for bearings, mirrors, optics, or some jewelry.

**33.21 For each of the surface lays shown in Fig. 33.2b, give an example of a manufacturing process which will produce that lay.**

By the student. Some examples are as follows: (a) Linear lay: turning, peripheral milling, surface grinding, belt grinding. (b) Angular lay: knurling. (c) Pitted: sand casting, shot blasting. (d) Circular: sawing, cutting off, face milling, rotary table grinding.

**33.22 Give several reasons why an originally round specimen in a ring-compression test may become oval after it is upset.**

The specimen may become oval for reasons such as:

(a) anisotropy of the workpiece material,

(b) the lay of the specimen surfaces, thus affecting frictional characteristics,

(c) the lay on the surfaces of the flat platens (dies) employed,

(d) uneven lubricant layer over the mating surfaces, and

(e) lack of symmetry of the test setup, such as platens that are not parallel.

**33.23 Explain how a shoe horn (metal or plastic) facilitates the process of putting on shoes.**

By the student. A shoe horn functions by (a) reducing friction between the back of the shoe and the heel or sock, (b) providing a wedge action, forcing the foot into the shoe, and (c) supporting the back of the shoe to permit a heel to be squeezed inward. Students should also note that shoe horns are made of various materials, including metal, plastic, wood, and from animal horns (from which the name shoe horn is derived).

**33.24 Describe what takes place in the running-in process.**

In running in, material from the peaks on the surface are removed (for a similar situation, see Fig. 33.4 on p. 1041), thus making the surface smoother. Running in is often accelerated by using chemically-reactive additives in lubricants (see p. 1053) for a run-in period, whereby the asperity peaks are attacked chemically and mechanically, producing very smooth surfaces.

**33.25 Why is the abrasive-wear resistance of a material a function of its hardness?**

Higher hardness means greater resistance to indentation (see pp. 80-81), hence less penetration of the abrasive particles or hard protrusions on the surface. The grooves produced will not be as deep and thus the volume of abrasive wear will be less. Hence, abrasive wear is a function of material hardness. This phenomenon can easily be observed by sanding soft materials, such as lead, versus hard materials such as steels. Before the proliferation of CAD software, draftsmen used pencils with a variety of hardnesses, and the volume of material transferred can be clearly shown to be related to the hardness for these pencils. Such pencils can still be obtained in art or office supply stores and this is a valuable demonstration.

**33.26 Make a list of parts and components in consumer and industrial products that have to be replaced because of wear.**

By the student. This is an open-ended problem that can have various answers, depending on the students experience and diligence in researching for applications. Typical examples will include brake shoes and pads, tires, belts, chalk, erasers, leads for mechanical pencils, shoe soles, drill bits, grinding wheels, and clothing. It should also be noted that original parts replacement at all levels is a very major industry.

**33.27 List manufacturing operations where high friction is desirable and those where low friction is desirable.**

By the student. Refer also to Problem 33.12. Noting that the terms high friction and low friction are relative, some examples are:

(a) The rolling operation (p. 349) cannot take place unless there is some friction between the workpiece and the rolls. However, if friction is high, roll forces and power will also be high; and if too low, the rolls will begin to slip.

(b) Friction welding (p. 983) must obviously have friction to be successful.

(c) The regulating wheel in centerless grinding supplies friction to feed workpieces through the grinding zone (p. 814).

(d) All fixtures need friction as well.

The students are encouraged to review all manufacturing processes to give other examples.

## QUANTITATIVE PROBLEMS

**33.28 Figure 33.1 shows various layers in the surface structure of metals. Consult the Bibliography at the end of this chapter and obtain data on the range of thicknesses for each of these layers. Comment on your observations.**

By the student. Although Fig. 33.1 on p. 1037 gives a general range of the thickness of these layers, the purpose of this question is to encourage students to search the literature and obtain more information on this topic. (See, for example, B. Bhushan, *Principles and Applications of Tribology*, 1999, p. 10.)

**33.29 Refer to the profile shown in Fig. 33.3 and place some reasonable numerical values for the vertical distances from the center line. Calculate the $R_a$ and $R_q$ values. Then, give another set of values for the same general profile and calculate the same two quantities. Comment on your observations.**

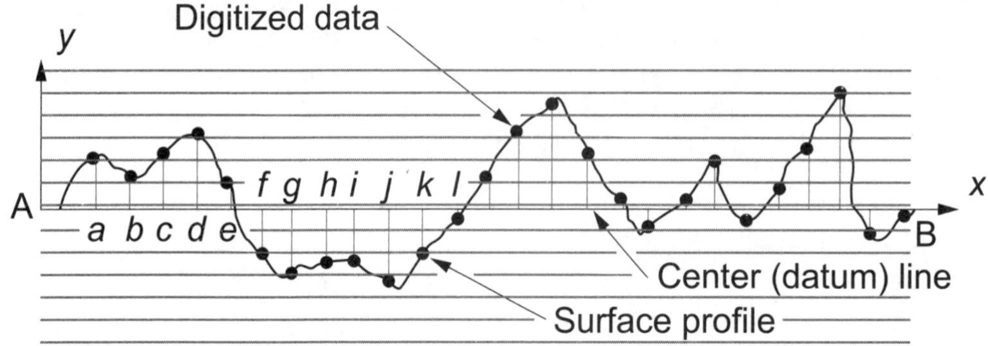


Horizontal lines have been added to the figure above so that the students can judge the accuracy of the estimated dimensions. The following data was used in the calculations:

| Point | Value | Point | Value | Point | Value |
|---|---|---|---|---|---|
| $a$ | 22.0 | $j$ | -33.2 | $s$ | 4.5 |
| $b$ | 15.0 | $k$ | -19.8 | $t$ | 21.9 |
| $c$ | 24.9 | $l$ | -4.2 | $u$ | 6.1 |
| $d$ | 33.8 | $m$ | 13.7 | $v$ | 10.1 |
| $e$ | 11.1 | $n$ | 35.1 | $w$ | 24.9 |
| $f$ | -19.9 | $o$ | 46.1 | $x$ | 49.6 |
| $g$ | -30.2 | $p$ | 24.8 | $y$ | -11.1 |
| $h$ | -23.9 | $q$ | 1.3 | $z$ | -3.1 |
| $i$ | -23.2 | $r$ | -7.7 | | |

Note that the mean of the curve is not zero; this is most likely due to the fact that this is only a partial surface profile. We will continue as if it were a zero mean. Consider the $R_a$ and $R_q$ values using all of the data. Also, note from the text on p. 1040 that all distances are absolute values, so only positive numbers are used in calculations. We then obtain

$$R_a = \frac{a+b+c+\dots}{n} = \frac{22.0+15+24.9+\dots}{26} = 20.0$$

Similarly,

$$R_q = \sqrt{\frac{a^2 + b^2 + c^2 + \ldots}{n}} = \sqrt{\frac{22.0^2 + 15^2 + 24.9^2 + \ldots}{26}} = 23.7$$

Note that if we use the first column only, we obtain values of $R_a = 22.67$ and $R_q = 23.5$. While these two numbers do not appear to be too far apart, better repeatability is generally desired in practice, depending on the application. In profile tracing, for example, the number of data points involved is typically between 3000 and 8000.

**33.30 Obtain several different parts made of various materials, inspect their surfaces under an optical microscope at different magnifications, and make an educated guess as to what manufacturing process or finishing process was used to produce each of these parts. Explain your reasoning.**

By the student. This is an open-ended problem and the answers will depend on the particular parts analyzed. Based on a review of the manufacturing process characteristics described throughout the preceding chapters, the students should be able to look for clues and signs regarding the manufacturing process. For example: (a) Is the part shape in bulk or sheet metal? (b) Does the part have machining or grinding marks? (c) Is orange peel or stretcher strains present? (See pp. 436-437). (d) Is there evidence of a sand mold, as may be evidenced from the workpiece surface?

**33.31 Refer to Fig. 33.6b and make measurements of the external and internal diameters (in the horizontal direction in the photograph) of the four specimens shown. Remembering that in plastic deformation the volume of the rings remains constant, calculate (a) the reduction in height and (b) the coefficient of friction for each of the three compressed specimens.**

Note that the photo shows an oblique view of the rings, so direct measurement of the diameters is difficult. Also, no scale is given in the figure, so students should not be strictly judged on their ability to obtain precisely the numbers given here. It should be noted that the original ring, shown in part 1, has a diameter of 19 mm, since it is a standard test specimen as shown in Fig. 33.7. The dimensions in the second and third columns of the table below can be scaled from this value.

| Ring No. | Outer diameter (mm) | Inner diameter (mm) | Height (mm) | Reduction in height (%) | Reduction in ID (%) | Friction coefficient ($\mu$) |
|---|---|---|---|---|---|---|
| 1 | 19 | 9.5 | 6.4 | 0 | 0 | — |
| 2 | 27 | 12 | 2.96 | 53.7 | -26.3 | 0.025 |
| 3 | 27 | 7.75 | 2.59 | 59.5 | 18.4 | 0.10 |
| 4 | 27 | 5 | 2.46 | 61.6 | 47.4 | 0.16 |

Since the volume is constant, we can obtain the following for comparing any ring to ring 1:

$$\frac{\pi}{4}\left(d_{o1}^2 - d_{i1}^2\right) h_1 = \frac{\pi}{4}\left(d_{o2}^2 - d_{i2}^2\right) h_2 \quad \rightarrow \quad h_2 = \frac{d_{o1}^2 - d_{i1}^2}{d_{o2}^2 - d_{i2}^2} h_1$$

Using ring 1 as the reference allows calculation of the heights given in the table above. The reduction in height, given in the 5th column, is calculated from

$$\text{Reduction in height} = \frac{6.4 - h}{6.4} \times 100\%$$

The reduction in internal diameter is calculated similarly, and the friction coefficient is then interpolated from Fig. 33.7 on p. 1046. The results shown above are typical of what is seen in a ring compression test.

**33.32 Using Fig. 33.7, make a plot of the coefficient of friction versus the change in internal diameter for a constant reduction in height of 40%.**

By the student. The graph is shown below:

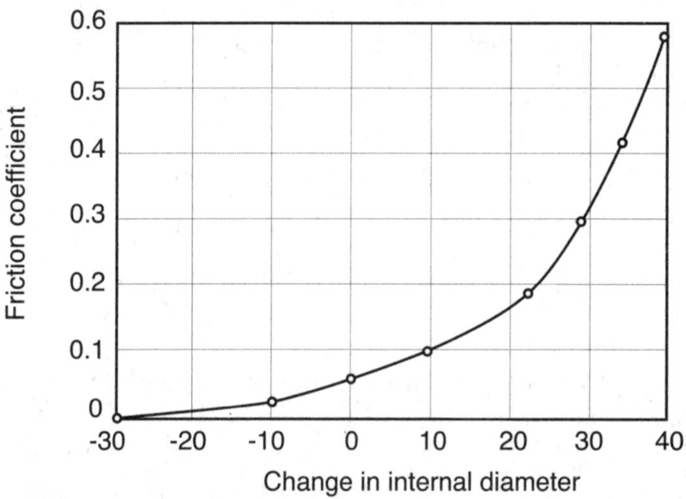


**33.33 Assume that in Example 33.1 the coefficient of friction is 0.15. If all other parameters remain the same, what is the new internal diameter of the specimen?**

By the student. Given: $\mu = 0.15$, and from Fig. 33.7 on p. 1046 we find that for this coefficient of friction and for a 50% reduction in height, the reduction in ID is 27%. Since the original ID is 15 mm, we have

$$\frac{(15 - \text{ID}_{\text{final}})}{15} = 0.27$$

Therefore, $\text{ID}_{\text{final}} = 10.95$ mm.

## SYNTHESIS, DESIGN, AND PROJECTS

**33.34 Would it be desirable to integrate surface-roughness measuring instruments into the machine tools described in Parts III and IV? How would you go about doing**

**so, taking into consideration the factory environment in which they are to be used? Make some preliminary sketches.**

By the student. The basic answer is that it would indeed be desirable; in fact, this is the trend in automated inspection, as described in Section 36.12 on p. 1137. As expected, there are difficulties in keeping such instrumentation clean and functioning in a somewhat hostile environment (air quality, airborne particles, temperature, humidity, vibrations from machinery) that may be present in manufacturing plants, such as in casting, forging, welding, and heat-treating operations. The students should comment extensively on various aspects concerning this important topic (as a project), and make appropriate sketches of typical setups.

**33.35 Section 33.2 listed major surface defects. How would you go about determining whether or not each of these defects is a significant factor in a particular application?**

By the student. This is a challenging topic and the necessary background information is covered in (a) Chapter 2, (b) Sections on defects in various chapters on manufacturing processes, and (c) Chapter 36 on Quality Assurance, Testing, and Inspection. It should be noted that surfaces are primarily important for some specific situations, such as fatigue, lubricant entrainment, and aesthetics. In some particular applications, surface finish is not critical.

**33.36 Why are the requirements for surface-roughness design in engineering applications so broad? Explain with specific examples.**

By the student. The basic reason is that engineering requirements are very broad, with some applications being surface sensitive while others very insensitive to surfaces. For example, parts such as shafts, gears, and metalworking dies are susceptible to fatigue failure (the cause of the majority of failures in mechanical components; see p. 83) unless the surfaces are very smooth (and depending on the quality of the material). On the other hand, the surfaces of the steel columns supporting a bridge do not have to be smooth; in fact, some roughness will help paint adhere to the surfaces.

**33.37 Describe the tribological difference between ordinary machine elements (such as gears and bearings) and metalworking processes. Consider such factors as load, speed, and temperature.**

Throughout various chapters we have seen that metalworking process involve a wide range of temperatures, contact stresses and relative speeds (between the workpiece and the tools and dies), and metalworking fluids (lubricants and coolants). Although machine elements such as gears and bearings also have a wide range of relevant parameters involved, only some of the factors listed above are common to metalworking processes. Thus, for example, contact stresses in machine elements are much lower than those in processing (for the simple reason that the stresses must be sufficiently high to deform the materials). On the other hand, speeds in gears and bearings are generally much higher than those in processing of materials, and machine elements typically operate at room temperature (whereas higher temperatures are necessary in hot working operations in metalworking).

**33.38 Explain why the types of wear in Fig. 33.11 occur in those particular locations in the forging die.**

By the student. Although difficult to generalize, the following observations may be made regarding Fig. 33.11 on p. 1049:

(a) Erosion occurs because the rough surface of the forging blank, and/or the wear particles produced during the early stages of forging, are abraded against those surfaces; also the workpiece slides against the inner corners of the protruding portions of the die as forging progresses.

(b) Pitting occurs (on lubricated dies only) in areas in the upper die where the lubricant will be subjected to high pressures, thereby penetrating small cracks developed on the die surface.

(c) Thermal fatigue appears to occur in areas exposed to high-temperature cycling which, in this case, is at the external corners of the die protrusions.

(d) Mechanical fatigue occurs in areas exposed to high reversing stresses, which in this case, appear to be on outer fillets of the protrusions.

(e) The geometry of the die suggests areas that undergo high contact stresses and high temperature, thus leading to plastic deformation.

**33.39 Wear can have detrimental effects in manufacturing operations. Can you visualize situations in which wear could be beneficial? Give examples.**

By the student. As a beneficial effect (see bottom of p. 1046) of small amounts of controlled wear consider, for example:

(a) Running-in periods in machinery (see also Problem 33.24),

(b) improvements in surface finish and appearance, such as polishing and buffing, and

(c) the fact that without it would not be possible to write with a pencil or a chalk (in which the words written consists of very small wear particles).

**33.40 You have undoubtedly replaced parts in various appliances and automobiles because they were worn. Describe the methodology you would follow in determining the type(s) of wear these components have undergone?**

By the student. This is a challenging question. One of the most valuable and simple method of investigation is microscopic examination of the surfaces. (a) A smeared surface, for example, is indicative of adhesive wear (p. 1047). (b) If the surface has longitudinal scratch marks, plowing and abrasion has likely occurred (p. 1048). (c) Rough, pitted surfaces are typical of corrosive wear (p. 1048). (d) Small surface cracks and spalls are typical of surface fatigue (p. 1049).

# Chapter 34

# Surface Treatments, Coatings and Cleaning

## QUALITATIVE PROBLEMS

**34.15 Describe how roller-burnishing processes induce compressive residual stresses on the surfaces of parts.**

Roller burnishing, like peening operations, subjects the workpiece surface to localized plastic deformation (as in Fig. 2.13 on p. 81). As a result, residual compressive stresses develop on the surface due to the fact that the surface layer tends to expand laterally during this deformation but the bulk prevents these layers from expanding freely. Consequently, compressive residual stresses are developed on the surface.

**34.16 Explain why you might want to coat parts with ceramics.**

There are several reasons for coating parts with ceramics (see also Example 34.3 on p. 1076). Ceramics are very hard and chemically inert (see Section 8.3 on p. 224), so it is natural that ceramic coatings be used for improving the wear resistance of parts, as is also done in coating cutting tools (see p. 659). Their high-temperature resistance also makes them attractive for coating gas-turbine components. Ceramics also can be made porous and hence thermally insulating. The chemistry and structure of ceramics also can be beneficial (as for orthopedic implants). Finally, there is an advantage to ceramic surfaces for their aesthetic appearance.

**34.17 Give examples of part designs that are suitable for hot-dip galvanizing.**

By the student. The basic concept is that hot-dip galvanizing (p. 1074) is an important process and economical for any application where corrosion prevention is important. Typical examples are: Sheet-steel water buckets, pipe, wire, plumbing supplies, and fasteners. Students are encouraged to develop other own ideas and give more examples.

**34.18 Repeat Question 34.17, but for cleaning.**

Any part that will be coated or painted has to be cleaned first to allow proper coating adhesion to surfaces. All containers with food-contacting surfaces must be cleaned, including the interiors of food and beverage cans, before they are filled. Other examples: close-tolerance hydraulic pistons, cylinders, and pumps, low electrical-resistance connectors, and medical implants. The students aee encouraged to give various other examples.

**34.19 Give some applications of mechanical surface treatment.**

By the student. Examples include roller-burnishing of shaft fillets to impart compressive residual stresses for improving fatigue life, knurling operations on handles (see Fig. 23.1(l) on p. 675), and peened surfaces for fatigue life (such as on helicopter shafts). (MORE?)

**34.20 It has been observed in practice that a thin layer of chrome plating (such as that on older-model automobile bumpers) is better than a thick layer. Explain why, considering the effect of thickness on the tendency for cracking.**

Observations have indicated that a thick chrome-plated layer on a bumper has a greater tendency to develop a few large cracks that penetrate to the substrate, thus causing corrosion of the substrate. Conversely, a thin chrome plating has been found to develop many but much shallower cracks. This explanation is similar to the observation that a thick oxide layer is more brittle (hence it develops large cracks) than a thin oxide layer (which has a higher compliance with the substrate body when subjected to strains). (See also Fig. 33.1 on p. 1037.)

**34.21 It is well known that coatings may be removed or depleted during the service life of components, particularly at elevated temperatures. Describe the factors involved in the strength of coatings and their durability.**

The strength of a coating is determined to a large extent by the quality of the bond between the coating material and the substrate. The strength depends on many factors, one of the most important of which is substrate-surface preparation to remove residual lubricants, oxides, and contaminants. In addition, a common difficulty with coatings is the presence of surface residual stresses, many being attributed to the thermal strains developed during the coating process. Coating thickness has a large effect as well. Since the maximum shear stress in Hertzian contact is at a depth between one-third and one-half its contact length, there is a critical coating thickness which leads to large-scale delamination and failure because of contact fatigue and the initiation and propagation of cracks.

**34.22 Roller burnishing typically is applied to steel parts. Why is this so?**

Steel (Chapter 5) is the most common material for fatigue and highly-loaded machine elements such as shafts, gears, and cams. For this reason, it is also the most commonly roller burnished material.

**34.23 Make a list of the coating processes described in this chapter and classify them as "thick" or "thin."**

By the student. This is an open-ended problem. Noting that the words "thick" and "thin" are relative, we can make the following general list:

(a) Thin coating operations: Physical vapor deposition, ion implantation, electroplating, electroless plating, and anodizing

(b) Thick coating operations: Mechanical plating, cladding, thermal spraying, chemical vapor deposition, hot dipping, ceramic coating, and painting (in all forms).

**34.24 Which of the processes described in this chapter are used only for small parts? Why is this so?**

By the student. Most of the processes that require a vacuum are used on small parts only; these include the PVD operations. It is very expensive to create a large evacuated space. The cost of the vacuum pumps makes the treatment of large parts uneconomical. Note also that the main purpose of surface-treating operations is to increase hardness and resistance to wear, temperature, and corrosion. Consequently, applications typically are confined to small parts, such as cutting tools and turbine blades.

**34.25 Shiny, metallic balloons commonly are made with festive printed patterns which are produced by printing screens and then plating the balloons. How can metallic coatings be plated onto a rubber sheet?**

As discussed on p. 1072, the plastic sheet must have a nickel coating, applied by electroless plating. The subsequent decorations are made through plating or anodizing.

**34.26 Why is galvanizing important for automotive-body sheet-metals?**

By the student. Hot-dip galvanizing is performed on most steel sheet for automotive bodies. The zinc serves as the anode in a galvanic cell, so that in the presence of ions (such as salt sprayed on roads in winter or in climates near oceans), all of the zinc must corrode before any of the steel begins to rust. This greatly prolongs the life of the automotive body.

**34.27 Explain the principles involved in various techniques for applying paints.**

By the student. These techniques are described on pp. 1077-1078; also, especially useful is Fig. 34.12 on p. 1078. While it is possible to dip a part into liquid paint, usually this leads to coatings that are too thick, and consequently, this is a less common technique. Flow coating and electrostatic spray use particles to produce a coating; small particles that are propelled at a surface are attracted because of high adhesion forces on the small-particle length scale, also aided by electrostatic forces.

## QUANTITATIVE PROBLEMS

**34.28 Taking a simple example, such as the parts shown in Fig. 34.1, estimate the force required for roller burnishing. (See Sections 2.6 and 14.4.)**

By the student. A simple method would be to estimate the contact area between the roller and the workpiece surface (based on geometric relationships) and multiplying it by the hardness of the material. See also the pressure required for piercing, as stated on p. 381.

**34.29 Estimate the plating thickness in electroplating of a 50-mm solid-metal ball using a current of 10 A and a plating time of 2 hours. Assume that $c = 0.08$ in Eq. (34.1).**

Note that the surface area of a sphere is $A = 4\pi r^2$, so that the volume of the plating is $V = 4\pi r^2 h$, where $h$ is the plating thickness. From Eq. (34.1) on p. 1070,

$$V = cIt = 4\pi r^2 h$$

Solving for the plating thickness, and using proper units, we find

$$h = \frac{cIt}{4\pi r^2} = \frac{(0.08)(10)(7200)}{4\pi(25)^2} = 0.73 \text{ mm}$$

## SYNTHESIS, DESIGN, AND PROJECTS

**34.30 Which surface treatments are functional and which are decorative? Are there any that serve both functions? Explain.**

By the student. A review of the processes described in this chapter indicates that most surface treatments are functional. A few, such as electroplating, anodizing, porcelain enameling, and ceramic coating, may be regarded as both functional and decorative. The students are encouraged to give specific examples from their experience and observations.

**34.31 An artificial implant has a porous surface area where it is expected that the bone will attach and grow into the implant. Make recommendations for producing a porous surface and then review the literature to determine the actual processes used.**

There are various approaches used by different manufacturers:

(a) Metal beads can be sintered to the substrate.

(b) powders can be plasma sprayed onto the workpiece

(c) powders or fibers can be diffusion-bonded in a furnace.

(d) A recent development is the use of metal foams as bone in-growth material.

(e) Research is now being conducted on developing collagen and ceramic-based surfaces for these applications.

**34.32 If one is interested in obtaining a textured surface on a coated piece of metal, should one apply the coating first or apply the texture first?**

The answer depends on the scale of the features that one wishes to impart. If the features are much larger than the coating thickness, the features can be produced before applying the coating. If, on the other hand, the features are on the order of the coating thickness or less, they should be applied after coating the surface.

**34.33 It is known that a mirror-like surface finish can be obtained by plating workpieces that are ground (that is, the surface finish improves after coating). Explain how this occurs.**

The key to plating very smooth surfaces is to have long-chain molecules (typically animal fats) in solution and on fairly smooth surfaces. The plating process then preferentially takes place in the valleys of the workpiece surface. A literature search on the composition of these brighteners can be performed by the students.

**34.34 Outline the reasons why the topics described in this chapter are important in manufacturing processes and operations.**

By the student. This is an open-ended problem, and the students should be encouraged to develop their own rationales for the importance of surface-treatment operations. There are several ways of responding this question. Students can comment on the need for surface properties that are different from the bulk properties, for a number of operations such as cutting tools where wear resistance is required for the cutting surfaces of the tool, but ductility and high heat transfer is desired for the bulk. Students can also make this argument by listing applications for each process, or by examining information such as given in Fig. 22.6 on p. 658 which clearly shows the performance advantage that can be achieved from coatings.

**34.35 Because they evaporate, solvents and similar cleaning solutions have adverse environmental effects. Describe your thoughts on what modifications could be made to render cleaning solutions more environmentally friendly.**

By the student. This is an open-ended problem, and is suitable for research and development for a brief report, if desired. There are many issues in this area which already have received much attention. For example:

- Water-based paints, stains, and inks continue to be developed to eliminate harmful solvents.
- A recent innovation is the use of ionic liquids as solvents. These unique materials do not lose their effectiveness with time, hence their disposal becomes a non-issue.
- Some solvents can be reduced to harmless byproducts by burning them in a furnace.

**34.36 When an electrically insulating specimen is to be placed in a scanning electron microscope for examination, the specimen is first coated with a thin layer of gold. How would you produce this layer of gold?**

Such coatings are usually sputtered on. Note that electroplating will not be effective because the workpiece is electrically insulating. Because the coatings are so thin. the material costs of the gold coating are negligible.

**34.37 A roller burnishing operation is performed on a shaft shoulder to increase fatigue life. It is noted that the resultant surface finish is poor, and a proposal is made to machine the surface layer to further improve fatigue life. Will this be advisable? Explain.**

It is possible to improve fatigue life by making the surface smoother (see Fig. 2.28 on p. 93), but this is a very difficult prospect. Very special care must be taken to remove material only on the order of the surface roughness - a micrometer or so. Normal depths of cut are a few orders of magnitude larger than this depth, so machining may not be the best option. Some grinding operations may be a better approach. The concern, of course, is that the surface that is removed is the region with the compressive residual stress, and therefore machining eliminates the usefulness of the burnishing operation.

**34.38 You can simulate the shot-peening process by using a ball-peen hammer (in which one of the heads is round). Using such a hammer, make numerous indentations on the surface of a piece of aluminum sheet (a) 2-mm and (b) 10-mm thick, respectively, which placed on a hard flat surface. You will note that both pieces will develop curvatures but one will become concave and the other become convex. Describe your observations and explain why this happens. (Hint: See Fig. 2.13)**

By the student. Figure 2.29 on p. 95 is a useful figure to refer to, because the answer to this problem lies in the residual stresses that are produced. With the flat sheet, the hammer causes deformation through the thickness, not just at the surfaces. However, with a 10-mm thick sheet, the deformations are restricted to the surface only, and this results in a compressive residual stress on the surface. Since the sheets are not constrained, they can deform to relieve the stresses, and the compressive residual stress is relieved by contracting, causing a concave surface.

**34.39 Obtain several pieces of small metal parts (such as bolts, nuts, rods, and sheet metal) and perform the waterbreak test on them. Then clean the surfaces using various cleaning fluids and repeat the test. Describe your observations.**

By the student. This is a good experiment to perform, especially if the instructor prepares special samples beforehand. For example, a steel plate can have a thin paraffin oil film placed on it, and mostly removed with a paper towel. This can be compared to the same surface where the paraffinic oil has been removed by rubbing it vigorously with acetone. Another example is a painted and waxed surface compared to a painted surface without wax. There are also commercial products that are intended to increase surface tension on glass (Rain-XTM) and these can be effective learning examples as well.

**34.40 Inspect various products around your house (such as small and large appliances, silverware, metal vases and boxes, kitchen utensils, and hand tools) and comment on the type of coatings they may have. Also comment on those products that do not appear to have any coatings, stating the possible reasons for it.**

By the student. This is an open-ended problem, and the specific answers can vary depending on the experience of the student and their diligence in seeking solutions. Examples of answers are:

- Tableware is coated with silver for corrosion resistance, resulting in safer food consumption.
- A large number of products, including appliances such as washers, dryers, refrigerators and the like, are painted for aesthetic reasons.
- Electrical wire is co-extruded to provide protection against electrical shock.

- Note that aluminum items are not coated, nor are stainless steel products such as tableware, because these materials naturally develop good-looking functional surfaces.

**34.41 Survey the technical literature and prepare a brief report on the environmental considerations regarding the application of the processes described in this chapter.**

By the student. This is an open-ended problem, but is rich with potential problems for investigation. Examples of directions this research can take are the environmental impact of exhausted working gases, especially for processes such as chemical vapor deposition, the treatment of electroplating fluids, the generation of volatile organic compounds (VOC) in polymer coating operation or the exhaust associated with painting operations.

# Chapter 35

# Engineering Metrology and Instrumentation

## QUALITATIVE PROBLEMS

**35.14 Why are the words "accuracy" and "precision" often incorrectly interchanged?**

They are often confused because we usually think of object dimensions as both accurate and precise. Accuracy is the degree of agreement of the measured dimension of a part with its true magnitude; the dictionary describes it as conforming to a standard, and suggests that it is somewhat synonymous to the word correct or exact. Precision is the degree to which an instrument gives repeated measurement of the same standard; the dictionary describes it as again being equivalent to exactness. It is interesting to note that the first use of the word accuracy was in 1662, and for precision in 1740, and as an adjective in 1875.

**35.15 Why do manufacturing processes produce parts with a wide range of tolerances?**

By the student. This is an open-ended problem and the answers will depend on the particular process (or family of processes) considered. Typical reasons would be:

(a) variations in the manufacturing-process parameters
(b) machine performance as a function of time (such as wear)
(c) variations in machine location, temperature, etc.
(d) variations in lubricant performance
(e) environment, and
(f) unreliability of workers.

**35.16 Explain the need for automated inspection.**

Automated measurement and inspection is needed for feedback in highly-automated manufacturing systems. Automated inspection is especially useful where work is untended (see Factory of the Future, p. 35). In-process inspection reduces the number of rejects, as described in Section 36.12 on p. 1137.

**35.17 Dimensional tolerances for nonmetallic parts usually are wider than for metallic parts. Explain why. Would this also be true for ceramics parts?**

Nonmetallic parts have wider dimensional tolerances because they often have low elastic modulus and strength, are soft, and have high thermal expansion (see, for example, Chapter 7); they are therefore difficult to manufacture accurately. Also, some nonmetallic parts (such as injection-molded polymers or slip-cast ceramics) are produced with metal molds. In such circumstances, the best achievable dimensional tolerances are equal to the tolerances of the mold, but because of warpage and shrinkage of the parts made, these tolerances are never achieved.

**35.18 Comment on your observations regarding Fig. 35.20. Why does dimensional tolerance increase with increasing surface roughness?**

By the student. As shown in Fig. 35.20 on p. 1104, dimensional tolerance increases with surface roughness for a number of reasons, depending on the specific process. For example, in turning operations, a roughing cut will lead to high metal removal rates but also large variations in tool force, so that the small tolerances cannot be maintained; roughing cuts also give rough surfaces. In contrast, in polishing, smoother surfaces are obtained by using extremely small abrasive particles; these particles cannot remove as large of chips as in turning. Therefore, the dimensional tolerances are far better.

**35.19 What are the advantages and limitations of gage blocks made of zirconia?**

The possible advantages of zirconia gage blocks (see p. 1094) are hardness, abrasion resistance, light weight, and lower cost. The principal limitation could be its relatively low toughness, hence the tendency for chipping in case of being mishandled or dropped.

**35.20 Review Fig. 35.19 and comment on the range of tolerances and part dimensions produced by various manufacturing processes.**

By the student. This is an open-ended problem, and various comments can be made by the students that could be valid. The students can examine the processes that are suitable for obtaining a desired dimensional tolerance, and evaluate them based on cost. Also, there is a range of tolerances that can be achieved, and the students should be encouraged to explain the reasons for the ranges.

**35.21 In the game of darts, is it better to be accurate or to be precise? Explain.**

In darts, one could consider an accurate set of throws to have their mean at the center of the dartboard, while a precise set would be very close to each other. It is difficult to decide which is better, as both are needed. With some games, there is an advantage to striking a desired location on a dart board multiple times, in which case precision is the better characteristic.

**35.22 What are the advantages and limitations of GO and NOT GO gages?**

The advantages of GO and NOT GO gages (see p. 1094) are that they are relatively simple to manufacture and very easy to use. The main disadvantage is that they do not provide a numerical reading; this limitation makes the application of statistical quality control methods and Taguchi methods impossible (see Chapter 36).

## QUANTITATIVE PROBLEMS

**35.23 Assume that a steel rule expands by 0.08% due to an increase in environmental temperature. What will be the indicated diameter of a shaft whose diameter at room temperature was 1.500 in.?**

The indicated diameter of the shaft will be 1.500 - (0.0008)(1.500) = 1.4988 in.

**35.24 If the same steel rule as in Problem 35.23 is used to measure aluminum extrusions, what will be the indicated diameter of a part that was 1.500 in. at room temperature? What is the actual dimension? What if the part were a thermoplastic?**

By the student. For a steel rule to expand by 0.08%, the expansion will be $e = \alpha\,\Delta T = 0.0008$. From Table 3.1 on p. 103, the coefficient of thermal expansion, $\alpha$, for steel is $6.5 \times 10^{-6}$ per °F, and for aluminum, $\alpha = 12.9 \times 10^{-6}$/°F. Therefore, for an expansion of 0.0008, the temperature change is

$$\Delta T = \frac{0.0008}{6.5 \times 10^{-6}} = 123^\circ\text{F}$$

For this temperature change, the actual dimension of the aluminum part will be:

$$e = \frac{\Delta L}{L} = \alpha\,\Delta T$$

Solving for $\Delta L$,

$$\Delta L = \alpha L\,\Delta T = \left(12.9 \times 10^{-6}/^\circ\text{F}\right)(1.5 \text{ in.})(123^\circ\text{F}) = 0.0024 \text{ in.}$$

Note that this means $L = 1.5024$ in. Since the steel rule has expanded by 0.08%, the actual reading will be

$$\frac{1.5024}{(1 + 0.0008)} = 1.5012 \text{ in.}$$

**35.25 A shaft must meet a design requirement of being at least 1.25 in. in diameter, but it can be 0.01 in. oversized. Express the shafts tolerance as it would appear on an engineering drawing.**

The dimension could be expressed in terms of a unilateral tolerance:

$$1.25 \text{ in.} \begin{array}{l} +0.01 \text{ in.} \\ -0.00 \text{ in.} \end{array}$$

or in terms of limit dimensions:

$$\begin{matrix} 1.01 \\ 1.00 \end{matrix} \text{ in.}$$

Both of these concepts are shown in Fig. 35.18 on p. 1103.

## SYNTHESIS, DESIGN, AND PROJECTS

**35.26 Describe your thoughts on the merits and limitations of digital measuring equipment over analog. Give specific examples.**

By the student. This is an open-ended problem and can be answered in a number of ways depending on the experience of the student. Some of the advantages of digital equipment over analog are:

- Readings can be taken much more quickly.
- Digital gages can be computerized more readily.

Some of the disadvantages are:

- They are more expensive.
- It is more difficult to judge when a gage is giving an erroneous reading.

**35.27 Take an ordinary vernier micrometer (Fig. 35.2a) and a simple round rod. Ask five of your classmates to measure the rod diameter with this micrometer. Comment on your observations.**

By the student. This is a simple and useful experiment, and variations are possible with a wide variety of products. For a simple round rod the students are likely to obtain reasonably close results; however, it is rare for each student to get exactly the same measurement. With larger numbers of readings, one can demonstrate that the measurements are normally distributed about a mean value (see Fig. 36.3 on p. 1122). This simple experiment will demonstrate to students that there are tolerances associated with parts, but there are also errors associated with measurements.

**35.28 Obtain a digital micrometer and a steel ball of, say, 1 in. diameter. Measure its diameter for the following conditions when the ball has been placed in (a) freezer, (b) boiling water, and (c) held in your hand for different periods of time. Note the variations, if any, of measured dimensions, and comment on it.**

By the student. The difference in size (from a freezer to boiling water) is around 0.00016 in., which can be registered and read on a digital micrometer.

**35.29 Repeat Problem 35.28 but with the following parts: (a) plastic lid of a small jar, (b) thermoset part such as the knob or handle on the lid of a sauce pan, (c) small juice glass, (d) ordinary rubber eraser.**

By the student. These parts will have much more noticeable and measurable variation in their dimensions (because of their lower coefficients of thermal expansion; see Table 3.1 on p. 103). This topic will be an interesting project to be carried by different groups of students to see how different, if any, the results would be.

**35.30 What is the significance of the tests described in Problems 35.28 and 35.29?**

The tests demonstrate a number of concepts, including:

- The phenomenon of thermal expansion among a wide variety of materials.
- How small the actual expansion or contraction is for metals over a fairly large temperature range.
- How measurements may vary using different instrumentation and taken by different people.
- The importance of this topic in actual manufacturing operations and measurements.

**35.31 Explain the relative advantages and limitations of a tactile probe versus a laser probe.**

By the student. This is an open-ended problem with several possible answers depending on the background and diligence of the student in pursuing and investigating this topic (see also Section 37.7 on p. 1171). Some of the advantages and disadvantages of probes are:

- Laser probes may not function well with some surfaces, especially anodized surfaces because the light is absorbed or diffused.
- Laser probes will not function well for surfaces at steep angles.
- Laser probes can be more expensive.
- Tactile probes may not trace a surface properly (see Fig. 33.4b on p. 1041).
- Tactile probes may not be suitable for very soft and flexible surfaces.
- Tactile probes are much more susceptible to damage.

**35.32 Make simple sketches of some forming and cutting machine tools (as described in Parts III and IV of this book) and integrate them with the various types of measuring equipment discussed in this chapter. Comment on the possible difficulties involved in doing so.**

By the student. This is a challenging problem. For example, a student could design the following:

- Incorporation of a touch probe to sense the presence or absence of a tool on a lathe; this would then determine if an untended operation requires a tool change.
- In-machine measurement of the dimensions of a workpiece or tool could be performed as part of an adaptive-control setup to produce less deviations from part to part (see Section 37.4 on p. 1161).
- Indirect measurements can be taken to gage the effectiveness of operations, such as measuring rotational speed of work rolls in rolling and inlet speed of the strip to obtain a neutral point (see Fig. 13.2 on p. 349).

- In automated machinery too check, for example, if a cold-extruded piece has been removed from the die (either by the worker or by a robot) before another blank is placed into it.

**35.33 What method would you use to measure the thickness of a foam-rubber part? Explain.**

By the student. This can be a challenging problem, because of the following reasons:

- The foam may not provide a sufficiently smooth surface (unless it is very dense); it may have a porous surface where the pore depth is greater than the nominal tolerance.
- The foam is extremely compliant, and any attempt to use tactile instrumentation (such as micrometers) would have large errors because of the deflection of the foam.
- The foam may have a waviness that must be flattened before a surface can be measured

There are established practices for measuring foams, including using low-force touch probes, using projection methods with optical comparators, or for flat workpieces, loading them between two platens to eliminate waviness and then measuring the thickness.

**35.34 Obtain one or more of the following parts and describe how you would measure as many of the key dimensions as possible; include the type of instruments to be used and the measurement method.**

**(a) An automotive brake pad.**

**(b) A plastic soft-drink bottle.**

**(c) A compact disc or floppy disk.**

By the student. This is a good laboratory exercise. The challenge in this problem is to encourage students to use as many different instruments as possible, and to encourage them to use creative solutions.

**35.35 Inspect various parts and components in consumer products (including small appliances) and comment on how tight dimensional tolerances have to be in order for these products to function properly.**

By the student. This is a challenging and valuable exercise, and would make a good project for groups of students. It should be noted, for example, that the shaft and the bearings of a motor in an appliance must have much tighter dimensional tolerances than the sheet-metal or plastic housing of the unit.

**35.36 As you know, very thin sheet-metal parts can distort differently when held from various locations and edges of the part, just as a piece of paper or aluminum foil does. How then could you use a coordinate measuring machine for "accurate" measurements? Explain.**

By the student. This is a challenging problem, and after appreciating the significance of the question, the students should be encouraged to provide their own answers (perhaps also contacting some companies). It should be pointed out, however, that even though a thin sheet may be quite flexible, when made into a component such as a fender or door panel, it has become much stiffer by virtue of the presence of flanges and seams along its periphery. In response to the question posed, the logical approach would be that, in preparation for measurements, the piece should be supported in a manner and in locations where it would be assembled with the other components.

# Chapter 36

# Quality Assurance, Testing and Inspection

## QUALITATIVE PROBLEMS

**36.16 What is the consequence of setting lower and upper specifications closer to the peak of the curve in Fig. 36.4?**

In SPC, setting the control limits closer to the center of the distribution will cause more of the sample points to fall outside the limits, as can be seen in Fig. 36.4 on p. 1124. This will make the spread of the distribution worse because the process will be adjusted even though it is still in control, and thus causing unnecessary adjustment time and expense.

**36.17 Identify several factors that can cause a process to become out of control.**

By the student. For example, a process can become out of control because of changes in inputs (materials, tools, lubricants), environment (temperature, humidity), or operator (training, skill, time of day). Students are encouraged to give other examples.

**36.18 Describe situations in which the need for destructive testing techniques is unavoidable.**

By the student. As described in Section 36.11 on p. 1136, destructive techniques include determining the bursting speed of grinding wheels and the bursting pressure of pressure vessels. Thus, for example, for large production quantities, the first part or parts produced in such product lines would be tested until they fail. The results would give a confidence level for the reliability of these products. Also included are hardness tests, which inevitably leave an impression on surfaces (except in using durometers; see p. 82). The size of these impressions is important for more brittle materials as they can lead to premature failure.

**36.19 Which of the nondestructive inspection techniques are suitable for nonmetallic materials? Why?**

By the student. Ultrasonic, acoustic, thermal, and holographic methods could be applied to nonmetallic parts.

**36.20 Give examples of products where 100% sampling is not possible or feasible.**

By the student. For mass-produced common items such as gears, valves, light switches, pencils, or paper clips, 100% sampling would not be feasible because the number of tests to be performed would place undue economic burden, and such testing would not be necessary. Statistical sampling techniques are commonly used for such products. However, in critical applications such as in aircraft engines and medical instrumentation, 100% testing is imperative.

**36.21 What are the advantages of automated inspection? Why has it become an important part of manufacturing engineering?**

By the student. Automated inspection (p. 1137) is advantageous because it can often be performed between stages of manufacturing operations without stopping production, thus allowing in-line and continuous monitoring of part quality. This method has obvious and important quality implications, especially with regards to just-in-time production (Section 39.5 on p. 1225).

**36.22 Why is reliability important in manufacturing engineering? Give several examples.**

By the student. The intended reliability of a product affects manufacturing engineering through design, processing, and cost that reliability goals require. For example: (a) An engine connecting rod or a shaft may be shot-blasted for improved fatigue life, depending on the desired reliability (b) A gasket joint can be held by many or few fasteners, depending on the desired reliability. (c) The level of inspection and functional testing during manufacturing will vary, depending on the desired reliability.

**36.23 Give examples of the acoustic-impact inspection technique other than those given in the chapter.**

By the student. This is an open-ended problem and students are encouraged to give various additional examples. For instance, in helicopter-blade inspection, the acoustic-impact technique is used to detect delamination in the composite material that makes up the blade. This technique also was employed to detect flaws on a composite main rotor blade, steel highway bridges, and internal defects in encapsulated computer chips (see www.sensorsmag.com/articles/0400/56/main.shtml).

**36.24 Explain why GO and NOT-GO gages (See Section 35.4.4) are incompatible with the Taguchi philosophy.**

The Taguchi philosophy, as expressed by the Taguchi Loss Function, requires that a variation from a target value be measured. GO and NOT-GO gages do not give a measurement (see pp. 1094-1095); they only can ascertain whether a dimension falls between two limits.

**36.25 Describe your thoughts regarding Table 36.1.**

By the student. This is an open-ended problem. Many students have expressed surprise over the short expected life of dollar bills shown in Table 36.1 on p. 1112, and also have suggested that the muffler life appears to be low. An interesting topic that can be assigned is to add applications to this table, either by specifying individual products (see also Table 40.3 on p. 1244) or by asking the students to list their own products and find data. This topic can lead to an interesting discussion, such as the life expectancy of paper versus metal currency.

**36.26 Give examples of robust design in addition to that in Fig. 36.1.**

By the student. There are many examples and students are encouraged to apply creativity and diligence in responding to this problem. A good example, for instance, is the stiffness, $k$, of a simple cantilever spring (beam) with a rectangular cross-section, given by

$$k = \frac{P}{\delta} = \frac{Ebh^3}{6L^2}$$

where $P$ is the load at the end, $\delta$ is the deflection, $b$ is the width, $h$ is the height (thickness), and $L$ is the length of the cantilever beam. Based on this equation, a hypothetical question would be: Which of the beam dimensions will cause the most variation in stiffness, and which dimension should be most tightly controlled to achieve a robust design? It will be noted that the height of the beam has the largest effect since it has the highest exponent.

## QUANTITATIVE PROBLEMS

**36.27 Beverage can manufacturers try to achieve failure rates of less than one can in ten thousand. If this corresponds to $n$-sigma quality, find $n$.**

This is an advanced problem because one must be able to apply statistics theory to evaluate the probability that a value will be outside certain limits. If one assumes that there is a normal distribution of data, then one can refer to a tabulated normal distribution. For failure rates of 0.0001, 0.00005 parts occur on each side of the distribution curve. The position of interest is where the normal-distribution function has the value of 1-0.00005=0.99995. This is found to be $3.9\sigma$. Therefore, the quality is $\pm 3.9\sigma$.

**36.28 Assume that in Example 36.3, the number of samples was 8 instead of 10. Using the top half of the data in Table 36.4 recalculate control limits and the standard deviation. Compare your observations with the results obtained by using 10 samples.**

We follow the same procedure as given in Example 36.3 on p. 1128, but only for the top-half of the data (rows 1 through 5). Note that in this case the average of averages is

$$\bar{\bar{x}} = \frac{4.438 + 4.428 + 4.410 + 4.446 + 4.430}{5} = 4.430$$

and the average of $R$ values is

$$\bar{R} = \frac{0.06 + 0.08 + 0.13 + 0.18 + 0.04}{5} = 0.098$$

If the sample size is 8, then from Table 36.3 on p. 1126, we have $A_2 = 0.373$, $D_4 = 1.864$, $D_3 = 0.136$ and $d_2 = 2.847$. Thus, from Eqs. (36.6) and (36.7) on p. 1125,

$$\text{UCL} = \bar{\bar{x}} + A_2\bar{R} = 4.430 + 0.098 = 4.528$$

$$\text{LCL} = \bar{\bar{x}} - A_2\bar{R} = 4.430 - 0.098 = 4.332$$

Therefore, from Eq. (36.10) on p. 1126, we find that

$$\sigma = \frac{\bar{R}}{d_2} = \frac{0.098}{2.847} = 0.0344$$

**36.29 Calculate the control limits for averages and ranges for the following: (a) number of samples = 6, (b) and (c) $R = 5$.**

From Table 36.3 on p. 1126, we find that for a sample size of 6, we have $A_2 = 0.483$, $D_4 = 2.004$, and $D_3 = 0$. Therefore, for the averages, using Eqs. (36.6) and (36.7),

$$\text{UCL}_{\bar{x}} = \bar{\bar{x}} + A_2R = 65 + (0.483)(5) = 67.415$$

$$\text{LCL}_{\bar{x}} = \bar{\bar{x}} - A_2R = 65 - (0.483)(5) = 62.585$$

and for the ranges, from Eqs. (36.8) and (36.9), we have

$$\text{UCL}_R = D_4\bar{R} = (2.004)(5) = 10.02$$

$$\text{LCL}_R = D_3\bar{R} = (0)(5) = 0$$

**36.30 Calculate the control limits for the following: (a) number of samples = 5, (b) and (c) $\text{UCL}_R$=5.75.**

For a sample size of 5, we have $A_2 = 0.577$, $D_4 = 2.115$, and $D_3 = 0$ from Table 36.3 on p. 1126. We first calculate for the ranges. From Equations (36.8) and (36.9), we find

$$\text{UCL}_R = 5.75 = D_4\bar{R} = (2.115)\bar{R} \quad \rightarrow \quad \bar{R} = 2.719$$

$$\text{LCL}_R = (0)(2.719) = 0$$

Since we know $R$, we can now calculate for the averages from Eqs. (36.6) and (36.7):

$$\text{UCL}_{\bar{x}} = \bar{\bar{x}} + A_2\bar{R} = 36.5 + (0.577)(2.719) = 38.069$$

$$\text{LCL}_{\bar{x}} = \bar{\bar{x}} - A_2\bar{R} = 36.5 - (0.577)(2.719) = 34.931$$

**36.31 In an inspection with sample size 12 and a sample number of 50, it was found that the average range was 12 and the average of averages was 75. Calculate the control limits for averages and for ranges.**

Note from Table 36.3 on p. 1126 that for a sample size of 12, $A_2 = 0.266$, $D_4 = 1.716$, $D_3 = 0.284$, and $d_2 = 3.258$. If $\bar{R} = 12$ and $\bar{\bar{x}} = 75$, then the control limits for averages are, using Eqs. (36.6) and (36.7) on p. 1125,

$$\text{UCL}_{\bar{x}} = \bar{\bar{x}} + A_2\bar{R} = 75 + (0.266)(12) = 78.192$$

$$\text{LCL}_{\bar{x}} = \bar{\bar{x}} - A_2\bar{R} = 75 - (0.266)(12) = 71.808$$

The control limits for ranges are given by Eqs. (36.8) and (36.9) on p. 1126:

$$\text{UCL}_R = D_4\bar{R} = (1.716)(12) = 20.592$$

$$\text{LCL}_R = D_3\bar{R} = (0.284)(12) = 3.408$$

**36.32 Determine the control limits for the data shown in the table below.**

| $x_1$ | $x_2$ | $x_3$ | $x_4$ |
|---|---|---|---|
| 0.57 | 0.61 | 0.50 | 0.55 |
| 0.59 | 0.55 | 0.60 | 0.58 |
| 0.55 | 0.50 | 0.55 | 0.51 |
| 0.54 | 0.57 | 0.50 | 0.50 |
| 0.58 | 0.58 | 0.60 | 0.56 |
| 0.60 | 0.61 | 0.55 | 0.61 |

We construct the following table, where we add a sample number for reference purposes and calculate the average and the range for each sample number:

| Sample No. | $x_1$ | $x_2$ | $x_3$ | $x_4$ | $\bar{x}$ | $R$ |
|---|---|---|---|---|---|---|
| 1 | 0.57 | 0.61 | 0.50 | 0.55 | 0.557 | 0.11 |
| 2 | 0.59 | 0.55 | 0.60 | 0.50 | 0.580 | 0.05 |
| 3 | 0.55 | 0.50 | 0.55 | 0.51 | 0.527 | 0.05 |
| 4 | 0.54 | 0.57 | 0.50 | 0.50 | 0.527 | 0.07 |
| 5 | 0.58 | 0.58 | 0.60 | 0.56 | 0.580 | 0.04 |
| 6 | 0.60 | 0.61 | 0.55 | 0.61 | 0.592 | 0.06 |

From this table, we can calculate the average of averages and the average range as

$$\bar{\bar{x}} = \frac{0.557 + 0.58 + 0.527 + 0.527 + 0.58 + 0.592}{6} = 0.561$$

$$\bar{R} = \frac{0.11 + 0.05 + 0.05 + 0.07 + 0.04 + 0.06}{6} = 0.0633$$

Since the sample size is 4, Table 36.3 on p. 1126 gives $A_2 = 0.729$, $D_4 = 2.282$, $D_3 = 0$, and $d_2 = 2.059$. Therefore, from Eqs. (36.6) and (36.7) on p. 1125,

$$\text{UCL}_{\bar{x}} = \bar{\bar{x}} + A_2\bar{R} = 0.561 + (0.729)(0.0633) = 0.607$$

$$\text{LCL}_{\bar{x}} = \bar{\bar{x}} - A_2\bar{R} = 0.561 - (0.729)(0.0633) = 0.515$$

The control limits for ranges are given by Eqs. (36.8) and (36.9) on p. 1126:

$$\text{UCL}_R = D_4\bar{R} = (2.282)(0.0633) = 0.144$$

$$\text{LCL}_R = D_3\bar{R} = (0)(0.0633) = 0$$

**36.33 The average-of-averages of a number of samples of size 8 was determined to be 124. The average range was 17.82 and the standard deviation was 4. The following measurements were taken in a sample: 120, 132, 124, 130, 118, 132, 135, and 121. Is the process in control?**

Note that for this case the average is

$$\bar{x} = \frac{120 + 132 + 124 + 130 + 118 + 132 + 135 + 121}{8} = 126.5$$

and the range is $R = 15$. The upper and lower control limits on averages are obtained from Eqs. (36.6) and (36.7) on p. 1125 as

$$\text{UCL}_{\bar{x}} = \bar{x} + 3\sigma = 124 + 3(4) = 136$$

$$\text{LCL}_{\bar{x}} = \bar{x} - 3\sigma = 124 - 3(4) = 110$$

If the sample size is 8, then $D_4 = 1.864$ and $D_3 = 0.136$ (from Table 36.3 on p. 1126). Thus, from Eqs. (36.8) and (36.9) on p. 1126:

$$\text{UCL}_R = D_4\bar{R} = (1.864)(17.82) = 33.2$$

$$\text{LCL}_R = D_3\bar{R} = (0.136)(17.82) = 2.42$$

Since both the average and the range of the sample are within the limits, the process is in control.

**36.34 The trend in the electronics and computer-chip industries is to make products where it is stated that the quality is approaching six sigma ($6\sigma$). What would be the reject rate per million parts?**

This is a very challenging problem and can be done in a number of ways. Most tabular forms of the normal probability function do not consider numbers as far from the mean as six times the variance or six sigma. If the student can find such a table, they can find that this means there will be 3.4 defects per million parts. This can also be shown by obtaining a numerical solution to the normal distribution function:

$$F(x) = \int_{\infty}^{x} \frac{1}{\sqrt{2\pi}} e^{-t^2/2} dt$$

where for this case $x = 6$.

**36.35 A manufacturer is ring-rolling ball-bearing races (see Fig. 13.15). The inner surface has a surface roughness specification of 0.10 ± 0.06 $\mu$m. Measurements taken from rolled rings indicate a mean roughness of 0.112 $\mu$m with a standard deviation of 0.02 $\mu$m. 50,000 rings per month are manufactured and the cost of discarding a defective ring is \$5.00. It is known that, by changing lubricants to a special emulsion, the mean roughness could be made essentially equal to the design specification. What additional cost per month can be justified for the lubricant?**

The approach to this problem is similar to Example 36.1 on p. 1117. Note that in this problem we have USL = 0.16, LSL = 0.04, $T = 0.10$, $\sigma = 0.02$, and $Y = 0.112$. From Eq. (36.2) on p. 1117,

$$k = \frac{\text{Replacement cost}}{(\text{LSL} - T)^2} = \frac{\$5.00}{(0.04 - 0.10)^2} = \$1389.00$$

For the initial case, the loss cost is obtained from Eq. (36.1) on p. 1117 as

$$\text{Loss cost} = k\left[(Y - T)^2 + \sigma^2\right] = \$1389\left[(0.112 - 0.10)^2 + (0.02)^2\right] = \$0.76$$

After the improvement, $Y = T$, so that

$$\text{Loss cost} = k(0.022) = \$0.56$$

The improvement per part saves \$0.20; for 50,000 rings per month, the additional cost that can be justified is \$10,000.

**36.36 For the data of Problem 36.35, assume that the lubricant change can cause the manufacturing process to achieve a roughness of 0.10 ± 0.01 $\mu$m. What additional cost per month for the lubricant can be justified? What if the lubricant did not add any new cost?**

We use the initial approach from Problem 36.25. Note that in this problem we have USL = 0.16, LSL = 0.04, $T = 0.10$, $\sigma = 0.02$, and $Y = 0.112$. From Eq. (36.2) on p. 1117,

$$k = \frac{\text{Replacement cost}}{(\text{LSL} - T)^2} = \frac{\$5.00}{(0.04 - 0.10)^2} = \$1389.00$$

For the initial case, the loss cost is obtained from Eq. (36.1) on p. 1117 as

$$\text{Loss cost} = k\left[(Y - T)^2 + \sigma^2\right] = \$1389\left[(0.112 - 0.10)^2 + (0.02)^2\right] = 0.76$$

Afterwards, the new values are $Y = T$ and $\sigma = 0.01$. Therefore the loss cost is

$$\text{Loss cost} = k(0.012) = \$0.14$$

Therefore, the improvement saves \$0.62 per part, or \$31,000 per month.

## SYNTHESIS, DESIGN, AND PROJECTS

**36.37 Which aspects of the quality concepts of Deming, Taguchi, and Juran would be difficult to implement in a typical manufacturing facility? Why?**

This is an open-ended, challenging problem and is subjective in nature. The students should demonstrate a good command of the subject matter in their answer. The main difficulty is in interpreting the word "difficult." In some respects, all aspects of these philosophies are difficult to implement because they all demand an organizational structure and environment that is quality-driven, and also require personnel to develop new skills. Also, note that the question can suggest that there are components (where some components are easy and others are difficult), and it must be emphasized that the quality approaches require that the entire philosophies be adopted, not just components.

**36.38 Should products be designed and built for a certain expected life? Explain.**

By the student. This is an open-ended problem. For example, there are some products such as high-speed shafts that are designed for infinite life from a fatigue viewpoint, and it is proper that they be designed so. However, larger components result in lower stress levels and usually result in higher life; but these components often are more expensive. Thus there is an unnecessary expense in making a product that lasts longer than its intended life. Consider an extreme case: Should a computer keyboard or a mouse be designed to last 20 years if it adds $10.00 to the cost, and when the computers life is only 2 or so years? As an assignment, the students are strongly encouraged to investigate the somewhat controversial topic of planned obsolescence.

**36.39 Survey the available technical literature, contact various associations, and prepare a comprehensive table concerning the life expectancy of various consumer products.**

By the student. This is a good problem and it complements the information given in Table 36.1 on p. 1112. See also the answer to Problem 36.26.

**36.40 Is there a relationship between design specifications on blueprints and limits in control charts?**

There should, ideally, be a relationship. The designer should consider manufacturing processes and assign dimensional tolerances on the engineering drawings (or blueprints) based on the capabilities of the processes required to produce the desired part geometry. Because designers may not always have full knowledge of manufacturing-process capabilities, the tolerance data is updated in the first part revision, and there is often no attempt to base the design specifications on control chart data.

**36.41 Would it be desirable to incorporate nondestructive inspection techniques in various metalworking machinery? Give a specific example, make a sketch of such a machine, and explain its features.**

By the student. This is an open-ended, challenging problem and the students are encouraged to develop creative solutions (see also Problem 35.32). As examples, nondestructive testing techniques (p. 1132) that can be incorporated include:

- Acoustic sensors in machine tools, capable of detecting and discarding defective incoming blanks.
- Surface gloss (similar to reflectivity) can be monitored and measured to ensure that the surface roughness being produced is acceptable.
- Surfaces can also be monitored for any defects, especially those involving deep cracks.

- Inspection of parts in machinery for producing composite materials.

**36.42 Name several material and process variables that can influence product quality in metal (a) casting, (b) forming, and (c) machining.**

By the student. This is an open-ended problem and the students are encouraged to develop their own answers. Acceptable answers could include the following:

| Process | Material variables | Process variables |
|---|---|---|
| Casting | Melting temperature, coefficient of thermal expansion, specific heat, thermal conductivity, impurities | Superheat, mold material and its temperature, mold design |
| Forming | Ductility, stiffness, hardness, strain-rate sensitivity, strain-hardening exponent | Deformation rate, temperature, die temperature, metalworking fluid |
| Machining | Strength, hardness, ductility, chemical reactivity with tool materials, thermal conductivity | Cutting speed, depth of cut, feed, tool angles, cutting fluids |

**36.43 Identify the nondestructive techniques that are capable of detecting internal flaws and those that detect external flaws only.**

By the student. Typically, nondestructive techniques that detect internal flaws include ultrasonic, acoustic, radiographic, eddy-current inspection, thermal inspection, and acoustic holography. External flaws can be detected by liquid penetrants, magnetic-particle inspection, eddy-current inspection, thermal inspection, holography, and radiography.

**36.44 Explain the difference between in-process and post-process inspection of manufactured parts. What trends are there in such inspections?**

As the names infer, in-process inspection is performed while the product is being manufactured, whereas post-process inspection takes place after the part is manufactured. There are increasing trends for in-process inspection, but this still is relatively rare compared to post-process inspection. The advantage to in-process inspection is that defects can be detected much more rapidly than in post-process inspection of batches produced. It is also important to note that adaptive-control techniques (see Section 37.4 on p. 1161) can be applied to in-process inspection.

**36.45 Assume that you are in charge of manufacturing operations for a company that has not yet adopted statistical process control techniques. Describe how you would go about developing a plan to do so, including providing for the training of your personnel.**

By the student. This is an open-ended problem and because the information given in the problem statement is not detailed, a number of approaches may be reasonable, including:

- Someone in charge of manufacturing operations may have limited time available, so this task would probably be delegated to other staff members, or a consultant could be hired for this task.

- A review can be done of the several quality-control software packages now available. Commonly, training on software packages can be arranged to be conducted in-house, which would also include discussions of quality theory.
- One could personally conduct the training and implement the procedures, but this is time consuming and it is a large task, even for small shops. There is usually at least one staff person delegated to this task.
- Professional societies such as the Society of Manufacturing Engineers can be contacted to provide in-plant training on these topics.

**36.46 Many components in products have minimal effect on part robustness and quality. For example, the hinges in the glove compartment of an automobile do not really impact the owners satisfaction, and the glove compartment is opened so few times that a robust design is easy to achieve. Would you advocate using Taguchi methods (like the loss function) on this type of component? Explain.**

The Taguchi methods are powerful for developing robust designs. It is recognized, however, that some components impact impressions of quality and others do not. The methods used in identifying these components are also well-developed and can be found in design textbooks. The Taguchi approach advocates spending time in optimizing the components that have a major impact on quality, and minimizing the cost of components that do not have this effect. Thus, Taguchi loss functions would not be applied to such part, where the goal instead is to minimize their cost.

# Chapter 37

# Automation of Manufacturing Processes

## QUALITATIVE PROBLEMS

**37.15 Giving specific examples, discuss your observations concerning Fig. 37.2.**

By the student. This is an open-ended problem and the students' answers will vary depending on their experience and effort expended. A few observations are described here. Fig. 37.2 on p. 1148, which can be presented in different ways, shows the incompatibility between flexibility and production capacities. As expected, conventional job shops have low productivity but are capable of making a wide variety of parts, including prototypes. Conversely, transfer lines are designed and arranged for a specific line of products, and flexibility is not a priority. Other systems on the figure can be assessed accordingly. The choice of a system obviously depends on the type of products to be manufactured.

**37.16 What are the relative advantages and limitations of the two arrangements for power heads shown in Fig. 37.4?**

One of the advantages of the circular pattern in transfer mechanisms (see p. 1151) is that the process starts and ends at the same location; this is very convenient because the pallets are in a closed circuit (thus easier to implement). On the other hand, having the part return to the same location is not always desirable if the part has to be moved further to another machine for subsequent processing. For this case, the linear pattern is more convenient because the movement of the part takes place along with the manufacturing sequence. Also, with the linear pattern, modifications are easier to implement, whereas with the circular pattern it is very difficult to add one or several more powerheads. Furthermore, the linear transfer line can accommodate larger workpieces and a larger number of operations can be included in the line (see, for example, Fig. 37.5 on p. 1152).

**37.17 Discuss methods of on-line gaging of workpiece diameters in turning operations other than that shown in Fig. 37.15.**

By the student. This is an open-ended problem with various possible solutions. The number and quality of solutions will depend on the students' experience and diligence in searching for answers. For on-line gaging (Fig. 37.15 on p. 1163), there has to be some method of fixturing the part and a measurement system that can send a signal to a computer. Laser and pneumatic gages can perform such tasks, as can a large number of touch probes. See Figs. 35.11 and 35.14 on pp. 1096 and 1098, respectively, for illustrations of these gages.

**37.18 Are drilling and punching the only applications for the point-to-point system shown in Fig. 37.10a? Explain.**

The point-to-point system, shown in Fig. 37.10a on p. 1158, is also used in operations such as turning operations (grooving, cutting off) and in shearing and punching applications (p. 429). With appropriate tooling, punching systems can be very flexible (see nibblers; p. 430). Also, there is a wide variety of machines that can use the point-to-point system, such as stereolithography and fused deposition modeling systems (see Chapter 20), computer-controlled sewing machines, laser-beam cutting machines, and water-jet cutting machines.

**37.19 What determines the number of robots in an automated assembly line such as that shown in Figs. 37.22 and 37.32?**

The number of robots in an automated assembly line is determined mainly by the number of operations to be performed (see pp. 1171 and 1182). The robot could be used for material handling, assembly, and inspection. The total operation must be decomposed into individual operations, and for each, the best method of implementation should be chosen (which may not necessarily require a robot). If a robot is appropriate, it can be arranged in (a) a robot-centered manufacturing cell (see Section 39.2 on p. 1219), where the robot serves one or more workstations, (b) an line-robot cell where one or more robot cells are located along a line conveyer, or (c) in a mobile-robot cell where the robot can be transported to perform various tasks in different locations.

**37.20 Describe situations in which the shape and size of the work envelope of a robot (Fig. 37.20) can be critical.**

By the student. The students are encouraged to respond comprehensively to this question. The shape and size of the envelope (see Fig. 37.20 on p. 1169) must be chosen according to the application involved. Note that the larger the envelope, the higher are the risks of collision of the arm of the robot with another device, machine, or even personnel. On the other hand, the smaller the envelope, the lower the access capabilities of the robot. The load to be carried is also an important factor, as robots are very sensitive to moment of inertia (which is determined by the mass of the load and the distance of the load from the axis of rotation). With spherical-envelope robots, an increase in the size or shape of the envelope will lead to a decrease in the load-carrying capacity.

**37.21 Explain the functions of each of the components of an industrial robot.**

By the student. In addition to viewing Fig. 37.17a on p. 1167, the students are encouraged to investigate various other robots from different manufacturers. The major components are designed to give the robot flexibility in movements in various degrees of freedom, with due considerations to stiffness of the components, including bearings, and other characteristics as described in Section 37.6. End effectors are also important. For example, vacuum lines and electromagnets are used to carry small as well as large parts that cannot be handled with grippers; the robot must first move up to the part and then activate either the vacuum or the magnet. For small parts, a gripper (Fig. 37.18f on p. 1167) can be used. Usually, grippers are activated through pneumatics to allow constant-controlled pressure of handling or they can be equipped with sensors. For machining operations, devices such as deburring tools (figure c) are used; the robot first brings the tool into position and then activates it. For assembly lines, devices such as nut drivers are common as are dial indicators for inspection of parts and their dimensions.

**37.22 Explain the difference between an automated guided vehicle and a self-guided vehicle.**

By the student. The students are encouraged to review the designs of various guided vehicle manufactured by different manufacturers. An automatic guided vehicle follows a preprogrammed path, using tape or embedded wires as guides for determining its path. Self-guided vehicles, such as the one shown in Fig. 37.16 on p. 1165, calculate in real-time their own paths and correct for deviations as necessary. Some vehicles have the capability of detecting obstacles in their path and taking preventing measures.

**37.23 Give two specific examples for which (a) an open-loop and (b) a closed-loop control system would be desirable.**

By the student. Refer to Fig. 37.8 on p. 1156. The students are encouraged to investigate this topic to respond to this question. Recall also that open-loop control, although not as accurate, is less expensive because of lower hardware costs. Some examples of open-loop control applications are:

- Inkjet printer mechanisms, where the inkjet printer head is moved to a location without any feedback.
- Tensioners for web handling machines use an open-loop control system on position.
- Pneumatic power systems that use a solenoid driven valve to control velocity usually are open-loop systems. Examples include hydraulic presses and actuators.

Examples of closed-loop control are:

- Segway transportation vehicles (www.segway.com) use sensors to confirm desired positions from a complicated dynamic model of the scooter.
- Industrial robots use kinematic models for motion and rotary encoders on revolute joints in a closed-loop control system.
- Automotive ignition control systems use a number of closed-loop control systems. For example, an oxygen sensor in the exhaust modifies the air flow into the engine to achieve desired exhaust products and to make sure there is not an excess of fuel or air in the combustion chamber.

**37.24 Explain why sensors have become so essential in the development of automated manufacturing systems.**

By the student. As can be appreciated after reviewing sensors on pp. 1171-1176, automated manufacturing systems will be greatly limited in their potential unless various control systems can be incorporated into them. Note also that, by definition, closed-loop control systems (p. 1156) require a feedback signal, which must come from a sensor. In automated manufacturing, it is important that information from sensors be readily available for control and documentation purposes, at the very least as part of a troubleshooting or preventative maintenance program. For automated systems, it is natural that the sensors be incorporated with the computer control systems.

**37.25 Why is there a need for flexible fixturing for holding workpieces? Are there any disadvantages? Explain.**

By the student. This is an open-ended problem with a large number of potential solutions based on the background of the student. There are a number of reasons, but mostly this is because production quantities can be moderate and cannot justify the cost of dedicated fixturing. Also, with the goal of minimizing set-up times, flexible fixturing becomes an important tool.

**37.26 Table 37.2 shows a few examples of typical products for each category. Add several other examples to this list.**

By the student. This question could become fine project for students to explore this topic further. The following are some additional examples:

- Experimental or prototype: All products go through a prototype phase (see also Chapter 20) where quantities may range from 1 to 10. It should be noted, however, that some products are made in such small quantities, such as highly-specialized test equipment, specialized and dedicated machinery, aircraft carriers, custom-made fixtures, and wheelchair cushions (because they are fitted individually).
- Piece or small batch: Products with 10-5000 parts per year include machine tools, cranes, off-road equipment, military aircraft, and custom orders for a variety of applications.
- Batch or high-volume: Products with 5000-100,000 annual production include bowling balls, golf clubs, tractors, and overhead projection systems.
- Mass production: Computers, iPods, hand tools, drill bits, cutting tools, and small and large appliances.

**37.27 Describe applications of machine vision for specific parts similar to the examples shown in Fig. 37.25.**

By the student. The students are encouraged to explore this topic further. It should be apparent that machine vision can be used for a large number of parts, ranging from hardware parts to food products.

**37.28 Sketch the workspace of each of the robots in Fig. 37.19.**

By the student. The workspaces are fairly straightforward. (a) Figure 37.19a shows a Cartesian robot, which will have a workspace as shown in Fig. 37.20a. (b) The robot in sketch b has a cylindrical workspace, same as that shown in Fig. 37.20b. (c) The robot in sketch c has spherical workspaces, same as that shown in Fig. 37.20c. (d) The robot is similar to that in sketch c with the exception that, because it has more joints, its reach and flexibility is greater.

## SYNTHESIS, DESIGN, AND PROJECTS

**37.29 Give an example of a metal-forming operation that is suitable for adaptive control.**

By the student. This is a good project for the students and encourages them to review the processes described and illustrated in Part III of the book. There are several metal-forming operations that are suitable for adaptive control (see Section 374 on p. 1161), such as:

- Metal rolling can have adaptive control in the rolling-mill control system (Chapter 13). The mill can use the measured force and torque values, as well as surface roughness and sheet thickness and its variation across the width as feedback parameters, and adjust these quantities accordingly for optimal production.
- In extrusion (Chapter 15), there is an initial high force requirement until a fluid film has been generated, and an adaptive control program could sense the higher forces and trigger the pressing stem to slow down or even back up slightly before proceeding, so that a lubricant film can be generated.
- In sheet-metal forming operations (Chapter 16), the springback in bending can be monitored and controlled by making adjustments in the processing parameters.

**37.30 List and discuss the factors that should be considered in choosing a suitable material-handling system for a particular manufacturing facility.**

By the student. The students should choose a particular manufacturing activity (such as casting, forming, machining, plastics shaping, welding, etc.) and elaborate as appropriate. Among the many considerations are:

- Whether the facility needs to move solids, granular materials, liquids, or combinations of these materials.
- The distances that the material has to be moved from one location to the next.
- Requirements to avoid vibrations transmitted to the workpiece.
- Ambient conditions, such as materials to be moved through furnaces or heat treating or painting facilities.
- The size and shape of the workpieces to be moved, and features such as how they will be gripped or clamped.
- The characteristics of the material to be moved, i.e., magnetic, electrically non-conducting, toxic.

**37.31 Describe possible applications for industrial robots not discussed in this chapter.**

By the student. This is an open-ended problem, with answers limited only by the imagination of the student. As it is also known, potential applications involve replacing operators or personnel, include cleaning floors, dispensing medicines and providing health care, and aiding in communications. There are other applications as well, such as bartending, pitching baseballs for batting practice, sweeping homes and walking dogs.

**37.32 Design two different systems of mechanical grippers for widely different applications.**

By the student. There are several potential applications and similarly a large number of grippers that can be designed (see also Fig. 37.18 on p. 1167). The students are encouraged to develop gripping systems for a variety of applications, including hardware of various shapes and sizes, very small screws and washers, soft or delicate products, fruits and vegetable, and parts at various temperatures.

**37.33 Give some applications for the systems shown in Fig. 37.25a and c.**

By the student. The system shown in Fig. 37.25a on p. 1174 could be used, for example, for the inspection of parts from powder-metallurgy production (Chapter 17), in which each camera would inspect one view related to the dimension to be inspected; the operators on the line then remove the defective part. A robot or some other automatic device can be used to perform this operation. Regarding Fig. 37.25c: In some processes, parts are presented to the robot always in the same position; the robot is programmed to pick them up always with the same movement. If one part happens to be improperly placed, the robot cannot grip it. With the system shown in (c), the camera detects the precise position of the part and sends the information to the robot so that it can grab the part properly, whatever its position. Another application is the sorting of parts: The camera detects what part is presented to the robot, so that it can grab it properly and place it at the right location.

**37.34 For a system similar to that shown in Fig. 37.26, design a flexible fixturing setup for a lathe chuck.**

By the student. This is an open-ended design problem that can, for example, use Fig. 37.26 on p. 1177 as a guide. The students have to obtain specifications on lathes and various related accessories (see Section 23.3 on p. 686), and consider workpieces with a wide range of shapes, surface features, hardness, stiffness, etc., as well as production quantities. They should also keep a record of costs when investigating various fixture design options.

**37.35 Think of other part shapes that can be guided such as those shown in Fig. 37.33.**

By the student. The students are encouraged to search the literature on this important topic as a background for their own suggestions. As an example, consider the following for U-shaped parts (from G. Boothroyd, *Assembly Automation and Product Design*, 1991):

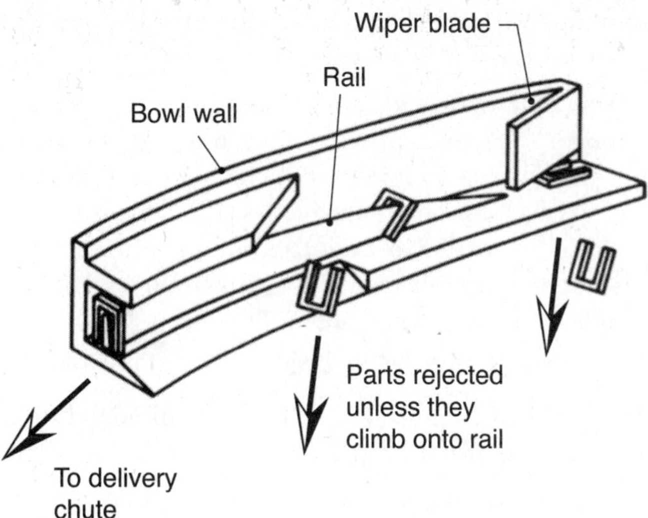


**37.36 Give examples of products that are suitable for the three types of production shown in Fig. 37.3.**

By the student. This is an open-ended problem, and students should be encouraged to develop answers based on their experience and training. Examples of answers are:

- Job shop: Fixtures, dies, customary replacement parts, prototypes.
- Batch production: Pleasure boats, surf boards, books, cookies, airplanes and components.
- Mass production: Automobiles, computers, televisions, cookies, garbage bags, diapers, medications.

**37.37 Give examples where tactile sensors would not be suitable. Explain why.**

By the student. The main factors to be considered are (a) the properties and characteristics of the objects being contacted by the tactile probe, (b) whether the probes may cause any surface damage, such as scratching, and (c) whether the object is sufficiently rigid to withstand the contact force (e.g., a thin plastic part or metal foil). Note also the high cost of tactile sensors; they can be justified only for continued use for large production runs and only if less expensive alternatives are not practical.

**37.38 Describe situations where machine vision cannot be applied properly and reliably. Explain why.**

By the student. Machine vision cannot be applied properly in situations where the lack of light or visibility would prevent the camera from viewing the particular event. This situation would happen, for instance, in processes where smoke, fumes, or metalworking fluids are present (as in machining using cutting fluids). The machine-vision system must be set on a stable support and cannot be used effectively in the vicinity of vibrating machinery or equipment. If the environment is subject to changes (lighting, for instance), processing of the image can take too long and thus it is not suitable for high production-rate control. Also, complex parts make the control very difficult.

**37.39 Choose one machine each from Parts II through IV and design a system in which sensor fusion can be used effectively.**

By the student. This is an open-ended and challenging topic, and would make a fine project for groups of students. For example, a rolling mill (see Section 13.4 on p. 358) may be equipped with torque, roll speed, workpiece speed, and workpiece-thickness sensors to control the whole process. Sensor fusion would be essential to properly control the whole system in real-time. As another example, consider machining operations where cutting forces, temperatures, vibrations, etc. are all monitored simultaneously and adjustments are made for optimizing the whole operation. The students should be made aware that a large number of such applications already exist in manufacturing operations.

**37.40 Why should the level of automation in a manufacturing facility depend on production quantity and production rate?**

There are several reasons. If production rate is low, the need for automation obviously is also low, as the cost of automation cannot be justified. Furthermore, there probably will be a need for increased flexibility, depending on quantity of production (see Fig. 37.2 on p. 1148). As can be seen, there may be an optimum system for the desired production level. Note also that for obvious economic reasons, as production quantity increases, so should the production rate.

**37.41 Think of a product and design a transfer line for it similar to that shown in Fig. 37.5. Specify the types of and the number of machines required.**

By the student. This is a good and challenging project, To help layout the transfer line, the students should first develop a list of the processes that would be required to manufacture the particular product and in the proper sequence. A routing sheet, such as the one shown in Fig. 38.10 on p. 1204, is helpful. For example, a simple transfer line for a small engine-block for a lawn mower (starting with a casting) may consist of a boring mill, a drill press, a tapping machine, a surface broach, an internal grinder, a vapor degreaser, a coordinate-measuring machine, and possibly an ultrasonic tester.

**37.42 Describe your thoughts on the usefulness and applications of modular fixturing consisting of various individual clamps, pins, supports, and attachments mounted on a base plate.**

By the student. This is an important topic for students to investigate further. Modular fixturing (p. 1176) can be very effective and time saving for small production runs, and if different parts are to be produced on the same machine. The primary advantage of modular fixturing is that a fixture can be disassembled when the production run is completed, and the components can be reassembled and used in a different fixture. The fixture can be readily reconstructed from drawings or even photographic records. Their reuse allows the rapid construction of complex, high-precision fixtures while limiting the capital investment in fixture components.

**37.43 Inspect several household products and describe the manner in which they have been assembled. Comment on any product design changes you would make so that assembly, disassembly, and servicing are simpler and faster.**

By the student. A very common method to simplify assembly operations is to consolidate fasteners into the housing of the product, especially using integrated snap fasteners (see Fig. 21.19 on p. 1026). Such fasteners are commonly found in all types of appliances. The students should note that a large number of threaded fasteners can be found in a very wide range of products such as small appliances, hair dryers, and housings for computers and television sets.

**37.44 Inspect Table 37.1 on the history of automation and describe your thoughts as to what new developments could possibly be added to the bottom of the list in the near future.**

By the student. This is a challenging area of inquiry for students, and they should be encouraged to develop future concepts and applications. We have found this question to be a very effective for reviewing various topics described in this book, as well as good topic for discussions in class. Consider, for example, the following questions:

(a) Are there implications of wireless communication that will be exploited in future manufacturing facilities and machines?

(b) If computers continue to increase in speed and software capabilities, what will be the nature of CAD and CNC systems?

(c) What would be the effect of speech recognition on the design and operation of future machinery?

**37.45 Design a robot gripper that will pick up and place the following: (a) eggs - without breaking them; (b) an object made of very soft rubber; (c) a metal ball with a very smooth and polished surface; (d) a newspaper; and (e) tableware, such as knives, spoons, and forks.**

By the student. This is a challenging topic with many possible solutions, depending on the imagination and creativity of the students. As one suggestion for eggs, a simple method would be a cantilever (with low stiffness) mounted on an actuator, with its tip equipped with a piece of soft foam. When the actuator closes in over the egg, the force applied by the cantilever is limited by its stiffness and no stress concentrations are present on the egg shell (because of the foam tip). Thus, even fragile products like eggs can be handled by robots (see also Fig. 37.24 on p. 1173). It should be noted that numerous "Rube Goldberg" type solutions also can be developed which are far more complex. The other products listed in the problem require similar approaches, including considerations of the shapes and the materials involved, stiffness, hardness, and surface characteristics.

**37.46 Review the specifications of various numerical-control machines and make a list of typical numbers for their (a) positioning accuracy, (b) repeat accuracy, and (c) resolution. Comment on your observations.**

By the student. This is a challenging problem because the statement is deliberately open-ended. This question can be interpreted as comparing particular machines, such as robots from different manufacturers or with different payloads, or by comparing different drives (stepper motor, ball screw drives, piezoelectric, etc.), etc. The students should be encouraged to contact manufacturers and suppliers of NC machines and develop their responses accordingly.

**37.47 Obtain an old toaster and disassemble it. Explain how you would go about assembling it by automated assembly.**

By the student. This topic is especially useful and it gives a good opportunity to evaluate the assembly efficiency using Eq. (37.1) on p. 1186. Toasters today, which are relatively inexpensive, have designs that are efficient for assembly; they are mass produced and much thought has been given on optimizing their assembly. An older-model toaster is valuable because it will not have solid-state controls and therefore will have more components for assembly. However, any toaster (or indeed any inexpensive appliance) is useful for this laboratory exercise. Students should also be encouraged to suggest design modifications to facilitate assembly (see also Section 37.10 on p. 1183).

**37.48 Perform a literature search and determine how a bowling pinsetter operates. Explain how the pins are never placed upside down on a bowling lane.**

By the student. This is a good project for students. It will be noted that a bowling pinsetter uses an orientation plate which operates on a principle similar to the guides shown in Fig. 37.33 on p. 1183. The pins are conveyed on a belt so they are either pin-first or bottom-first. At the orientation plate, a pin-first orientation is rotated 180°, while a bottom-first pin passes as is.

# Chapter 38

# Computer-Aided Manufacturing

## QUALITATIVE PROBLEMS

**38.14 Describe your observations regarding Fig. 38.1.**

Figure 38.1 on p. 1193 shows the integration of computer control and network communication systems with machinery and equipment in a computer-integrated manufacturing system. It shows a hierarchical structure, where higher levels of control are exercised over the computers controlling the machines. The nature of the network (not shown) can be Ethernet or wireless without introducing any inaccuracy into the system.

**38.15 Give examples of primitives of solids other than those shown in Figs. 38.4a and b.**

Primitives are any shape, as can be seen in Fig. 38.4a and b on p. 1198. Cylinders and rectangles are primitives that are simple and common. Triangular- and prismatic-based pyramids, spheres, cones, dodecahedrons, gears, etc., are all examples of primitives, although not as common.

**38.16 Describe your understanding of the octree representation in Fig. 38.6.**

The octree representation (Fig. 38.6 on p. 1199) shows a volume (or area for quad tree representation) in terms of voxels (or pixels) that are filled by the object. This type of representation is not an unusual concept, as computer terminals and television images operate on the same principal. Octree representations are, for example, useful in biomedical applications where the geometries are very complex and where geometry data is obtained from scanning instruments.

**38.17 Explain the logic behind the arrangements shown in Fig. 38.13b.**

The arrangement shown in Fig. 38.13b on p. 1210 uses the group-technology (cellular) method (p. 1208), where the parts are grouped according to their manufacturing similarities.

The layout is made such that machines are grouped by functions; parts enter and exit the total operation at different points according to their design. All parts that require the same operation are made together in the same batch. This batch is then split and the parts are dispatched to other machines for subsequent operations, joining some other parts from other previous operations, and so on. With this system, each machine is set once for an operation and the redundancy is avoided.

**38.18 Describe your observations regarding Fig. 38.2.**

Figure 38.2 on p. 1196 various types of modeling and representations for computer-aided design. The students should review these types and comment on their characteristics, noting the differences between 2D, 2 1/2 D, and 3D representations. Note also, for example, that the surface model does not show the hidden features of the part.

**38.19 What are the advantages of hierarchical coding?**

The advantage of hierarchical coding (p. 1212), also called monocode, is that, since every symbol's value depends on the previous symbol, a short code can contain a very large amount of information. This system is widely used in industry to define part numbers for catalogs.

**38.20 Referring to Fig. 38.3, what are the advantages of a third-order piecewise Bezier curve over a B-spline or a conventional Bezier curve?**

It should first be noted that any curve can be described using B-splines, Bezier curves, or third-order Bezier curves. The main disadvantage of a Bezier curve is that if a point is modified, then the entire curve also is modified. Curve modification is therefore difficult for a designer. Consider the case where sheet-metal part periphery is clamped, but the contour or profile needs to be modified - this is very difficult to accomplish with a Bezier curve. When endpoints need to be maintained but the curvature needs to be modified, a third-order piecewise Bezier curve is very powerful. Note that, since most modern CAD programs use these constructs, students can examine these curves and experiment with them as they wish.

**38.21 Describe situations that would require the design change at its larger end of the part in Fig. 38.5.**

The main strength of parametric design is that such changes, which occur all the time, can be made quickly. For example, reasons that one end in Fig. 38.5 on p. 1198 may be redesigned include:

- A new model of a product may be desired with a larger or smaller capacity.
- Field reports may indicate a large failure rate, necessitating an increase in the size of some components.
- Interference between parts in an assembly operation may require reducing the size of some features.
- Castability or other manufacturing concerns may require modification of designs. Students are encouraged to cite additional reasons.

## SYNTHESIS, DESIGN, AND PROJECTS

**38.22 Review various manufactured parts described in this book and group them in a manner similar to those shown in Fig. 38.12.**

By the student. This is an open-ended problem. For example, the students may compare parts, such as that shown in Fig. 11.1a on p. 287 as sand castings; parts as in Fig. 13.16 on p. 363 as thread-rolled parts; or rotary swaged parts such as in Fig. 14.14d on p. 384. These are all parts that have very different geometries but have similar manufacturing attributes. Now, consider the shape of a coffee cup. The cup can be slip cast, injection molded, machined, metal-injection molded, or made from paper; the cups will have identical geometries but different manufacturing histories. There are many such examples; the students can, for example, list processes suitable for making a 2-in. diameter solid sphere (ball bearing) as well as one that is 0.1-in. in diameter.

**38.23 Think of a product and make a decision-tree chart similar to that shown in Fig. 38.14.**

By the student. This is an open-ended problem and a difficult one unless the students first does some research and identifies a coding scheme that can be worked out before characterizing parts. Students should be wary of selecting geometries that are too complex, because most coding schemes tend to converge to the same code (irregular or complex default codes in Fig. 38.14).

**38.24 Outline the benefits of a manufacturing system, giving specific examples.**

By the student. The ultimate benefit is the dramatic increase in productivity and reduction in manufacturing cost, especially for medium-sized (lot) production lots. Agility is an ever-present concern in modern manufacturing, and the global economy demands economic manufacturing practices be held paramount. Thus, such systems are not only beneficial, they are perhaps essential.

**38.25 How would you describe the principle of computer-aided manufacturing to an older worker in a manufacturing facility who is not familiar with computers?**

By the student. Computer-aided manufacturing is based on the use of computers, machines which have the capability to perform a variety of tasks at very high speeds and as many times as needed, consistently and without complaining as humans might. These exceptional characteristics can be utilized in manufacturing operations to save time and decrease the extent of data manipulation (thus leading to a reduction of errors). Consider, for example, CNC machines (Section 37.3 on p. 1153). An operator must first write a program describing the tool path, which actually corresponds to a description of the part to be made. If this part has already been designed (using a computer), there is no need to describe it again in order to develop the CNC programs; this information can be retrieved and used directly. Furthermore, the CAM system can compute the tool path and generate the CNC blocks; all repetitions and risks of errors during programming are thus reduced. In the CAM system, having generated all the information needed for each operation (including the time required for machining), this information can then be used to schedule production, plan the use of machines, and so on. In such planning, a computer can automatically download the machines with the appropriate CNC program.

**38.26 Think of a simple product and make a routing sheet, similar to that shown in Fig. 38.10. If the same part is given to another person, what is the likelihood that the routing sheet developed will be the same? Explain.**

By the student. The routing sheets (p. 1204) created by different people could be very different unless there are some restrictions placed on the production processes to be used. For example, a connecting rod for an internal-combustion engine could be cast, forged, machined, or made by powder-metallurgy techniques. If there is a requirement that they be cast, for example, students should be able to make fairly similar routing sheets, with a logical flow of processes, such as cast, bore holes, and grind surfaces, but not cast, grind, and bore. It is obvious that a proper response to this question requires a good understanding of the capabilities of various processes.

**38.27 Review Fig. 38.10, then suggest a routing sheet for one of the following: (a) an automotive connecting rod, (b) a compressor blade, (c) a glass bottle, (d) injection-molding die, or (e) a bevel gear.**

By the student. The students are expected to review all relevant primary and secondary processes described in the book for making these parts, as well as searching the literature and manufacturers for information on these products.

(a) For a connecting rod see, for example, Fig. 14.7a on p. 377, where the processes involved would typically be:

   i. various forging operations performed on a blank (obtained from an extrusion),
   ii. trimming the flash,
   iii. cutting the larger end,
   iv. boring operations for the circular ends,
   v. finishing the holes for assembly with the crankshaft and the piston pin, and
   vi. inspection.

   Note also that some smaller connecting rods may be made by powder metallurgy or even with ceramics. For the others parts listed in the problem:

(b) Compressor blade, where the processes may be similar to the connecting rod, with additional machining, grinding, deburring, and finishing operations because all surfaces of the blade will require appropriate surface finish and dimensional accuracy.

(c) Glass bottle; see, for example, Fig. 18.10 on p. 524, which describes the sequence of operations.

(d) Injection-molding die; see, for example, die-manufacturing methods described in Section 14.7 on p. 388.

(e) Bevel gear; see, for example, Section 24.7 on p. 749.

# Chapter 39

# Computer-Integrated Manufacturing Systems

## QUALITATIVE PROBLEMS

### Qualitative Problems

**39.15 Would machining centers be suitable for just-in-time production? Explain.**

By the student. Because of their capability to machine different workpieces and in batches of as low as one, machining centers could be suitable for just-in-time production (p. 1225), depending on the type of parts to be produced. The students could explore this topic further, noting that a machining center is basically a versatile machine tool. Its operations are programmed and can be changed rapidly for another type of workpiece. It should also be noted that, as the word infers, machining centers perform material-removal operations and not forming or other metalworking operations.

**39.16 Give an example of a push system and of a pull system. Indicate the fundamental difference between the two methods.**

By the student. This is an open-ended problem and the answers given will depend on the experience and diligence in searching the literature. A push system has high inventory levels which mask production problems (see top of p. 1226). For example, large quantities of fasteners may be produced and stored, even though (at least for a while) the demand may not be there. Unless there is continuous quality control, there may be defective parts (due for reasons such as die wear or poor maintenance of machinery) in storage. A pull system has low inventories and thus allows identification of problems (such as poor surface finish and dimensional accuracy) at the earliest stages of production.

**39.17 Is there a minimum to the number of machines in a manufacturing cell? Explain.**

By the student. A manufacturing cell (p. 1219) consists of a group of machines, arranged logically to produce certain specific features on a family of parts. The cell usually consists of a number of machines and a material handling system for the movement of parts in various stages (see Fig. 39.1 on p. 1220). It can be noted that the minimum number of machines in a manufacturing cell would be two, as otherwise the term cell cannot be used properly. An example of a minimum number of machines would be a cell where the first machine would perform an operation such as turning of a shaft, and a second machine to grind the outer diameter. It should be apparent, however, that a minimum number of machinery may not be an optimum number for a particular set of operations on products.

**39.18 Are robots always a component of a FMC? Explain.**

By the student. The material-handling system in an FMC (see Fig. 39.1 on p. 1220) is an essential and important component; it must have high flexibility because of the variety of parts and operations taking place in the cell. Whether or not this task can be performed with a robot or some other material-handling system depends on factors such as the type of products, process capabilities, how many machines are involved in the cell and how far they are from each other. Using a variety of end effectors (see p. 1166), robots can handle various parts-in-progress, but they may not be capable of handling complex, delicate, or heavy parts. In that case, the material-handling system may require special conveyors, manipulators, automated guided vehicles, or even individual workers.

**39.19 Describe the elements of artificial intelligence. Is machine vision a part of it? Explain.**

By the student. The students should discuss the details further, but as described in Section 39.8, the basic elements of artificial intelligence are expert systems, natural language processing, and machine vision. Machine vision can be considered as an interface. It supplies data to the system in different ways. It can be in the form of a picture (array of pixels) or as the result of an image-processing software (a contour). A robot guided by machine vision (Fig. 39.7 on p. 1232) is a typical example of such a system.

**39.20 Are there any disadvantages to zero inventory? Explain.**

While the concept of JIT suggests that there should be zero inventory, in practice this may be difficult to justify. Consider, for example, the case when a critical machine in the production line unexpectedly breaks down (in a manner not preventable through maintenance programs and schedules). Such an occurrence could shut down the entire production line, and in the absence of sufficient inventory, this situation would have major economic impact. Furthermore, there is also the consideration that a strike in one manufacturing plant can shut down and thus adversely affect the entire set of operations of a large corporation.

**39.21 Give examples in manufacturing processes and operations in which artificial intelligence could be effective.**

By the student. This is a challenging topic and the students should consult books and publications that are now widely available on artificial intelligence and neural networks, with various applications in design, automation, and the economics of manufacturing operations (see also the Bibliography at the end of this chapter). It should be noted that expert systems, for example, have a wide range of applications such as diagnosing problems in manufacturing, modeling and simulation, and computer-aided design, process planning, and production scheduling. A typical example is when one is given a specific part drawing and is asked to generate a manufacturing plan, including selection of processes, tooling, die, and fixture design, and selection of processing parameters. See also Problem 39.22.

**39.22 Describe your opinions concerning the voice-recognition capabilities of future machines and controls.**

By the student. The subject of voice recognition of future machines is a good topic for class discussion, noting also that significant progress already are being made in this area. Although the current technology is highly demanding on computer memory, voice-recognition capabilities would, for example, allow an operator to give verbal instructions to a machine (as well as to a computer), using words such as stop, start, slower, faster, etc., thus eliminating the need to type commands on a keyboard or manually adjust machine controls.

**39.23 Evaluate a process from a lean-production perspective. For example, closely observe the following and identify, eliminate (when possible), or optimize the steps that produce waste when (a) preparing breakfast for a group of eight, (b) washing clothes or cars, (c) using internet browsing software, and (d) studying for an exam, or writing a report or a term paper.**

By the student. It is important to first understand and appreciate the main features of lean production, as also described in Section 39.6 on p. 1227. In lean manufacturing it is essential to consider whether or not a certain activity is adding value, and also to not the importance of the various items listed on pp. 1227-1228. The four topics listed in the problem can then be subjects of interesting discussion by groups of students.

## SYNTHESIS, DESIGN, AND PROJECTS

**39.24 Think of a product line for a commonly used household item and design a manufacturing cell for making it. Describe the features of the machines and equipment involved.**

By the student. In this open-ended problem, the specific answers will depend on the particular products selected and how complex their manufacture would be. It is important that students consider relatively simple products, such as containers for food and beverages, electric razors, and small appliances.

**39.25 What types of (a) products and (b) production machines would not be suitable for FMC? What design or manufacturing features make them unsuitable? Explain with examples.**

By the student. Examples of such products and production machines would be:

(a) products that are not intended for batch production, such as a rolling mill,

(b) processes and equipment that require long cycle times (chemical etching, electroplating, or composites manufacturing) as they would be impossible to synchronize efficiently with other activities in the cell,

(c) machinery that may not be compatible with other equipment such as, for example, a large drop hammer (see Section 14.8 on p. 390) placed on the same shop floor and near a precision grinder or a coordinate measuring machine. The students can elaborate further on these and other ideas, also discussing the design and manufacturing features that make them unsuitable for inclusion into FMC.

**39.26 Surveys have indicated that 95% of all the different parts made in the United States are produced in lots of 50 or less. Comment on this observation and describe your thoughts regarding the implementation of the technologies outlined in Chapters 37 through 39.**

By the student. This is a challenging problem; a comprehensive answer will require students to review the capabilities and limitations of the various manufacturing systems and methodologies described in Chapters 37 through 39. The low production quantity is quite challenging in that it is too large for prototyping equipment (Chapter 20), but far too small to justify dedicated equipment or hard automation. With this level of production quantity, there is a great need to use the machinery that possess flexibility and agility in manufacturing and with extensive computer controls (such as machining centers, grinding centers, EDM centers, etc. described in Chapters 25 through 27.) In fact, a visit to manufacturing facilities of various sizes will indicate the preponderance of such machinery.

**39.27 Can a factory ever be completely untended? Explain.**

By the student. This is an interesting and a controversial topic for class discussion. It should be noted that while some machinery (such as a machining center) or sets of machinery (such as those in a flexible manufacturing cell or system; see Fig. 39.3 on p. 1222) can perform untended operations, it is very difficult to conceive of a factory that is truly untended. It should be apparent that untended factories will, at the very least, still require maintenance and setup personnel.

**39.28 Assume that you own a manufacturing company and that you are aware that you have not taken full advantage of the technological advances in manufacturing. However, now you would like to do so, and you have the necessary capital. Describe how you would go about analyzing your companys needs and how you would plan to implement these technologies. Consider technical as well as human aspects.**

By the student. This is a challenging problem and can be discussed in class, and has broad industrial implications. Also, responses to this, as well as to many other problems in Chapters 37 through 39 of this book, should also come from students in industrial engineering and business administration programs, as they will bring a larger perspective the discussions. Students should be encouraged to consider, among others, the following:

- Not all product lines require flexible manufacturing systems or advanced material-handling systems in transfer lines (see, for example, Fig. 37.2 on p. 1148). A thorough assessment must be made concerning the applicability of advanced manufacturing approaches to the types of products being manufactured.

- There have been several situations where replacing workers with robots has not been as attractive an alternative as originally thought.
- Even if capital is available, flexible manufacturing systems are very expensive and may not be justifiable on a cost basis. An economic analysis of alternative production methods is therefore essential.
- There are social implications to the application of automation and modern technology at the expense of jobs, a topic that should be discussed in class. It is important to also note that such moves may well be necessary in order to maintain competitiveness in a global marketplace.

**39.29 How would you describe the benefits of FMS to an older worker in a manufacturing facility whose experience has been running only simple machine tools?**

By the student. This is a challenging problem and the students will have their own way of responding, especially in class discussion. Some students may be assigned to be the older workers, listening to other students who, based on their knowledge of Section 39.3 on flexible manufacturing systems are assigned to describe the benefits of FMS. It should also be noted that, in spite of their limited experience with simple machine tools, the workers are older and have much experience with parts making.

**39.30 Artificial neural networks are particularly useful where problems are ill defined and the data is vague. Give examples in manufacturing where ANN can be useful.**

By the student. This is a challenging problem and requires some literature search. As also described on p. 1233, it will be noted that ANN can have a variety of applications in manufacturing such as process control, speech recognition, predicting performance in machining (based on several input parameters).

**39.31 Consider a routing sheet for a product, as discussed in Chapter 38. If a holonic manufacturing system is to automatically generate the manufacturing sequence:**

**(a) What is the likelihood that it will be the same as produced manually?**

**(b) What is the likelihood that a holonic system will produce the same sequence every time? Explain.**

Holonic manufacturing systems are intended to self-organize into a system that will produce the desired product. It is possible (and likely, under some circumstances) that the holonic system will generate a routing sheet that is identical to a sheet produced manually, and that it is the same every time. However, if the resource pool is limited, it is also likely (under most circumstances) that the self-organized system could have some deviations, as for example, using a CNC milling machine for drilling holes when drill presses are unavailable.

**39.32 It has been suggested by some that artificial intelligence systems will ultimately be able to replace the human brain. Do you agree? Explain.**

By the student. This is a good and challenging topic for class discussion. As a matter of general principle, one should never claim that something is impossible. Presently, there are tasks which the human mind can perform easily and which cannot be performed even by the most advanced computers. Computers have great difficulty with creative thought processes as well as with the handling of simultaneous inputs.

# Chapter 40

# Product Design and Process Selection in a Competitive Environment

## QUALITATIVE PROBLEMS

**40.15 Explain why the value of the scrap produced in a manufacturing process depends on the type of material and processes involved.**

By the student. Materials have different raw-material market values, which can fluctuate with supply and demand. A major consideration is the processing required to make the scrap material usable. The purity of the material is also important as various other materials that may have been mixed with it. The cleanliness of the material is also a factor; for example, metal chips from dry machining have more value than those in which cutting fluids have been used, which can contribute to pollution during recycling.

**40.16 Comment on the magnitude and range of scrap shown in Table 40.6.**

By the student. Referring to Table 40.6 on p. 1250, note that, as expected and even by definition, a near-net-shape process (such as powder metallurgy) produces very little scrap. Machining, being a material-removal process may produce the highest percentage of scrap, depending, for example, on the initial and final dimensions of the workpiece machined from a blank. Note also that processes such as forging, cold or hot extrusion, and permanent-mold casting produce a rather consistent amount of scrap (by way of flash, runners, etc). The rolling process is well controlled and, as a result, scrap is very low (generally by way of trimming the material). However, it should be recalled that sheet metals typically are subsequently subjected to various secondary forming processes, thus the scrap can increase significantly (see also Fig. 16.51 on p. 472).

**40.17 Describe your observations concerning the information given in Table 40.5, and the reasons for it.**

By the student. See also Problems 40.26 and 40.32. The major observations regarding Fig. 40.5 on p. 1265 are:

(a) most processes (especially grinding; Chapter 26) have a rather wide range of surface-finish capabilities (see also Fig. 23.13 on p. 698)

(b) as expected, the finer the surface finish, the longer the production time (with a difference of at least an order of magnitude; a fact that has major influence on economics),

(c) the finest finish is obtained by grinding (although other processes are also capable of the same performance (see, for example, Fig. 23.13 on p. 698 and Fig. 27.4 on p. 839) but are not included in this figure, and

(d) the roughest finish is obtained by various traditional machining processes, described in Chapters 23 and 24.

**40.18 Other than the size of the machine, what factors are involved in the range of prices in each machine category shown in Table 40.9?**

By the student. As one would expect, and as also noted in the caption of Table 40.9 on p. 1263, the wide ranges of machinery base prices are due to factors such as

(a) size and capacity of the machines

(b) machine quality and the level of precision

(c) level of automation and computer controls, and

(d) options, such as additional equipment or tool-magazine capacity in machining centers.

A good class project would be to contact various suppliers of machinery and provide numbers to this table, which will range from a few thousand dollars to millions.

**40.19 Explain how the high cost of some of the machinery listed in Table 40.9 can be justified.**

By the student. Cost justification may be summarized as follows:

(a) Although a particular machine may first appear to be expensive, its cost must be put into proper perspective, particularly in view of return on investment (ROI; see p. 1266). As we have seen throughout this book, machines may be used in mass production (for very large quantities) as well as in a shop setting (individual jobs; dedicated machines) typically over the course of many years. The products from these activities are always in demand.

(b) High-quality machines will be more expensive but their various characteristics (such as stiffness, reliability, high precision, and productivity) will easily pay off, by avoiding product quality problems.

(c) Machines for transfer lines may be one-of-a-kind units with only a few in existence; consequently, though essential, such machines are likely to be more expensive.

**40.20 Based on the topics covered in this book, explain the reasons for the relative positions of the curves shown in Fig. 40.2.**

By the student. Numerous observations about the relative positions and shapes of the curves in Fig. 40.2 on p. 1253 may be made, including:

(a) Note that the overall trend for larger web dimensions, $w$, to involve larger web thicknesses, $h$. This is often necessary to avoid problems such as warping, wrinkling, nonuniform thickness, material handling, and various other issues.

(b) The curves for hot and cold rolling are horizontal; this is because rolling can easily produce thin sections over the range of widths (shown in the figure) and even larger.

(c) Cold rolling may produce thinner sections than hot rolling, as the difficulties in controlling dimensional tolerances caused by thermal expansions and contractions from heat are generally not present.

(d) Thin sections can be produced for thermoplastics and thermosetting polymers (due to their excellent formability, with thermoplastics allowing even thinner sections).

(e) Thin sections also can be produced by casting, by proper mold design and control of processing parameters.

(f) The curves from thick to thin sections are, respectively, sand casting, shell casting, plaster-mold, investment, and die casting.

(g) Forging processes produce relatively thick sections. Recall that thin forgings can require very high forging forces, and the dies can be complicated to design and expensive to produce.

**40.21 What factors are involved in the shape of the curve shown in Fig. 40.4? Explain.**

By the student. Various factors are involved in the shape of the curve in Fig. 40.4 on p. 1255. Overall, it indicates that as the dimensional tolerance required falls below about 0.25 mm (0.010 in.), the relative cost begins to rapidly increase. Tighter tolerances require extra care, possibly reducing production efficiency and increasing labor costs (which already may be high as more skilled labor is required for precision work). Tighter tolerances usually require additional processing and finishing operations. Also, tighter tolerances may result in higher reject rates and better equipment may also be required, as well as better tool and die materials.

**40.22 Is it always desirable to purchase stock that is close to the final dimensions of a part to be manufactured? Explain and give some examples.**

As expected, it is often very beneficial to purchase stock that is close to the final desired dimensions; this choice minimizes the additional machining, forming, finishing, etc., that have to be performed, thus reducing the production time and cost. The quality of the stock also is an important consideration; for example, hot-extruded, hot-forged, or hot-rolled blanks may not have the desired dimensional tolerances, surface integrity, and surface finish. Thus, operations such as machining or grinding may be necessary in order to remove sufficient material for the desired surface characteristics; this extra amount of material must be accounted for in selecting the stock size.

**40.23 What course of action would you take if the supply of a raw material selected for a product line becomes unreliable?**

By the student. It should be noted that unreliable materials supply means that the material is not being delivered to a plant as required; it does not necessarily mean that the quality and other characteristics of the material are unacceptably fluctuating. If the material supply is unreliable for geopolitical or other reasons, such as random or continued strikes, then material substitution has to be considered. Examples would, for instance, be substituting imported materials for cutting tools or for gas-turbine blades. Substitution can be a challenging task, as can be appreciated by reviewing Section 40.6 on p. 1250.

**40.24 Describe the potential problems involved in reducing the quantity of materials in products. Give some examples.**

By the student. For economic reasons, it is often desirable to reduce the quantity of material in products; this reduction can be accomplished by using and optimizing cross-sections or by using materials with higher strength-to-weight or strength-to-stiffness ratios (see, for example, Fig. 3.1 on p. 105). Numerous examples of creative solutions can be given, such as the use of a copper layer to achieve a smooth surface finish in electroplating applications in electronics, followed by a much thinner layer of gold for improved corrosion resistance and electrical conductivity. It should be apparent that to reduce the variety of materials in a product, as well as the number of fasteners in it, a systematic review of the processes and materials must be done. It should be recalled that this topic is discussed in some detail on p. 1241, and several examples have been given.

**40.25 Explain the reasons why there is a strong desire in industry to practice near-net-shape manufacturing.**

By the student. Refer also to p. 31. The costs associated with finishing operations are usually very high. Thus, if a part can be made to near-net shape, then the machining and finishing operations can be greatly reduced or eliminated (see, for example, Fig. 26.34 on p. 828), thereby reducing much of the expense in part manufacture (see also p. 31). Also, the manufacturing processes associated with near-net-shape manufacturing (such as die casting, precision forging, powder metallurgy, and injection molding) are high-production-rate operations, thus the lead time and labor costs are also reduced.

**40.26 Estimate the position of the following processes in Fig. 40.5: (a) centerless grinding, (b) electrochemical machining, (c) chemical milling, and (d) extrusion.**

Referring to Fig. 40.5 on p. 1255, we can state the following:

(a) Centerless grinding (p. 813) will give a similar range of roughness as cylindrical grinding, but the production time will be much lower because the process is continuous.

(b) Electrochemical machining (p. 841) will produce very smooth surfaces (to 0.05 $\mu$m or so) but involves a much higher production time than cylindrical grinding.

(c) Chemical milling (p. 836) will give a roughness ranging from ground surfaces to surfaces typical of end milling, depending on the workpiece properties and process parameters. The processing time is difficult to define for this process because it depends to a large extent on the workpiece material and surface roughness to be produced.

(d) Extrusion (p. 402) will have surface finish ranges similar to shaping and drilling (although the surface texture is different; see also Fig. 23.13 on p. 698), and the production time will be lower than all the processes shown in the figure.

**40.27 In Section 40.9, there is a breakdown of costs in today's manufacturing environment maintaining that design costs contribute only 5% to the total cost. Explain why this figure is reasonable.**

Design involves only 5% of the total cost because the design cost is distributed over a large production run. However, it should be noted that design has the largest impact on costs. For example, a poorly designed part may require expensive manufacturing processes, but if manufacturing is considered simultaneously by the designers (concurrent engineering; Section I.2 on p. 11), this contribution to cost can be significantly reduced.

## SYNTHESIS, DESIGN, AND PROJECTS

**40.28 As you can see, Table 40.8 on manufacturing processes, includes only metals and their alloys. Based on the information given in this book and other sources, prepare a similar table for nonmetallic materials including ceramics, plastics, reinforced plastics, and metal-matrix and ceramic-matrix composite materials.**

By the student. Students are encouraged to respond to this question by reviewing process capabilities throughout this book, as well as conducting a literature search. A partial answer is given below:

| Process | Ceramics | Thermoplastics | MMCs |
|---|---|---|---|
| Casting | A | A | A |
| Extrusion | B | A | B |
| Rolling | B | A | B |
| Sheet-forming | - | A | - |
| Machining | | | |
| Chemical | B | - | A |
| ECM | B | - | A |
| EDM | B | - | A |
| Grinding | A | A | A |
| Welding (joining) | B | A | A |
| Injection molding | A | A | B |
| Blow molding | - | A | - |

**40.29 Review Fig. I.4 in the General Introduction and present your thoughts concerning the two flow charts. Would you want to make any modifications, and if so, what would they be?**

By the student. The students are encouraged to investigate similar flow charts in other books and publications. It will be observed that, as to be expected, such flow charts have different stages, with more or less emphasis placed on them, depending on the priorities of those who develop them. For example, the planning or marketing stages may be emphasized with far more detail than shown in these charts.

**40.30 Over the years, numerous consumer products have become obsolete (or nearly so - such as rotary-dial telephones, analog radio tuners, turntables, and vacuum tubes), while many new products have entered the market. Make a comprehensive list of obsolete products and one of new products. Comment on the reasons for the changes you observe. Discuss how different manufacturing methods and systems have evolved in order to produce the new products.**

By the student. This would be an interesting student project. As resource materials, it would be helpful to (a) search for newspaper and magazine advertisements in archives of large libraries and (b) to interview people of different age groups for their recollection of various products that they purchased or used in the past. Among examples of obsolete products are record players, typewriters, analog radios, early videogames, daisy-wheel printers, and oil-based printing inks. New products which correlate to these obsolete products are compact disks, word processors, digital radios, modern videogame systems, laser printers, and water-based inks. It is apparent that the newer products and devices are made possible by the rapid advances being made in materials, design, and manufacturing.

**40.31 Describe how you could reduce each of the costs involved in manufacturing of products.**

By the student. Refer to Section 40.9 on p. 1261 for coverage of this topic, noting the cost-reduction approaches outlined on pp. 1265-1266. The students are encouraged to develop their own additional ideas on this very important aspect of manufacturing in a competitive global marketplace.

**40.32 Make suggestions as to how to reduce the dependence of production time on surface finish (shown in Fig. 40.5).**

By the student. The production time for a certain specified surface finish (shown in Fig. 40.5 on p. 1255) may be reduced by implementing some or all of the following:

(a) First note the characteristics and the times for various processes by comparing them for a surface finish of, say, 1.6 $\mu$m.

(b) Make certain to specify the minimum surface finish acceptable for each part to properly perform its function.

(c) Choose the appropriate process or processes to obtain the desired surface finish, and do not attempt to produce a finer surface finish than a process is capable of (see, for example, Fig. 23.13 on p. 698 and Fig. 27.4 on p. 839).

(d) The greater the number of processes involved, the longer the workpiece-handling time. In the same manner, do not use too few processes, either. For a typical forging, for example, a machining process should be an intermediate step between forging and grinding, otherwise the grinding operation, with its generally slow material-removal rate, will take much longer time to remove the irregularities inherent to a forged surface.

(e) Whenever necessary, use higher quality raw materials for the workpiece.

(f) Follow basic guidelines such as using stiffer machines in machining processes, using the proper type and amount of cutting fluid, proper tool materials, and maintaining the tooling in good condition.

**40.33 There is a period between the time that an employee is hired and the time that the employee finishes with training during which the employee is paid and receives benefits but produces nothing. Where should such costs be placed among the categories given in this chapter?**

Although the costs associated with such employees can be placed in a number of categories, it is reasonable to consider this cost as a labor cost, further classifying it as an indirect labor cost. It is also reasonable to consider such costs as overhead costs. There is no category that fits such a situation exactly, but this is certainly considered in hiring decisions.

**40.34 Select three different products and make a survey of the changes in their prices over the past ten years. Discuss the possible reasons for the changes.**

By the student. This topic presents challenging and interesting possibilities. For example, computers can be shown to have approximately the same wide range of price, from low-performance 'bare-bones' systems to top-of-the-line models. However, the performance of computers has improved dramatically over the period of ten years, such that a comparison is not appropriate. As now widely observed, the manufacture of many labor-intensive products have been moved to countries with low wages (see Table I.4 on p. 40), thus keeping manufacturing costs low.

**40.35 Figure 2.1a shows the shape of a typical tensile-test specimen having a round cross-section. Assuming that the starting material (stock) is a round rod and that only one specimen is needed, discuss the processes and the machinery by which the specimen can be made, including their relative advantages and limitations. Describe how the process you selected can be changed for economical production as the number of specimens required increases.**

By the student. If only one specimen is needed, the best and most economical method would be to

(a) take round, drawn bar

(b) cut it to length, and

(c) machine the profile on a CNC lathe.

An alternative would be to investment cast a single part, if a cast specimen is acceptable. If the specimen is to be made of plastic, it is still possible to machine it, as with metal. A ceramic specimen would require casting it into the desired shape and then firing it; some finishing operation may also be necessary. As the number of specimens increases, however, one would begin to consider processes such as casting, roll forging, swaging, and machining them on automatic bar machines. Note that processes a process such as forging would require costly dies which can only be justified if the number of specimens is very large (see, for example, Fig. 14.19 on p. 394)

**40.36 Present your thoughts concerning the replacement of aluminum beverage cans with steel ones.**

By the student. Aluminum has an economic advantage as long as the material costs remain competitive and if the aluminum is recycled numerous times. Aluminum requires a large amount of energy to produce from ore (see p. 173), so the initial cost is higher, but once produced, aluminum requires less energy to re-melt. Steel is used for beverage cans in Europe and Asia, and these have some benefits over aluminum. Steel is generally easier to form (because of its higher strain-hardening exponents), so its shape can be more easily optimized, further reducing material cost and resulting in negligible weight increase over aluminum cans. Note also the appearance of an aluminum can over steel (which could corrode), its high thermal conductivity, as well as light weight. (CHECK)

**40.37 Table 40.4 listed several materials and their commercially available shapes. By contacting suppliers of the following materials, extend this list to include: (a) titanium, (b) superalloys, (c) lead, (d) tungsten, and (e) amorphous metals.**

By the student. Students are encouraged do contact suppliers of these materials and expand on this table. A typical response could be as follows:

| | |
|---|---|
| Titanium | B, f, I, P, S, T, W |
| Superalloys | B,I,P |
| Lead | B,I,P |
| Tungsten | B,w |
| Amorphous metals | F |

**40.38 Select three different products commonly found in homes. State your opinions on (a) what materials were used in each product, (b) why they were chosen, and (c) how the products were manufactured, and (d) why those particular processes were used.**

By the student. The students are encouraged to investigate each product and, based on a review of the topics described in this book, comment on each of the four questions.

**40.39 Inspect the components under the hood of your automobile. Identify several parts that have been produced to net-shape or near-net-shape condition. Comment on the design and production aspects of these parts and on how the manufacturer achieved the near-net-shape condition.**

By the student. Several components can be identified, which can also be discussed in class. As examples, consider the following: engine block, pulleys, belts, hose clamps, wiring, plastic containers (such as for the windshield fluid), fasteners, fan blades, and springs.

**40.40 Comment on the differences (if any) between the designs, the materials, and the processing and assembly methods used for making products (such as as hand tools and ladders) for professional use and those for consumer use.**

By the student. There is a realization that professional use implies a far more rugged and repeated use, often under adverse conditions. For example, the intended uses for hand tools and ladders for home use are not nearly as extensive as professional ones; thus, they usually are produced with greater emphasis on cost reduction. For example, drills for home use typically are less powerful and with less rugged motors; drill bits are not be made with as high a quality material and are likely to wear more rapidly; aluminum ladders are lighter and less rigid.

**40.41 The capabilities of some machining processes are shown in Fig. 23.1. Inspect the various part shapes produced and suggest alternative manufacturing processes. Comment on the properties of materials that would influence your suggestions.**

By the student. The parts shown in Fig. 23.1 on p. 675 could be difficult to produce without using machining processes. However, many of the features can, for example, be cast, cold extruded, or injection molded (depending on the material), but at a noticeable reduction in dimensional tolerances, thread accuracy, and surface finish.

**40.42 If the dimensions of the parts in Problem 40.38 were (a) two times larger or (b) five times larger, how different would your answer be? Explain your responses.**

By the student. There are several factors to be considered for larger parts, such as:

(a) possible difficulties in producing parts with larger sizes and in their heat treatment (if required),

(b) the size and cost of machinery, dies, and tooling required,

(c) difficulties in achieving desired dimensional tolerances (see, for example, Fig. 23.14 on p. 699), and

(d) various cost considerations.

**40.43 The cross-section of a jet engine is shown, in Fig. 6.1. On the basis of the topics covered in this book, select any three individual components of such an engine and describe the materials and processes that you would use in making them in quantities of, say, 1000. Remember that these parts must be manufactured at minimum cost, yet maintain their quality, integrity, and reliability.**

By the student. This is a very challenging problem and, because of the many factors involved, would be suitable for a class project.

**40.44 Discuss the tradeoffs involved in selecting between the two materials for each of the applications listed here:**

**(a) steel or plastic paper clips**

**(b) forged or cast crankshafts**

**(c) forged or powder-metallurgy connecting rods**

**(d) plastic or sheet-metal light-switch plates**

**(e) metal or plastic intake manifolds**

**(f) sheet metal or cast hubcaps**

**(g) steel or copper nails**

**(h) wood or metal handle for hammers**

**(i) steel or aluminum lawn chairs**

**Also, discuss the typical conditions to which these products are subjected in their normal use.**

By the student. Appropriate responses to these questions will require a review of all the materials characteristics, as described in Part I of this book.

**40.45 Discuss the manufacturing process (or processes) suitable for making the products listed in Problem 40.44. Explain whether they would require additional operations (such as coating, plating, heat treating, and finishing). If so, make recommendations and give the reasons for them.**

By the student. A wide variety of manufacturing processes would be suitable for making these products. As in Problem 40.44, appropriate responses will require a thorough review of all the manufacturing processes described in various chapters of this book, including also additional operations such as heat treating, coating, plating, and finishing. The descriptions given below are only as a general guide and are not meant to be comprehensive.

(a) Steel paper clips (see Fig. I.2 on p. 8) typically are made from drawn wire, bent to shape, and cut, without any additional operations. An alternative method (for flat paper clips) could be to punch them from sheet metal (which would likely produce sharp edges that have to be deburred). Plastic paper clips could be injection molded; if they have metal wire inside, then the process would be similar to making electrical wiring (see p. 540).

(b) Forging (Chapter 14) and casting (Part II) would both be suitable methods for producing a crankshaft, although both would require numerous secondary and finishing operations (especially on their bearing surfaces (see Fig. IV.1 on p. 603). A forged crankshaft would first have to have the flash trimmed while a cast one, depending on the process, may require the runners, gates, and sprues to be removed. The forged crankshaft would next has to be hot twisted (for the proper angles of the arms of the shaft), whereas the cast crankshaft would already be in the proper shape. Beyond these initial steps, processes such as machining and grinding would be similar in both processes.

(c) Forging, powder metallurgy (Chapter 17), and casting would be suitable processes for producing a connecting rod. A forged connecting rod (see p. 377) would have to be trimmed and have the holes at each end punched out. The large end would then be drilled and tapped, and then split. The holes would then have to be machined to size. Powder metallurgy would not require any trimming or holes to be punched out. Heat treatment (Chapter 4) might be required for strength. A cast connecting rod may need sprues, gates and runners removed. The holes could be integral to the casting, but would require machining for improved dimensional accuracy and surface finish. Machining for balancing would be more involved for a cast or forged connecting rod than for a powder metallurgy one. Finally, heat treatment for strength might be required on the casting, but possibly for the forging as well.

(d) Light-switch plates may be made from plastic or sheet metal. Plastic light- switch plates may be injection molded, thermoformed, compression molded, cast, or cold formed (Chapter 19). The choice would depend on many factors but mostly upon the complexity of the plate (plain versus decorative), material, cost, and production quantity. Although all of the processes listed could produce the light-switch plate, injection molding is perhaps the most appropriate, being capable of high production rates with few secondary operations. Thermoformed plates would be impractical, as secondary and costly operations would be required. Plastic plates would generally not require any polishing or painting operations. Sheet-metal light plates would be stamped and punched.

(e) Water pitchers can be made of glass or metal. Glass pitchers are often blown (Section

18.3) but, depending upon their shape complexity, they may be pressed or centrifugally cast. Secondary operations would be required to form and attach the handle. Metal pitchers would most often be deep drawn and then, if necessary, bulged to produce the desired shape; rubber forming, spinning, or hydroforming may also be considered (see Chapter 16). Secondary operations to produce and attach the handle would be required, as well as possibly deburr the rim (Section 26.8).

(f) Inexpensive hubcaps are generally stamped from sheet metal, with little or no secondary operations; they are snapped in place on the wheel. Cast hubcaps (such as permanent-mold cast from aluminum or similar lightweight metals) are much more expensive and have limitations to minimum thickness and can have different means to attach them to wheels. On the other hand, there is more design flexibility and a certain customer appeal to such hubcaps.

(g) Nails are typically made from drawn wire; there would no major differences between steel and copper in the manufacturing techniques, which also involves the heading operation. Steel nails may further be galvanized or coated, such as with resin for better bonding to wood.

(h) Wood handles typically would be shaped by woodworking processes, whereas metal handles would generally be formed, usually from a tubular blank by processes like swaging or forging (for heavy duty hammers). Composite-material handles, which are lighter, would be filament wound on an anvil or molded, and subsequently cured in an autoclave (Section 19.13).

(i) Sheet-metal chairs can be manufactured by the processes described in Chapter 16, and reinforced-plastic chairs would involve processes described in Section 18.12 on p. 496.

**40.46 Inspect some products around your home and describe how you would go about taking them completely apart quickly and recycling their components. Comment on their design regarding the ease with which they can be disassembled.**

By the student. Refer also to Section I.3 on p. 14 and Section 37.10 on p. 1183. It will be noted that most such products utilize a wide variety of metallic and nonmetallic materials, which must be separated into types before they can be recycled. This aspect has not have been considered in the product design stage, whereby disassembly cannot be done quickly and economically. For example, plastic housings that are riveted in place are more difficult to separate than those attached with snap fasteners. A more challenging task is how to disassemble microelectronic and micromechanical devices and electronic components for recycling, such as those described and shown in Chapters 28 and 29. A study of this important topic can demonstrate that while material costs are certainly considered during design, the ease of recycling the materials has not, until now, generally been the main concern.

**40.47 What products do you know of that would be very difficult to disassemble for recycling purposes?**

By the student. The students are encouraged to carefully analyze various products and provide their own answers (referring also to Section I.3 on p. 14 and bottom of p. 1248). It will be obvious that products constructed from one material are relatively easy to recycle, but those made of several different metallic and nonmetallic materials are much more difficult, such as computers, television sets, radios, calculators, and automobiles. Welded structures are difficult to take apart, as are riveted assemblies and brazed or adhesively-bonded connections. It should be apparent that although recycling is always an important consideration, it has to be cost effective (which also means less time for disassembly).

**40.48 Junction boxes for electrical wiring are available either in galvanized sheet metal or in injection-molded plastic (in colors such as white or blue). Considering all their various features, describe your thoughts on how you would go about deciding which one to purchase, and explain why.**

By the student. Refer also to Fig. P40.54b and c, and note that junction boxes are usually hidden behind walls. Metal boxes (a) are electrically conducting, hence they also serve the important purpose of grounding (with wires attached with green screws), and (b) although galvanized, they may corrode in moist environments. Plastic boxes do not have these characteristics and are generally less expensive. They are also available in colors such as white or blue, although color coding (unlike in electrical wiring) does not have any particular benefits; their grounding is done through separate grounding wires. Note from the figure that plastic boxes have nails embedded and are easily installed on wood stud. Metal boxes are typically supported by metal conduits, and may also be nailed or screwed in place.

**40.49 Discuss the factors that influence the choice between the following pairs of processes:**

**(a) sand casting versus die casting of a fractional electric-motor housing;**
**(b) machining versus forming of a large gear;**
**(c) forging versus powder-metallurgy production of a gear;**
**(d) casting versus stamping a sheet-metal frying pan;**
**(e) making outdoor furniture from aluminum tubing versus cast iron;**
**(f) welding versus casting of machine-tool structures;**
**(g) thread-rolling versus machining of a bolt for a high-strength application;**
**(h) thermoforming a plastic versus molding a thermoset to make a fan blade for a household fan.**

(a) Sand casting versus die casting of a fractional electric-motor housing. The sand-cast housing would be less expensive for low quantities and for situations requiring very little finishing operations (see also Table 11.2 on p. 288). For high volumes, however, and depending on size, die casting could prove more cost effective, especially when less finishing operations are required. The type of metal will also dictate the process to be chosen. Depending on the application (such as commercial heavy-duty versus residential light-duty motors), the mechanical-property advantages that die casting offers over sand casting should also be considered.

(b) Machining versus forming a large gear. Refer also to Section 24.7 on p. 749. Machining is almost always more expensive than forming, except in low quantities. The mechanical properties of the formed gear would be superior to those of a machined gear. However, for lower quantities or in cases where higher dimensional tolerances are required, machining